EVOLUTIONARY CONNECTIONS

ADVANCES IN HUMAN ECOLOGY, Supplement 1 (Part A)

Editor: Lee Freese, *Department of Sociology, Washington State University*

EVOLUTIONARY CONNECTIONS

by: LEE FREESE
Department of Sociology
Washington State University

 JAI PRESS INC.

Greenwich, Connecticut   *London, England*

Copyright © 1997 JAI PRESS INC.
55 Old Post Road, No. 2
Greenwich, Connecticut 06830

JAI PRESS LTD.
38 Tavistock Street
Covent Garden
London WC2E 7PB
England

ISBN: 0-7623-0230-5 (Part A)
*   0-7623-0211-9 (Set)*

ISSN: 1069-0573

Manufactured in the United States of America

to Dorothy V. Boring,
with Love and Gratitude

CONTENTS

List of Figures

List of Tables

Acknowledgments

In producing this work, I profited in numerous ways from several colleagues, most of whom serve as Editorial Advisors for this series. The advice provided by John H. Bodley, Eldon Franz, and Richard B. Norgaard for the different chapters they reviewed saved me many embarrassing mistakes. So did the advice, reviews, and continual intellectual interchange provided by Chuck Dyke, who sets as fine a standard for intelligent thought and expression as one could hope to reach. Riley E. Dunlap, Alexandra Maryanski, Eugene A. Rosa, and Gerald L. Young, each in their distinct ways, contributed to a general atmosphere of encouragement for the investigation of human ecology as here conceived, from the inception of the work, and to specific choices in paths to follow during its course. All of the above have served as teachers for me although, except in Young's case, I never took any of their courses.

William R. Catton, Jr., has influenced this work and contributed to its betterment from virtually every possible angle of intersect. By providing line-by-line marginal comments for the entire work, Catton, too, saved many embarrassing mistakes and improved its logic, expression, and choice of material. Of course, he provided intellectual and moral support, but much more. Insofar as persons may be causes, Catton caused this work. It was his 1980 volume, *Overshoot: The Ecological Basis of Revolutionary Change,* that diverted my intellectual interests and pursuits, which had centered on social psychology and formal theory, to a human ecological paradigm. *Overshoot* was intended to communicate to social scientists a different vision, and to me, it did. More than anyone, Bill Catton has shaped my vision of human ecology and its significance, and energized me to pursue its implications. I am grateful to have had Bill for a colleague, teacher, and friend.

This volume is dedicated to my mother, whom I regard as my most significant evolutionary connection and who is probably wondering why I would ever dream to think of her in such a way.

Preface

This work, consisting of two volumes, is the first supplement to *Advances in Human Ecology*. Part A of the supplement—this volume—traces themes by which human ecology connects to evolution. Part B, the companion volume *Environmental Connections*, traces themes by which human ecology connects to (or, in the treatment of some scholars, disconnects from) contemporary environmental conditions. The annual publication of diverse papers in the series proper is inherently unsuited to covering the truly broad scope of human ecology except over the very long term. Taken as a whole, this supplemental work is supposed to compensate by providing a broad overview and theoretical framing of scientific human ecology. The premise, or thesis, of the work is that human ecology connects human evolution to human environments.

The premise sets the problem of the work: to address the range of matters that a general science of human ecology must consider, in the terms of the premise, to be complete. But there is no general science of human ecology now, so this work obviously is not complete. Often I had to content myself with just identifying, without filling in, empty spaces. I am uneasy about what has been left out, especially the empty spaces I fear I failed even to identify. My excuse is that human ecology crosses from biology to the social sciences, and the more of this I took in, the more I had to leave out, at times sacrificing depth for breadth of coverage and at other times breadth for depth. I explain in the first chapter why so much ground has to be covered and why an understanding of human ecology has to incorporate both social and biological sciences. If that argument isn't convincing, I'm confident the work itself shall be. I recognize the excuse is not fully exculpatory. However, I assume this work is not the last of its kind, so I am confident that other human ecologists will remedy what they here may take to be incomplete or miscast.

About some other things, I am not so confident. One is locating the perfect groove for common discourse between the biological and social sciences. The first time I taught a graduate course (to a class of students all in social sciences) covering the material in this work, I had a chastening experience. I intended to spend a couple of hours discussing some technical but elementary facets of neo-Darwinian theory, and by way of rhetorical prelude, I referred in an offhanded manner to the standard textbook paragraph or two that is often used to characterize Darwin's original theory. When I saw the students taking notes on *that*, I knew I was in trouble. I would now have to be deliberate with the technical discussion and devote more time to it than I cared to, in order to draw out the points I needed. I would have to do that again with other subjects, for I could not presume too much in the way of background knowledge. In subsequent seminars, biology students were observed to be taking notes on some elementary ideas of social science. Cross-disciplinary ignorance runs both ways.

That's bad enough, but matters are really much worse. A reviewer of the first version of this work, seeking to provide friendly advice, suggested that I ought not to use the phrase bioecological forces, for it would mystify biologists. Maybe it would. But if it does, it would have to mystify someone steeped in the *culture* not just the information content of the natural and physical sciences. Social scientists casually, and often carelessly, refer to various "forces" not in allusion to anything like the four physical forces, which have some definition in physical theory, but to vaguely articulated conditions they believe affect sociocultural processes. This usage is a part of *their* culture (and they have even been known to use the word forces in names for their journals). The communication of even simple ideas across disciplines can be difficult just because people trained in the different disciplines carry with them implicit understandings and interpretations that derive from their different cultural world views. As a social scientist, I can not claim to comprehend the nuances of the unspoken cultural understandings that come with training in the natural and physical sciences, nor do I expect those with training in natural and physical sciences to comprehend the implicit cultural understandings I have unconsciously let influence this work. In seeking some perfect groove for cross-disciplinary discourse, which I doubt I have found, I don't assume that the entire intended audience will have either the foreground information or the background culture that I wish them to have, nor do I assume I have all I need. But, fortunately, many lenses can be focused on human ecology, and many good ones are now focused on various facets of it. This work provides a wide-angle lens, and it leaves room for many others to come forth to better focus their lenses, and to use better lenses, than I have made available.

It has been half a century since a prominent human ecologist, the sociologist Amos H. Hawley, presented what he called an attempt at a full theory of human ecology. I have no such ambitions for this work, because I don't think such is possible at present. But it is possible, and this I intend, to sketch the boundaries and some of the substance—in language that biologists and social scientists equally can comprehend—that a full theory is going to have to cover. Put in other terms, a main purpose of this work is to provide some reasonable, arguable definition of the scope of human ecology.

The purpose is reflected even in the organization of the two volumes. The choice to focus the volumes differently actually was dictated by the thoughtways and practices of contemporary analysts and by the economics of publishing, not by any intellectual concept that human ecology can be neatly partitioned into evolutionary or environmental modes within which definable problems can be isolated and effectively reduced. I do not affirm that possibility, for reasons I explain at the outset, although I do think the two volumes can be read independently. But as a practical matter, I hope that *Evolutionary Connections* will be read by those whose primary interests tend toward human environmental problems, and that *Environmental Connections* will be read by those whose primary interests tend toward human evolutionary problems. It is unfortunate from my point of view that so many serious scholars and beginning students as well seem to be interested mostly in one but not the other class of problems. The comprehension of either requires the comprehension of both. Although neither volume can provide full comprehension, and for neither do I claim much originality, taken together they are intended to advance the discussion and theoretical development of their subjects taken as a whole—taken as human ecology.

I consider it desirable that a full and general science be developed to incorporate all the matters pertaining to human evolutionary and environmental connections. This is why I deliberately forsake presenting human ecology as the potpourri it really is in favor of tracing themes I think may belong to the theoretical continuity there ought to be. But, if no general theory can be completed at present, that doesn't mean that the subject cannot be treated with general theoretical ideas, which I have always found to be useful for the sketching and framing of boundaries and empty spaces. That both volumes are far from complete in their presentations of theory and relevant data, given the framework of scope they adopt, is a fact the fuller specification of which by interested scholars I will take as a measure of the success of the work.

Lee Freese

Chapter 1

Conditions for Human Ecology

There is a condition often rumored to exist, which has been given various turns of expression in the twentieth century train of humanistic and social science thought. The condition is implicit in the analysis of Maryanski and Turner (1992), which finds humans to have biologically evolved to be not as social as we appear to be, notwithstanding their cultural development. Roy A. Rappaport, the anthropologist, turns this into an explicit dilemma. He makes the common observation that cultures take on a life of their own, so to speak, by organizing to serve the needs, goals, values, and purposes of humans. But, then, "It becomes no longer clear whether culture is a symbolic means to organic ends, or whether organisms are living means to culture's ends, for humans come to serve and preserve their cultures as much as, or even more than, their cultures serve and preserve them" (1990, p. 56). A possible, if not likely, effect is that the requisites of culture "may come to be at odds with the organic needs of the humans striving to live by and fulfill [the requisites], and may also violate the ecosystems in which they are fulfilled." Rappaport's Dilemma is that "the cultural properties of human populations may be inimical to their organic characteristics" (p. 56).

Rappaport omitted to elaborate, but let us be clear to state, that this condition may be imminent by virtue of the following cascade that has a self-reinforcing motion to it: (1) Humans are organically connected to ecosystems; (2) the prime impact of sociocultural organization on ecosystems has been to transform energy and food chains, shortening the chains and placing humans at the top; and (3) following upon their long-cascading interactions with human sociocultural systems, modern ecosystems give evidence of massive disorganization and correlative human environmental degradation—results that can hardly be said to be in the organic interests of humans. Is there something inherent in

1

human evolutionary or environmental connections to cause an increasing tension in the complex of sociocultural and organic-ecological interactions?

Rappaport's Dilemma is a problem for both theory and practice. But how in theory are we to characterize the disorganization of ecosystems due to sociocultural impacts; how are we to measure the consequences for sociocultural systems following upon environmental degradation; and what conclusions for practice should we draw? Indeed, how even should we frame the themes that emerge from the massive and often disparate literatures now devoted to these matters? In what theory-bracketing terms shall we interpret them?

There is a science that in principle can fully address the condition rumored in Rappaport's Dilemma, and there is no other science that can. The science is human ecology, and no other has the reach to produce a full, general theory of human evolutionary and environmental connections that an adequate account of the condition demands. For the most part, however, human ecology has paid its respects from afar, periodically noting the condition with assorted curtsies to human evolutionary and environmental connections but without fully describing them—and thus failing to explain the condition and even failing to establish whether the condition itself is true or is just a long standing rumor mongered by discomfited intellectuals.

Why?

THE INDIVIDUALIZING OF HUMAN ECOLOGY

Human ecology does not now have clear definition as a science in its own right. It is something of a tagalong to biology, anthropology, sociology, geography, psychology, and economics. All those sciences lay claim to human ecology in some sense or other. The only common thread is the concept of an environment. But what counts as an environment is not common, and so conceptions of human ecology abound, virtually all of them colored by the dependency that human ecological studies have had on the parent scientific disciplines that have nurtured them.

One result is that, for the most part, human ecology is pursued within the frameworks *of* those parent disciplines. To take one example, a sociologist usually considers human ecology as falling within the scope of sociology and so formulates problems of human ecology as essentially sociological problems that have an ecological or environmental cast. In practice, this means that something thought to be ecological is conceived, usually by way of analogy to a biological idea, and is incorporated into a sociological theory because it is thought that the explanation of a problematic sociological process requires reference to something environmental, something in the context in which the sociological process is situated. Since that something resembles the sorts of things that biological ecologists talk about in reference to their own systems, the result is called human ecology. The system now, in the case of the sociologist, is different from the system of the biologist, but retained is the attempt to identify something ecological about it. This is done in the service of solving a sociological problem, which is the focal point, with both the problem and solution oriented to a network of sociologists and their criteria for what counts as sociologically worthy. The orientation is not toward human ecology per se, but to the human ecology of sociology.

The example generalizes to biology, anthropology, geography, and economics in one particular: Human ecology is conceived by all these general sciences as a specialization that is individually tailored to their general science. The term human ecology is not always used.[1] Anthropologists sometimes use it and sometimes also speak of ecological anthropology, though only a lawyer could defend claims to a difference, while economists almost never use the term but, instead, speak of ecological or environmental economics. In all cases, except in biology, whose theory is more developed, ecology is thought to represent a unique perspective on their general subject matter. Social scientists, following the manner in which bioecologists can be heard to talk about the ecology of caves or of estuaries, may hold forth on the ecology of bureaucratic organizations, or built environments, or some preliterate tribe.

In addition to general sciences that individualize human ecology for the study of subjects x, y, or z, many scientists specialize in subjects that touch upon human ecology but are not devoted to it. The subjects include evolutionary biology, evolutionary ecology, ecosystems ecology, community ecology, primatology, socioecology, systems theory, environmental sociology, ecological economics, ecological demography, ecological geography, historical demography, epidemiology, population biology, archaeology, and others. To fully harvest human ecology, all these fields have to be picked. If one is looking for closure, matters are rather untidy.

Conceptions of human ecology, accordingly, differ by a wide margin—as wide as the sciences that claim it for a subject matter but including also some that do not. How wide is that? It extends to any process having to do with humans and any of their environments, and any of the environments humans create. Now, that takes in a great deal—so much that many conceptions of human ecology hardly overlap. Is human ecology the study of the conditions and strategies by which humans subsist in their environments? Some presume this. Is it the study of the social epidemiology of disease? Some presume that. Is it the study of the population-resource-environment dilemma? Many now seem to think so. Is it the study of the maintenance and change of human communities and residential areas in urban environments? Some still say that. If social environments are considered, must biophysical environments also be considered? Some say not, while others are astounded at the very thought of not. We could interpret all this intellectual diversity as a positive sign that augurs for the growth of human ecology as a general science. I don't think so.

An invitation to a general science issues forth only from general theory and its supporting evidence, not from a scientific cacophony gathered together under a single concept, in this case the environments and environizing of humans. Imagine, if you will, a symphony being performed without its movements first having been orchestrated, and without their having being scored, for the performers. There has to be something that ties that symphony together, and those ties have to be communicated to get a unified, structured, interpretable result. Otherwise, we get a cacophony of sounds called forth by the absence of common thematic structures and by each performer having a different concept of the composition. Human ecology today is like that unscored symphony. The general theory that would unify its different traditions has not been orchestrated. But I do not wish to gainsay the idea of human ecology as a general science. To the contrary, I want to promote it.

THE SPECIALIZING OF HUMAN ECOLOGY

Why should different academic sciences interpret the study of human ecology in different ways and not always refer to what they are doing as human ecology even when it is? If there is not a unifying general theory for human ecology which could make it a general science, is there reason to suppose such theory can be developed? What stands in the way?

One thing that stands in the way is the academic and professional organization of the sciences. They are departmentalized and institutionalized, and their ideas are specialized and sometimes compartmentalized. As a matter of historical fact, many scientific subject matters having certain common themes were investigated over the course of decades and, as American universities especially grew in number, scope, and influence and became more formal about a century ago, academic sciences that had slowly emerged became administratively organized. They had to be, to facilitate their teaching and further development. Frequently, in this century, particularly in recent times, the administrative organization of the general fields of science has been supported by special interests, such as governments or foundations or private parties (which universities actively solicit), who had some stake in the continued investigation of particular subject matters. All this has encouraged scientific specialization, now at its apex in our times in which we routinely find cause for interdisciplinary studies.

Once observation and discourse turn to the restrictive administrative organization of science within universities and within professional scientific organizations, over long periods of time, which permits the development of vested interests, we are no longer talking about science as a body of knowledge, nor about the world as the sciences describe it, nor about the formation and solution of scientific and intellectual problems that yield discoveries about natural phenomena. Now we are talking about the politics and sociology of formal organizations, especially of universities, governments, and private enterprises, and of the professional associations that serve and seek to maintain the privileged status of those who represent the institutionalized academic fields. When human interests become institutionalized in organizations that fund those interests, the interests and the activities in pursuit of them become entrenched—a condition that universities explicitly (if benignly) foster in their procedures for evaluating scientific personnel.

All this can get in the way of discovering general truths about natural phenomena, which is what I take science to be all about. The point has often been made: The academic organization of science encourages the specialization of ideas and discourages their generalization, ever the more as sciences become institutionalized, professionalized, and departmentalized. We know there is compartmentalized thinking in these sciences when we encounter a negative reaction, or just plain indifference, to a suggestion that some subject matters legitimately cross traditional discipline boundaries—cross them because, objectively speaking, that is how natural phenomena are constituted. Unfortunately for the narrow of mind, the administrative and professional organization of the fields of academic science does not always correspond to our knowledge of the laws of nature that describe how phenomena are constituted. Indeed, the organization of the sciences usually lags some measure behind science itself. But it is difficult to reason with people who have drawn lines in the dirt and dared you to cross. If administrative ways of organizing the sciences are taken as touchstones to define the natural organization of phenomena, with different turf assigned to different scientific fields, which then exert proprietary claims, the discovery of nature's laws is impeded. Unfortunately for the open of mind, so it has been with human ecology.

Scientific human ecology has been the creation of academic scientists, and modern research universities reflect the historical development of human ecological studies. Since human ecology has not yet been established as a general science, very few universities contain academic departments with that name. As a matter of administrative convenience, human ecologists are scattered. However, whether some subject matter is itself general or is a specialization within a more general subject matter, depends not at all on the organizational contrivances of universities. It depends upon how nature is organized and how well our theories and data describe that organization. Nature doesn't care how universities are organized.

THE GENERALIZING OF HUMAN ECOLOGY

Taking into account everything that gets called human ecology, a paradox presents itself. On the one hand, an implicit concept of human ecology has crystallized by default—the concept that human ecology entertains everything having to do with human environments and human environizing. This concept is so broad as to be vacuous and, perhaps, not even internally consistent. On the other hand, in service of the default, in no traditional science has the pursuit of human ecological studies extended its concept of human ecology far enough. Biologists go so far as to recognize that humans constitute populations of ecologically significant social animals—significant especially for our destructive impacts on natural habitats. But humans are more than this, as social scientists well know: We are socially *organized and acculturated* populations of animals. With few exceptions, biologists are disinclined to consider the ecological significance of those additional properties, which traditionally have been the turf of social scientists. Ecologically significant they are, however, so a general science of human ecology has to reach that far.

Yet, as I implied, the reach of social scientists doesn't extend far enough either. Social scientists have especially wanted to develop ecological explanations of culture, social organization, technology, and other such matters that have seemed important to them, and to integrate these subjects into an overall framework of sociocultural theory. In doing this, they have often drawn analogies from biological problematics, as we shall see, and have often contributed concepts in return that bioecologists have found useful. But an integrated body of human ecological theory that generalizes beyond provincial disciplinary problematics has not been social scientists' primary objective. So there have been and continue to be discontinuities in the development and practice of biological ecology and human ecology.

But there do not have to be discontinuities and, if nature is any guide, there ought not to be. Throughout this work, we shall adopt the position of John A. Moore, a biologist, who put the matter this way: "All human history is but a reflection of the workings of ecological principles" (1985, p. 377). Another way to put it is that all human activities bear some connection to natural environments. That thought, however obvious it may be to biologists, to many social scientists seems strange. Some of them just don't get it.

What, for instance, is the possible relevance of natural environments for a purely social and thoroughly mundane activity such as the filing of an income tax statement reporting the additional income afforded by the royalties being paid to me on sales of this book? Surely the activities of my accountant, who spends a lot of time reading the tax code, and the accountants who will read the form he prepares, according to the political, social, and cultural norms established for such activities and worthy of description on their own terms, have no connection whatsoever to natural environments.

Well, it isn't so. My accountant can spend his leisure time reading the tax code and his professional time interpolating it only because, in the meantime, his office is supplied with heat, his car with gasoline, and his refrigerator with food. If he had to chop his own firewood, care for his own horse, and grow his own corn, he could not be an accountant. Indeed, if all those creature comforts of his were not supplied to him by other segments of human society, there would be no profession of accounting for him to belong to. Sociologists call that a division of labor. Without a sufficient division of labor in human society, grounded to natural environments, my accountant would have to account for himself instead of the tax obligations of others. With a sufficient division of labor, which frees him from direct physical labor with natural environments, he can account for himself *by* accounting for the tax obligations of others. But his activities are no less dependent upon natural environments just because he is many orders removed from them.

The conditions of human existence that ground human ecology are these: Human beings have to eat and come in out of the cold. Pressed to provision ourselves for subsistence, we utilize or transform what we are naturally given. The givens all originate in some biophysical environment or process. Provided some culture to go with the biophysical givens, then humans can innovate but we need help even there. We cannot survive singly, as individuals. We have to organize socially. Dependent upon natural environments to survive and sociocultural environments to organize our survival, we are enabled ecologically to function. But the ecological function is not one way. In the natural course of going about our affairs, we perforce affect the natural environments we draw upon to survive. As we affect those, human social organization and the culture built around it are affected in turn. Thus, the web of human ecology is part and thread in the larger web of the ecology of life. This means that bioecology and human ecology in theory are all of a piece.

Human Ecology and the Ecology of Humans

Why, then, single out human ecology for special attention? Because human ecology is not a question just of the population dynamics and environmental impacts of humans treated as just one more species. Humans bring more than mere numbers that consume biomass in competition with other living things. Not that our numbers and biotic dominance are trivial. Total human population is doubling every 40 years now, and by one estimate, humans directly or indirectly consume (or waste) 40 percent of the net primary productivity of terrestrial ecosystems (Vitousek, Ehrlich, Ehrlich, and Matson 1986).[2] Facts like that, however, do not imply that human ecology "belongs" to biology, which is how biologists tend to see it, and that human ecological relationships can be accounted for with reference just to bioecological processes. The monumental impact on biophysical processes of systems of human sociocultural organization, in all its social, political, economic, urban, and demographic dimensions, and the impacts which that altered biophysical organization is having on our sociocultural organization in turn, and has had for a very long time now, make it impossible to reduce human ecology to human biology. We have to look to human sociocultural organization and its interactions with bioecological organization to understand the special ecology of humans.

To say there is a special ecology of humans in which society and culture play a substantial role is not to say that human ecology belongs to the social sciences either, even though they staked the first claim to it. A special ecology of humans is a complicated extension of the general ecology of living things. From a biological vantage point, it appears as if human ecology is the general ecology of humans. From a social science vantage point, it appears as if human ecology is *human* ecology—our ecology, the ecology of us. It is both, because one cannot be fully understood without the other.

To fully understand any species so dominant as humans, in relation to their environmental contexts, one has to fully understand *how biophysical and sociocultural systems adapt together, change together, integrate* and *disintegrate* as a function of each other. One further has to understand how those interacting systems affect, and are affected by, the individuals that function as interactants in the systems. In sum, one has to fully understand human evolutionary and environmental connections. A tall order, to be sure, but that is the promise of human ecology. It is a promise not now fulfilled. General theory that crosses over, together with supporting evidence, is the only means eventually to make good on it.

Human Ecological Theories versus Perspectives

Some investigators with an ecological frame of mind try to make good on the promise by applying something less than general theory to their subject matters—often what the investigators call an ecological perspective. Perspective is a term favored by social scientists for use in polite society when they have no real, testable theory. In its place, they will have an "approach" or "orientation"—an "ecological perspective" when they are thinking about their subject in ecological terms.

For instance, historians sometimes take an ecological perspective on history. We should be grateful that at least a few of them do this, but what does it mean to do this? It means applying ecological theory to develop and interpret patterns of historical data, for the purpose of gaining insights and learning truths not otherwise apparent. What sort of truths? Therein lies the difference between human ecological theories and an ecological perspective on humans. One could establish through investigation human ecological relationships not heretofore known, or historical relationships not heretofore known, or some combination. If one uses ecological theory to establish human historical relationships not heretofore known, one has an ecological perspective on history. Alternatively, one could use human historical data interpreted with ecological theory to extend the known domain of human ecological relationships. The first of these attitudes has been and continues to be dominant.

Because of that, human ecology is often referred to as a perspective in sociology or an approach to demography or an orientation in anthropology. This is a curious way to think. Is chemistry an orientation or political science an approach? An orientation or approach to what? The only reasonable answer is an orientation or an approach to *natural phenomena and their lawful organization.* What else could chemistry be an orientation to, a perspective on, or an approach toward? Chemistry is not a perspective on biology, or biology on chemistry, that eventually came to be called biochemistry. If we talk about biochemistry, we are talking about natural systems and processes that are organized in biochemical terms—that is to say, in the terms of systematic biochemical theory. Discovering empirical truths about these systems and processes can solve problems that neither classical chemistry nor classical biology could solve alone, which is why biochemical theory and data have been so extensively developed. To be developed, they had to cross over, which is to say a domain of investigation incorporating both biology and chemistry had to be defined.

It takes human ecology too lightly to call it a perspective or an orientation to humans and their environments. That's somewhat like saying hematology is a perspective on the blood, or pathology an orientation to disease. Sciences are bodies of theory applicable, together with their relevant evidence, to bounded domains of natural phenomena. To apply a "perspective" to a subject is to use theory implicitly, but to leave the theory so implicit as to be no more than perspectival is to render the domain of the subject undecidable and, in effect, to surrender knowledge of its lawful organization.

THE SCOPE OF HUMAN ECOLOGY

In the case of human ecology, there is no question that its domain extends farther than has traditionally and ordinarily been conceived. Different academic sciences have extended the study of human ecology in different ways. To bind human ecology to any of the general sciences that claim it is to foreclose entire classes of problems that *other* sciences can logically and empirically show are both human and ecological. Human ecology, in theory, cannot be a specialization within traditional sciences because its phenomena cannot be contained within their domains.[3]

We therefore cannot proceed here as if human ecological phenomena are the province of any particular established science. We have to proceed on the assumption that they form, at least potentially, a general science in its own right. The potential will be realized when the domain of the theory of human ecology includes phenomena that transcend the various special fields that can contribute. That hasn't happened much yet. The integration of human ecological ideas has not been a prime undertaking, so human ecology is not now practiced as a general science, nor often thought of that way. We shall think of it that way throughout this work, and will try to organize the ideas of human ecology, whatever their source, as if they belonged to a general science whose theory is in the process of developing.

For the present work, we exclude from the scope of our subject anything other than scientific human ecology. Thus, we omit consideration of numerous topics that some take to fall within human ecology but not within the science of it. Richard J. Borden[4] (1986) and Gerald L. Young (1994), to cite two influential examples, take the view that human ecology extends beyond science to include the humanities, the arts, and architectural design.

When ecological discourse ranges into the arts, humanities, and education, I am inclined to call it humanistic ecology. I recognize the boundaries between the sciences and the humanities can be fuzzy, and this work does not presume any hard and fast distinction between objective and subjective inquiries. But there is some purpose served by distinguishing human from humanistic ecology, and by focussing on the one and not the other. For one, the term ecology has been coopted by many who have felt the need to develop or proselytize for their personal environmental zeitgeist, and it can connotate meta-scientific matters ranging from what Bramwell (1989) calls ecologism to versions of ecological humanism and even environmental and spiritual cults—some of which pay little attention to scientific ecology, human or otherwise, and sometimes even distort scientific findings for political purposes. Whatever the merits of the philosophy, esthetics, and politics of ecology, and of various environmental movements, these subjects are different from the science and are not ours. We shall transcend the science of human ecology only to consider such matters briefly, and then only at the very end (in Part B, *Environmental Connections*), to see how they might inform the science.

No dogmatic attitude is intended by delimiting the subject so. Rather, this decision is pragmatic. A broader definition of human ecology would exceed the stated scope of the annual series to which these supplemental volumes belong, and our framing of the scope of scientific human ecology is broad enough to fully occupy us as it is.

So, with what concept shall we frame a proper scope for scientific human ecology? Colloquially speaking, some scientific matter should fall within human ecology if it concerns both humans and ecology, one would think, and this presumes that ecology is given biological interpretations. Formally, we may define human ecology as a domain of theoretical and empirical investigation of the following lawful phenomena: the structural and functional patterns and changes in human social organization and sociocultural behavior that are effects of, interdependent with, or identical to changes in evolutionary, ecosystemic, or ethological processes, factors, or conditions. Three degrees of scope are included in this definition of the domain of human ecology: (1) the adaptations of sociocultural to biophysical phenomena; (2) the interactions between sociocultural and biophysical phenomena; and (3) the integration of sociocultural with biophysical phenomena.

This definition of the scope of human ecology may seem rather unorthodox, depending upon one's scientific perspective.[5] But heterodoxy is demanded by our factual knowledge of the world. Consider the myriad of subjects arrayed in Figure 1.1.

The general sciences that appear at the top and the bottom of the figure provide source material for the multifarious subjects of investigation arrayed in the figure. These subjects, we shall find, all have some known bearing, to some degree or other, on human ecology. None concerns human ecology alone. However, all provide either pertinent principles or facts pertaining directly or indirectly to human evolutionary or environmental relationships. Since we know that evolution and environments connect, the domain of human ecology now

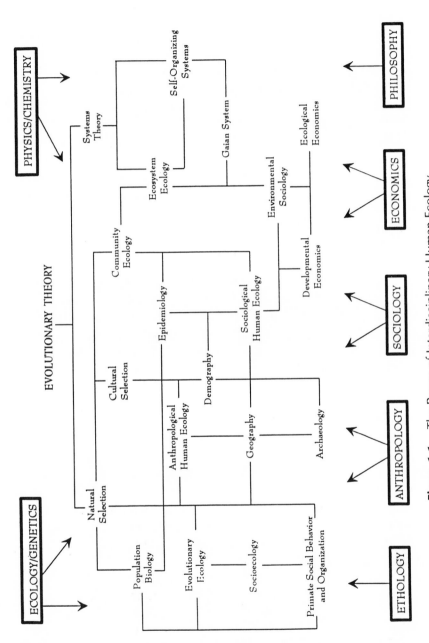

Figure 1.1. The Range of Interdisciplinary Human Ecology

13

becomes framed by nothing less than the relationships humans have and have had to their evolutionary past, biological and sociocultural, and to their biophysical environments.

It goes without saying that there are many empty spaces in, and much room to develop, the general human ecological theory that could integrate what the distinct bodies of knowledge arrayed in Figure 1.1 have to offer. Such development and integration implies, in my view, that no problem of human ecology can be fully comprehended if it is taken to exist in isolation or as a complete problem in its own right. For instance, if the human contribution to global warming is defined as a problem of human ecology, then first, this environmental connection humans now have must be explained in the context of other human environmental connections now extant, and second, the pattern of environmental connections in which anthropogenic global warming is embedded must itself be understood in the context of human evolution, which has set contingencies for the contemporary environmental processes and conditions in which humans are implicated. The premise generalizes to any human ecological problem: Where we are, environmentally speaking, is partly a function of our evolutionary heritage and trajectories, and even a tentative and incomplete mapping of evolutionary changes and environmental connections is necessary to define the terrain of human ecology.

Evolution tells about change and ecology tells about connections, and together they tell about changing connections. Human connections to environments have been changing not for any organic evolutionary change but for sociocultural evolutionary change. If Rappaport's Dilemma were irrelevant, then human ecology might not matter; perhaps it could be taken for granted and its science might have no significant problem to address.[6] But Rappaport's Dilemma is real. It is important to know how so, in what ways and under what conditions, because if the tension between ecological and human sociocultural systems continues to increase as the future unfolds, eventually something could snap. Without a general science of human ecology, we wouldn't know why.

NOTES

1. See, for instance, the excellent volume of human ecology by I.G. Simmons (1989), which the author hesitates to call human ecology. A psychologist, Paul C. Stern (1993),

has called for a second environmental science—of human-environmental interactions. That is another name for an old, underdeveloped science, human ecology. When the term is used, it often designates ostensibly different subjects with very little common ground. Anthropologists, such as Campbell (1995), usually strike wholly different attitudes from sociologists, such as Micklin and Choldin (1984).

2.   This estimate fell within the range provided earlier by Woodwell (1974).

3.   The problem here has been discussed before, and interdisciplinary approaches have often been proposed as the only solution. See, for example, a comparable statement by an anthropologist (Anderson 1973) and an economist (Daly and Cobb 1989).

4.   Borden, by academic training a psychologist, is human ecology's most effective entrepreneur. Co-founder of the Society for Human Ecology, Borden is president of the College of the Atlantic, located in Bar Harbor, Maine, an undergraduate institution of higher learning whose curriculum is devoted exclusively to human ecological studies. From Borden's point of view, human ecology is inseparable from educational development.

5.   Too broad for some, too narrow for others. Some human ecologists in the social sciences may think that this definition of scope, too broad for many of them, should be defended completely before proceeding any further. I defer a full defense until the opening chapter of Part B, *Environmental Connections*. There, I argue that it avails nothing to tacitly equate everything environmental with something ecological. I further argue against the notion, apparent in Young (1989, 1994), that human ecology incorporates the social sciences in all their glories. And I do not follow—I do not even understand—the position of those, such as Bennett, who claim that "Humans ... have the capacity to perceive the self in relation to the environment, which is *of course* the basis of human ecology" (1993, p. 31; emphasis added). Of course? There would be a basis to human ecology with or without that capacity. To emphasize for social scientists, who are so caught up in symbolic matters of the mind, the significance of biophysical matters, to which few of them attend, human ecology is framed throughout this work as if it had very little to do with matters of the mind.

6.   This is polite rhetoric offerred as an apparent concession to doubters whom I wish to persuade of the significance of human ecology; I don't really believe it. It just happens that the general problem of human ecology which I have here called Rappaport's Dilemma (he did not call it that) in one version or another has gained the most notice in current intellectual and public discourse and, therefore, provides the most reliable anchor in terms of which to cast human ecology. Of equal human ecological significance, in my view, and virtually certain to attract greater notice in future intellectual and public discourse—this is just now beginning—are questions of the epidemiology of infectious diseases (see Chapter 5). The combination of increased human population densities with modern sociocultural conditions and practices virtually assure increases in human mortality due to epidemic diseases and, therefore, assure that human ecology will have significant problems to address for a long time to come.

Chapter 2

Biological Evolution

There is no unbroken sequence of logic and fact by which can be traced, with parsimony and full justice, human evolutionary patterns and their connections to contemporary human environmental conditions. We shall eventually see that the logic and facts available at present to connect these matters finish in some paradoxes—a sure sign that various points of logic and fact are missing. Significant among the missing are connections of theory and fact to relate biological to cultural evolution and its ecology. Some vision of these connections is a necessary condition for Rappaport's Dilemma to unfold. One paradox to be revealed is how the validity of the Dilemma (not in full view until the end of the book) harks back to some of the concepts that guided the original formulation of the theory of evolution by natural selection.

There can be no ecological process without some biological evolutionary process or processes. Therefore, human ecology connects to the flow of biological evolution. Unfortunately, to try to connect the two straightway is to place the cart before the horse; for, it happens also, there are missing connections of theory to relate biological evolution to biological ecology. I can state the difficulty we confront in this work no better than did two authorities on the history and philosophy of evolutionary theory (Depew and Weber 1995, p. 404):

> ... although ecology was once closely linked to evolutionary thinking, evolution and ecology have for the better part of this century been in tension with each other. The original ecology emerged within a developmentalist vision of evolution. It was displaced with the rise of modern Darwinism.... We hear today calls for reunion between ecology and evolutionary theory ... ecology is fast becoming an architectonic discipline within which a new ethics of care for the earth and a "green politics" is [sic] being nurtured. It seems crucial to have an evolutionary theory that interfaces well with this vision of nature. Those who call for interanimation between evolutionary biology and ecology should not assume,

therefore, that what they are asking for will be easy to achieve. It will require radical changes in both evolutionary theory and in ecology. In particular it will require the resources of the [complex systems theory revolution] to revitalize, and demystify, the old developmental ecology, and to defend the claim that autonomous ecological dynamics are a powerful causal factor in evolutionary change.

Throughout, we shall have to consider and provisionally settle upon some presumed connections in ecological and evolutionary streams. We take the assessments of Depew and Weber as establishing our discursive base. Social scientists have been unable, from the time of the nineteenth century, to shake the notion that sociocultural evolution has a developmental component, and twentieth century human-environmental interactions have prompted increasing numbers of people to adopt this "new ethics of care for the earth" to which Depew and Weber refer and on which this work concludes. Finally, to serve the aim of continuity for subjects that otherwise may be unconnectable, we shall assume that future theoretical solutions to human ecological problems do, indeed, depend upon the development of the theory of nonlinear, complex, dynamical systems far from thermodynamic equilibrium. The various conceptual turns we shall take, especially as regards evolution, are intended to be consistent with these views. Unlike Depew and Weber, whose definitive work so marvelously describes the rich panoply of developments and implications in evolutionary theory in the past 30 years, we shall have to content ourselves merely with the incomplete recounting of uncontroversial facts or the taking of controversial positions, without presenting full defense, that only future theoretical developments will be able to vindicate. There is no alternative, for a domain as large as human ecology, but to undertake abbreviated treatments of the various boundary conditions that define the domain.[1]

Given the natural connection long presumed between evolution and ecology, the theory of natural selection must be adequately situated in an evolutionary framework that will accommodate the development of human ecological theory along the trajectory assumed above. Some evolutionary framework has always been implicit in human ecology, owing to the influence of Darwin. The idea of adaptation to environments was central to the Darwinian theory and has been a centerpiece of scientific ecology since then—a root out of which grew much of what is taken to qualify as ecological analysis. The concept has supplied a paradigm for human ecology from its outset, and is implicit or explicit in the diverse interpretations of the subject that abound. Geographers tell us that human spatial relations and physical arrangements are adaptations to environments. Anthropologists tell us that culture is an adaptation to environments. Sociologists tell us that social organization is an adaptation to environments. And some theoretical biologists and philosophers of biology tell us that natural selection is the selection *of* adaptations to environments, which are the sites of evolution.

As things stand, biologists and social scientists often do not have the same meanings in mind, nor the same intended interpretations, for the concepts of adaptation *or* environment. Social scientists employ a very general concept of adaptation (and not always the same one), which serves as an over-arching, interpretive frame—again, a paradigm concept. No such concept is part of the *nomenclature* of the modern biological theory of evolution (although more specialized concepts, such as adaptive value, can be found). In contrast to the original Darwinian theory, the elements of the modern theory can be rendered without much reference to an over-arching concept of adaptation, as did Grant (1991), on whom we rely here, although such a concept is often intended, inferred, or used to buttress the theory when it is interpreted to explain particular circumstances or to provide theoretical coherence (see, for example, Brooks and McLennan 1991, chap. 5).

A brief sketch of the biological theory of evolution by natural selection follows now, so that we may evaluate some issues of its interpretation which bear upon the grounding of human ecological explanations. Eventually, we shall see that the theory is never entirely adequate for human ecological explanations, but never entirely dispensable either.

THE EVOLUTION OF THE THEORY OF NATURAL SELECTION

If, as we said, there can be no ecological process without an evolutionary process, something like the converse is also true: There can be no biological evolution without a confluence of ecological plus genetic conditions. The original Darwinian theory emphasized ecological conditions. Subsequently, population-genetic and molecular-genetic foundations were added, and now they predominate for expository as well as explanatory purposes.

Ecological Foundations

Charles Darwin's interest in explaining the origin of species grew from his own natural history studies and from the intellectual ferment of his time, which accorded increasing significance to evolutionary theories. The idea of the evolution of species by descent with modification was in the air, but its acceptance awaited a satisfactory explanation. The explanation on which Darwin eventually settled was influenced by two of his contemporaries, Alfred Wallace, a biologist, and Herbert Spencer, an erstwhile biologist turned sociologist and philosopher. All three had read, and Darwin especially was significantly influenced by, an English political economist who had preceded them by more than a generation: T.R. Malthus.

Malthus, whose principal concern was the condition of English poor people and the laws governing them, observed their condition and thought he discerned in it a competitive struggle for survival that would manifest itself in population growth and decline associated with conditions of morbidity, owing to different mathematical functions he presumed to govern human reproductive potential compared to subsistence potential. Thus, Malthus hypothesized that more people could and would be born than could possibly survive and prosper, and there would be natural checks (a euphemism for war, pestilence, and famine) on growth in the size of human populations. Darwin, Wallace, and Spencer seized on this theory, knowing it to be factually correct for a large number of living species. Spencer supplied a phrase that became infamous—survival of the fittest—which Darwin reluctantly but eventually adopted at the urging of Wallace. Wallace had developed ideas about evolution similar to Darwin's and, in fact, had publicly presented them at the same conference at which Darwin first made known his version of natural selection. Spencer, a correspondent with different and far more extensive ideas about evolution, got lost in sociological implications.[2] With the passage of time, the contributions of Wallace were discounted (some say unfairly).[3] Of the three, it was Darwin who most fully developed the evolutionary implications of his own data into the logic of the theory of natural selection.

Today, it is called the Darwinian theory. Every standard rendering of it alludes to its ecological context for natural selection: (1) The members of a population vary in their morphological, physiological, and behavioral traits—their phenotypes; (2) a population tends to produce more offspring than can be supported by its habitat; (3) there ensues thus a competition for resources in the habitat; and (4) those organisms whose phenotypes better suit them to compete for resources are more likely to survive, thus more likely to reproduce, thus will leave more offspring—in a word, will be favored by natural selection because by virtue of their phenotypes they are better adapted to their habitat. Natural selection operates on individual organisms inasmuch as they, and nothing else, are selected for or against in this struggle of the fit to survive. But the result is the *population* of them is gradually changed by the preservation of favorable variations and the elimination of unfavorable variations. Provided there is phenotypic variation and habitat variation, this natural selection of better adapted organisms would gradually produce organic evolution over the very long term.

The Darwinian version is still rehearsed because no one seriously doubts the ecological foundation of natural selection that Darwin provided. Some qualifications have to be added, as befits the advance of ecology since Darwin's time, concerning the misleading impressions left by the idea of survival of the fittest. That unfortunate phrase of Spencer, inspired as it was by the world view of Malthus and the culture of entrepreneurial capitalism, which was expanding at the time, has been an unending source of intellectual mischief—prompting false or simplistic pronouncements about nature as well as society. In the case of nature, we know now that a couple of the assumptions listed above are not always true: Whatever the inherent reproductive potential of species, many do not "over-reproduce," and there is not always competition for resources to the point where nature is "red in tooth and claw." Early Darwinian theory was interpreted to imply that there is a natural and severe competition between organisms for survival. But competition need not be severe. Indeed, some evolutionary biologists argue that selection is most intense when competition is at its *lowest* (Williams 1966). Also, competition for survival and reproduction is not always a competition of individuals. Competition can involve entire populations, perhaps entire species, depending upon the scale of environmental habitat one is considering—a local habitat or the entire biosphere.[4]

Quaiifications notwithstanding (there are others besides these), the Darwinian theory supplies an ecological foundation for biological evolution in its emphasis on the natural selection of phenotypic variants according to their fit with the variable features of habitats in which selection occurs. Nowadays the emphasis is different. Instead of focusing on phenotypic variation, the modern evolutionary lens is trained on genetic variation, a subject of which Darwin never knew, although he might have, for the initial experiments in genetics by Gregor Mendel were done in Darwin's lifetime. The development of population genetics would provide a secure foundation for establishing the significance of natural selection.

Population-Genetic Foundations

Biological evolution, as a natural process, came to be accepted in intellectual circles perhaps half a century before the theory of natural selection enjoyed the same acceptance. In the early twentieth century especially, Darwin's preferred explanation fell into disfavor. It regained favor with the advances of population genetics.

The modern population-genetic theory of evolution by natural selection is called neo-Darwinian, sometimes genic selectionism, sometimes the Modern Synthesis. The modern synthesis of evolutionary theory (the term comes from a book by Julian Huxley in 1942) was forged in the 1930s and 1940s through the efforts of numerous biologists—Ernst Mayr, George Gaylord Simpson, and Theodosius Dobzhansky principal among them, but including also G.L. Stebbins, Bernhard Rensch, and Huxley. They all drew upon the work of many others, including Sewall Wright, J.B.S. Haldane, and R.A. Fisher, known for his statistical techniques. The synthesis consisted of integrating the theory and findings of population genetics, paleontology, and systematics, with the Darwinian theory. Prior to this time, there had been a bewildering array of biological theories of evolution, in some of which natural selection played little or no role. The modern synthesis of evolutionary theory, forged as a logical construction of principles and evidence, placed natural selection front and center among the faces of evolutionary theory.

Population genetics developed partly in desire to explain the results of breeding experiments that seemed to produce patterned outcomes, and early models focussed on patterns of the kind observed in the experiments of Mendel, whose long dormant work was revitalized in 1900. Experimenting for fully half a century prior to the critical discoveries of molecular biology, population geneticists found it convenient to assume the existence of genes as hypothetical entities constituted as definite, particle-like units. The term Mendelian gene is sometimes employed for this unit concept of the gene as idealized abstraction. With some additional simplifying assumptions, the properties of simple Mendelian systems with single gene variations may be characterized, which for our purposes should be sufficient to establish the flavor of genic selectionism.

To simplify, assume random mating in populations of a sexually reproducing species. Allow genetic recombination to occur with the pairing off and segregation of homologous chromosomes at the time of reproduction. Assume the population is diploid, meaning that the sex cells of males and females have only half the number of chromosomes as other somatic cells. Allow that, at the same locus (or point) on matching chromosomes, there may appear alternate forms, called alleles, of the same gene (then called polymorphic); that the different alleles may encode for the same trait, one of which might be dominant, notated A, and the other recessive, notated a; or that both could be dominant and both recessive, notated as A_1, A_2, or a_1, a_2, respectively. (Some alleles might be neither, but that is one of many complications we don't need.) Further allow that, for a given gene, there might be just one form of it or there might be many alternate alleles, and that different individuals may carry, though they need not express, the different alleles. Define the sum of all the alleles of a given individual as the individual's genotype (allowing that particular combinations, such as aa, also may be called genotypes). Define the sum of all the alleles in a reproducing population as the population's gene pool. Finally, assume that alleles are fundamental to the expression of phenotypic characters.

Infer, with this conceptual system,[5] that when the distribution of alleles in a gene pool changes, the change should be reflected in the distribution of phenotypes in the reproducing population. It was, of course, changed phenotypic distributions ranging from the appearance and disappearance of entire species that had given rise to the idea of evolution by descent with modification in the first place. With the Mendelian gene comes the idea to consider evolution from a microscopic point of view, the view that observable phenotypes reflect underlying lawful dynamics in the germ line. Early, it was assumed that phenotypic characters acquired from environmental influences on organisms could not be inherited through the germ line, an assumption that would simplify the underlying dynamics. Then it could be shown that simple lawlike ratios (called Mendelian ratios) could be generated from experiments that satisfied simple Mendelian systems. For example, the probability $= 1/2$ of obtaining offspring having a genotype Aa for a character when both parents have that same genotype, and the probability $= 1/4$ for either *AA* and *aa*. And then it was shown that considerations such as these had bearing on the theory of natural selection, once the Hardy-Weinberg equilibrium was described.

The Hardy-Weinberg equilibrium can be used as a model for the relative frequency of alleles in subsequent generations, given certain assumptions about known gene frequencies in an ancestor population. The assumptions include random mating in a large, isolated population with no limits on its size. Also, and significantly, there is the idealized assumption of no evolutionary change occurring in the population. By assuming this, gene frequencies in subsequent generations can be computed and, under the total set of given conditions, will quickly reach equilibrium values and stay there.[6] By describing a limiting theoretical condition, the Hardy-Weinberg model provided a standard against which to measure the magnitude of evolution by natural selection *in vivo*: Departures from the limiting condition, if observed in natural populations of sufficient size (with random mating), are a certain measure of evolutionary change. The Hardy-Weinberg model describes the statics not the dynamics of population gene frequencies; but biologists observed natural dynamics that departed from the model, and this helped to persuade the doubters (not all of them at once) of the significance of Darwin's theory.

Taking an evolutionary point of view with population-genetic foundations, the pressing question is: How and why do distributions of alleles in a gene pool change over time? With the description of these changes, the evolution of assorted characters of phenotype that define species can be described. Note that now the measure of evolution becomes allelic substitutions, giving evolution a microscopic interpretation, and that natural selection, so essential in the macroscopic Darwinian theory, can now become decoupled from evolution. So it was. With the population-genetic foundation there came to be recognized four types of evolution, only one of which is natural selection; and also four types of natural selection, two of which result in no evolution.

Modes of Evolution and Selection

The different modes of evolution and natural selection recognized in the Modern Synthesis can be illustrated by assuming an initial condition in which there is a distribution of a gene with one allelic form, A_1, which is more common than an alternate allele, A_2. At issue are allele substitutions, with some change in the distribution of their relative frequencies, that have some subsequent effect on reproductive fitness.

Modes of Evolutionary Change

One mode of evolutionary change is known as gene flow. If individuals carrying one allele, say A_2, physically move into the habitat of a reproducing population (of the same species) in which A_1 is found, the effect would be to increase the frequency of A_2 in the population, specifically its frequency relative to A_1. Individuals carrying A_1 could also migrate out, of course, which would also affect the respective frequencies. Gene flow results from the physical dispersal of individual organisms (or their gametes). When interbreeding between members of the same species in different populations occurs because of dispersal, it often results in the movement or migration of alleles, observed as changed relative frequencies of the alleles in a gene pool. Biologists count this as evolutionary change and assume it will be preserved if it enhances reproductive fitness.

A second mode of evolutionary change is mutation. A_1 could undergo biochemical alteration such that it becomes A_2 (or some other allele). Mutations are regarded as the ultimate source of allelic variations. A mutation of A_1 into A_2 would increase the relative frequency of A_2 in the gene pool of the population. Most mutant genes are lethal. But when they are viable, the distribution of alleles in a gene pool changes, so that too is counted as evolution. Evolutionary change due to mutation is believed to account for only a small fraction of the total change in itself because of generally low mutation rates and unfavorable survival probabilities for mutant genes, but mutation is significant to providing the variations on which natural selection can operate—often, only after generations have passed for mutant recessive alleles. In all cases, mutations are regarded as random in the sense that they impart no direction to evolution. Randomness in the Mendelian context introduces matters of chance to evolution.

Third, in very small natural populations, evolutionary change can occur by chance alone, when the populations become reproductively isolated, perhaps by colonizing new territory. Called genetic drift, sometimes the Sewall Wright effect, the chance part comes in thus: With very few matings in a small population, the resulting allelic frequencies may depart significantly from what would be expected by chance given sufficiently large N. But we are given very small N, in which departures from true values may be expected and even severe—errors of sampling, in a sense. Such "errors," should they occur, represent evolutionary change in the population.

Finally, the carriers of one allele may be more or less suited to survive and reproduce in their habitat by virtue of their phenotypes. If the carriers of A_1 and the phenotypic traits to which it contributes survive better so that, other things equal, they reproduce more offspring than the carriers of A_2, then there will be an increase and decrease, respectively, in the frequency distribution of those alleles in the population. This is evolution by natural selection.

There are several points to note: First, evolutionary change is interpreted as changes in allele frequencies, which is not what Darwin was talking about. It nonetheless is the conceptual currency of modern evolutionary biology. Second, evolutionary change understood as redistributed allele frequencies is interpreted for, applies to, and can occur only for populations across reproductive generations. The individuals within a population cannot evolve because *their genes* do not change in relative frequency. Individuals are born with inherited genotypes, and they die with them; from birth to death, they may undergo genetic change for a variety of reasons, but the heritable genotype is not affected. Within reproductive generations, there can be development but not evolution. Evolutionary change is change measured only from one reproductive generation to succeeding generations, and it is defined as a change in relative allele frequencies for a population at those reproductive intervals. Third, the first two types of evolutionary change produce variation in the gene pool, while the second two types sort it out. That is to say, migration and mutation are causes of changing allele frequencies within reproductive generations. Genetic drift and natural selection fix the frequency of variants across reproductive generations.

For any given population, a complete explanation of its evolutionary change for a chosen time frame may require reference to all of these types, for they may interact. All, incidentally, can be given mathematical coefficients and quantitatively measured. In their measurement, it is important to distinguish genotypes from alleles, since under certain conditions genotypes may change in frequency while allele (gene) frequencies do not. Genetic variation, as a term, comprehensively refers to genotypic and allelic variation. As to the types of evolution that sort allelic variation, conventional wisdom (currently being challenged) has held that drift is minor and of interest only in small populations. Natural selection, in the modes described below, has been regarded as the major sorter of allelic variations in a gene pool.

Modes of Natural Selection

Natural selection is recognized to occur in four different modes, depending upon how genetic variants are eliminated or preserved from generation to generation. The different modes are modeled as statistical curves that correspond to different observed frequency distributions that portray outcomes of the selection process.

The first mode is called directional selection, which is what Darwin seemed mostly to be talking about. It can occur when there is variation in habitat conditions and in reproducing individuals' genetic make-up. Assume a statistically normal distribution for some polymorphic gene in some population. Directional selection describes the case where, over reproductive generations, one tail of the distribution is gradually eliminated. The selection is called directional because the mean of the distribution shifts over time, as if there were some direction to it. The impression of direction is due to the fact that what one is describing is the gradual *replacement* of alleles in the gene pool, with one form becoming more frequent and another less frequent. Thus, the shifting mean. The shift reflects a changing genetic composition of the population, not random in origin, measured from one generation to the next with respect to some variant. When an allele is replaced by directional selection, the replacement often is not total. Also, the time frame need not be long, as shown by the oft-cited textbook example of industrial melanism (see Figure 2.1).[7]

By contrast, one can speak of stabilizing selection. For this mode to occur, assume habitat stability for some long period, for some population in which assorted genetic variants are phenotypically expressed. Stabilizing selection describes the case where *both* tails of a normally distributed polymorphic gene get lopped off. Here, the extremes are selected against. Directional selection is selection *for* particular variants, under the condition of habitat variability. But if a habitat stabilizes and a population continues to prosper in it, selection tends to stabilize so as to maintain the distributions of those alleles whose phenotypes are well matched to the habitat conditions. Those phenotypes will have more reproductive success than the peripheral variants. Figure 2.2 portrays this as the extinction of the peripheral variants within the population.

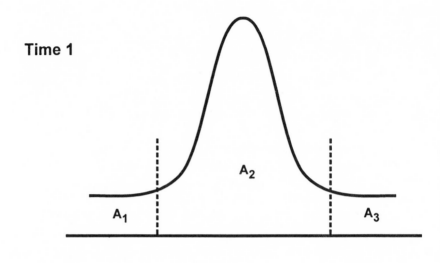

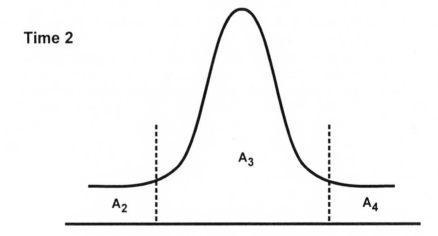

Figure 2.1. Directional Selection
A_3 becomes common, A_2 uncommon

Under stabilizing selection, an allele is gradually selected against if it appears in either tail of the distribution, whereas with directional selection, the variant in just one tail is eliminated. Directional selection gradually turns an extreme variant into a mean. Stabilizing selection describes the gradual elimination of extreme variants. Their elimination decreases

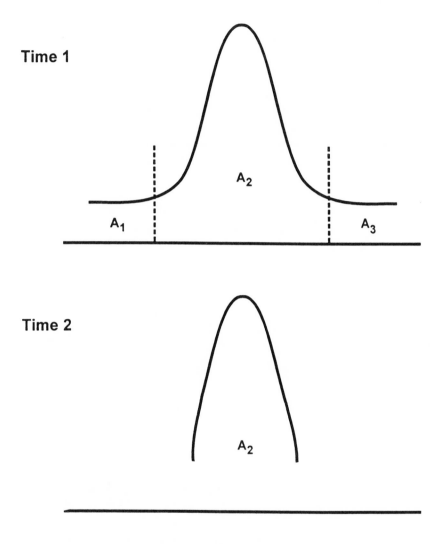

Figure 2.2. Stabilizing Selection
A_2 becomes fixed, A_1 and A_3 extinct

total genetic variation and lowers the probability that gene frequencies can change. Stabilizing selection is the process of evolution winding down. It is believed to be the most common form of selection in nature.

A third mode is called disruptive selection, sometimes better called diversifying selection. Again, assume a normal distribution for a

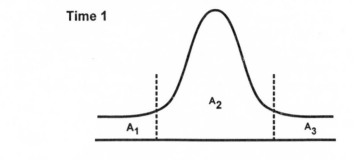

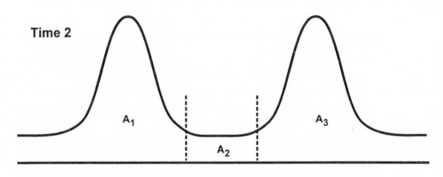

Figure 2.3. Disruptive Selection
A_2 becomes uncommon, A_1 and A_3 common

polymorphic gene. As disruptive selection occurs the distribution will become nonnormal, if not flat, because extreme variants are selected for and intermediate variants selected against. The effect of this is to accentuate polymorphisms in the population, as alleles in both tails of the distribution become more common (see Figure 2.3).

It is certain that disruptive selection can be made to occur experimentally, but less certain how often it happens in nature. Polymorphic phenotypes that are controlled by a single gene could easily be selected for, depending upon how heterogeneous are the habitat conditions. The more heterogeneous the conditions, other things equal, the greater the chance that polymorphisms can be selected for. Simple habitats cannot favor many forms; by definition, simple habitats provide fewer survival opportunities and, thus, room for fewer forms. In any case, the idea with disruptive selection is that a given distribution neither shifts its direction nor stabilizes but, in effect, gets broken up. The result is an accentuated polymorphism for the trait, or greater differentiation between phenotypes.

Finally, in contrast to disruptive selection, there is balancing selection, which is selection *for* heterozygotes. It happens that heterozygous genotypes (those with one dominant and one recessive allele, *Aa*) are often better able to survive and reproduce than either homozygous combination (*AA* or *aa*). Balancing selection refers to the case where the effect of natural selection is to preserve both alleles so that neither becomes extinct. Each allele represents a different type—thus, the polymorphism—but because of the selection for the heterozygous allele *pair* (*Aa*), a balanced polymorphism will evolve and be maintained. Because heterozygous genotypes are often more phenotypically viable, their selection is a common natural occurrence. Balancing selection can occur in tandem with disruptive selection or directional selection, as illustrated in Figure 2.4.

So, two forms of natural selection describe evolution and two do not. Stabilizing and balancing selection describe a condition in which, after a point, there is no evolutionary change. Directional and disruptive selection describe evolutionary change, for which the term evolutionary selection may serve as a general cover. Generally speaking, evolutionary change in a reproducing population is interpreted as the nonrandom, successive replacement of alleles in the population's gene pool. For a variant under stabilizing selection, alleles get fixed in their relative frequencies. For a variant under balancing selection, heterozygous combinations of them get fixed. For a variant under directional or disruptive selection, alleles get replaced.

For any mode of selection operating at a given time, one can never be sure whether that mode will be maintained over time. It depends upon habitat conditions—their variability, flexibility, and complexity— and the relation of those conditions to the phenotypic traits that correlate with genetic variants. All habitats change with time; it just depends upon the time frame. When a habitat changes, survival and reproductive chances in the population may be affected. If they are, a given genetic variant may come under different kinds of selection.

Molecular-Genetic Foundations

While the efforts of population geneticists to describe patterned changes in phenotypic distributions were well served by their abstract

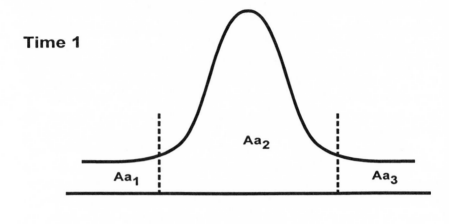

Time 1

Aa₂

Aa₁

Aa₃

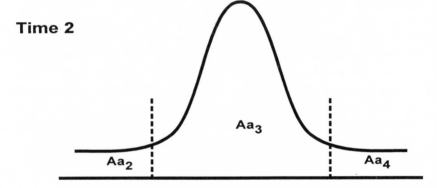

Time 2

Aa₃

Aa₂

Aa₄

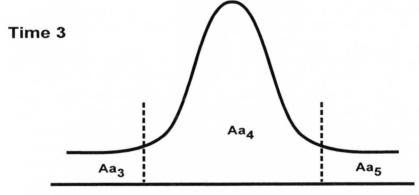

Time 3

Aa₄

Aa₃

Aa₅

Figure 2.4. Balancing Selection
(in combination with Directional Selection)
A and *a* both remain common

idealization of the gene, biochemically minded biologists knew there had to be a physical, molecular basis to the patterns and, thus, to the Mendelian gene. Around the middle of the twentieth century and following upon a rush of cumulative inquiry thereafter, the molecular basis was discovered. Genes were chunks of DNA residing on the chromosomes. With the locating of the molecular gene and the description of its structure and dynamics, the biochemistry of inheritance could now be described. It was, and continues to be.

It happens that there is no such thing as *the* molecular gene, for there are different kinds of molecular genes, with assorted functions. Not all molecular genes are way stations in the production of Mendelian phenotypes, but many are subject to mutation and recombination. It happens also that not all molecular genes are composed of DNA, for some viruses have no DNA (just RNA); not all DNA is found on the chromosomes of the cell nucleus, for some can be found in the mitochondria surrounding it (called mtDNA); some DNA has redundant structures for coding information and has uncoded regions; a considerable amount of DNA (called junk DNA) has no known function; and some genes are phenotypically significant because of only a small portion of the many fragments they may contain.

Special phenotypic significance has been identified for the structure, function, and context of those genes that encode for protein formation (in cells with a membrane-bound nucleus—the eukaryotes). These structural genes are chunks of DNA that represent no more than a small fraction of the total DNA in a genome, but their constituent compounds, the nucleotides, may number several hundred on a single gene. Triplets of nucelotides (codons) specify single amino acids, several hundred of which may be needed to synthesize a single protein—of which the average eukaryotic cell may contain perhaps ten thousand. Proteins matter because they function as enzymes to catalyze the hundreds or sometimes thousands of different metabolic reactions needed to sustain the cells. A structural gene encodes for the sequencing of the amino acids that constitute a particular protein. (A fine-grained resolution of the biochemistry of structural genes has shown that they contain clusters of noncoding base-pair sequences, called introns, that intervene between clusters that actually code for portions of proteins, called exons.) The transcription of the code produces a polypeptide chain whose sequence can be altered by the substitution, insertion, deletion, and rearrangement of its component amino acids—thus changing the protein that is synthesized and possibly the functioning of the cell. Any change in nucleotide sequencing constitutes a mutation. Depending upon the array of regulatory genes, which regulate the expression of structural genes during developmental sequences, changed proteins can affect cell growth and, thus, an organisms' physiology, morphology, and behavior.

This biochemistry of gene mutations is believed by many to be the key to evolution. If selected for, alleles with altered nucleotide sequencing can account for substantial differentiation between entire taxonomic groups. Humans and chimpanzees, for all their manifestly different phenotypes, are indistinguishable for more than 98 percent of their genes (which makes them genetically closer than mice and rats). mtDNA analysis suggests that humans and chimpanzees are phylogenetically closer than chimps and gorillas. In the protein chains found in hemoglobin, humans and chimps exhibit an identical sequence of amino acids, while humans and gorillas differ by a single amino acid. If just one amino acid is substituted at a known position in the human hemoglobin beta chain, which is 150 amino acids long, the phenotypic result is sickle-cell anemia and also, in the heterozygous condition, increased resistance to malaria. Nucleotide sequence changes are generally acknowledged to be the molecular source of allelic and phenotypic variation, and objects of natural selection.

But not all of them—perhaps not even most. To complicate the molecular and, hence, the evolutionary order of things, there appears to be a great deal of protein evolution that is selectively neutral and has no effect on fitness. Protein evolution in structural genes appears to be as regular as clockwork, and different species appear to have different mutation rates owing to the presence of so called mutator genes within their particular genomes. Selection for fitness in protein evolution apparently depends upon accompanying changes in the developmental program controlled by the regulatory genes. Then, phenotypic effects can be dramatic. Otherwise, and normally, the replacement of amino acids is regular and constant, although different proteins evolve at different average rates. Often, substitutions produce no demonstrable effects on the function of the altered protein. Natural selection cannot discriminate equifunctional amino acids that appear randomly and become fixed with predictable frequency.

The constant rate at which these neutral mutations become randomly fixed has been shown for some proteins to be linear with *geologic* time and, thus, provides a gauge for the purpose of evaluating evolutionary branchings by molecular assay. Alternate alleles for different populations can now be compared for the number of substitutions in nucleotide sequences, permitting the inference that the greater the number, the greater the evolutionary distance between the alleles and, therefore, the populations. (Nucleotide diversity is usually assessed using mtDNA, which has the advantages that it does not recombine and it mutates 10 times faster than nuclear DNA.) It all suggests a lawful molecular foundation for evolutionary phylogeny.[8]

A regular molecular clock for protein evolution is consistent with the theory that a large fraction of molecular changes result in alternate alleles that are functionally equivalent. But, if equivalent, there is no marginal fitness advantage, so selection cannot sort and retain them. The neutral theory (see Kimura 1983) was developed in the late 1960s and has not yet been fully accepted by evolutionary biologists, partly because of its radical theoretical implications. The most serious implication is that the theory accords a much-diminished role for natural selection in the explanation of evolutionary change. By attributing the cause of evolutionary change to the regular rate at which neutral mutations become randomly fixed, and by implying that this rate is the expected maximum for allelic substitutions, the neutral theory suggests a different computational baseline for microevolution in place of Hardy-Weinberg equilibrium. With this, the role that traditionally has been assigned to natural selection as the primary "creative force" in evolution is denied. If true, this cracks the edifice of the Modern Synthesis (see Depew and Weber 1995, pp. 362-368).

As if the neutral theory were not enough, the significance of the discoveries of the late Barbara McClintock is belatedly coming to be recognized and her discoveries are now being developed. What McClintock first showed to be true of corn has now been generalized *in vitro* and been found to occur (with as yet unknown frequency) *in vivo*: the transposition of DNA fragments from one site on a chromosome to another, and even to a different chromosome, without biochemical change in the transposed gene but with the effect of altering (often, deactivating) the functioning of the gene into which the "transposon" is inserted. The result produces changes in phenotype, but without allelic substitution. This theory of "jumping genes" is devastating for the explanation of evolution in terms of genic selectionism. It implies that evolutionary variation can become fixed without passing through Mendel's Laws of segregation and independent assortment, which are fundamental to classical population genetics.

These and other developments in molecular biology suggest that much more is needed for the explanation of evolutionary change than the Modern Synthesis has heretofore provided. Rather than producing a more integrated synthesis, in which microevolution and macroevolution clearly connect, the molecular revolution is seeming to suggest there may be some inherent discontinuities at the boundaries.

INTERPRETING BIOLOGICAL EVOLUTION

Where once, with the advent of molecular genetics, it seemed as if the Mendelian gene could be analytically reduced to molecular constituents, what has been described since is a microscopic system of inordinate structural and functional complexity. Endler and McLellan (1988), among many others, note that there is no one-to-one mapping of DNA sequence changes to functional effects within the genome or the cell, nor is there such a mapping to relate sequence and function from genome to cell to whole organism. The complexity of genomic systems and their developmental interactions with whole organisms suggest many-many relations, effectively prohibiting a one-to-one mapping of molecular to Mendelian genes for the general case. In other words, population genetics is not reducible to molecular genetics. Kitcher (1984) made this point, which Rosenberg (1985) elaborated in excruciating detail, a point even more valid in view of the evidence accumulated since: Background assumptions, foreground assumptions, processes and entities of interest, known genomic structure and function, as well as explanatory purpose, scope, and theory-based restrictions on inference, are sufficiently different between population and molecular genetics as to prohibit an effective reduction of the one to the other. Fogle (1990, pp. 350-351) goes farther:

> Recent molecular genetics investigations on the physical organization of the gene reveals [sic] that the delicate bridge connecting the Mendelian and molecular points of view is near collapse ... attempts by molecular biologists to find a coherent relationship to the Mendelian entity, at first successful, are currently strained by the robust architectural diversity of the molecular gene ... a gene is not constructed as a unit.... The molecular gene is more appropriately described as a set of embedded, tandem, and overlapping domains.

That was not to say there are no connections between population and molecular genetics or that they never intersect. Rather, the wished-for linear transformations simply are not there, and probably cannot be, because "genomic organization is vastly more complex than Mendelism ever revealed" (Fogle 1990, p. 367). Presumed and proved connections (such as the sickle-cell trait) notwithstanding, there is a break in the population-genetic and molecular-genetic foundations of evolution.

That now makes for two breaks, for one has always been festering: It had often been (and still is) affirmed that macroevolutionary processes such as speciation can be explained by the ordering of genetic variation by means of natural selection in ecological contexts, but one of the architects of the Modern Synthesis himself had to ruefully concede late in the day that:

> Among all the claims made during the evolutionary synthesis, perhaps the one that found least acceptance was the assertion that all phenomena of macroevolution can be "reduced to," that is, explained by, microevolutionary processes.... Now, 50 years later, the controversy still seems undecided (Mayr 1988, p. 402.)

Mayr continued:

> At the present moment, unfortunately, the genetics of microevolutionary processes has been unable to provide a full explanation of macroevolution, nor has the analysis of macroevolutionary phenomena provided any answers as to the nature of the genetic processes characterizing microevolutionary events (1988, p. 405).

Perhaps that is because macroevolution and microevolution are incommensurable.[9] What counts as microscopic and macroscopic, after all, is entirely relative to the human frame of perception. The description of macroevolutionary phenomena clearly is the description of complex systems, but the accumulated evidence from molecular biology suggests there is no reason to suppose that microscopic evolutionary phenomena behave in systems that are any less complex—just smaller in scale. With what justification, therefore, should we suppose that the one is reducible to the other, that macroscopic complexity represents the aggregated effects of microscopic complexity? It is a virtual certainty that ecological, population-genetic, and molecular-genetic processes of evolution are connected in fact and connectable in theory, but what reason is there to suppose linearity at their borders and points of interface? A wish to develop some unified evolutionary theory, analogous to the long-sought unified field theory of the physicists, perhaps explains the tenacity of the belief that microevolutionary phenomena determine macroevolutionary outcomes. The wish, however, is undermined by its own metaphysic: the notion of natural selection as an evolutionary mechanism and causal force.

For a long time, evolutionary biologists and some philosophers of biology have casually referred to natural selection as a causal force or evolutionary mechanism, in loose analogy to the four physical forces and the mechanistic and deterministic causality that can be described for physical systems of classical dynamics. The analogy usually appears in the presuppositional world views with which evolutionary inquiry is addressed and, thus, is exhibited in the ordinary language sometimes used in the discourse of the inquiry. But the analogy doesn't hold. The notion that natural selection is a causal force—on the genic interpretation of selection—is incoherent.

It would seem otherwise, especially since Hardy-Weinberg Equilibrium describes a perfect condition of no evolutionary forces acting on a reproducing population. To relax Hardy-Weinberg assumptions, therefore, is to admit some forces. But what forces? Certainly, natural selection as we described it earlier cannot "force" anything. It is not dynamical motion that can drive evolution, if the analogy is to classical dynamics, nor can it be a mechanism. Natural selection is the measurement of the result of the interactions produced by the forces of motion in distinct complex systems of differing scale, the ecological and the genetic. Let ecological and genetic dynamics proceed apace, and eventually *these* forces will interact to permit observable changes in populations or gene pools to be statistically arrayed at discrete intervals. Natural selection is the name for the differences observable, if any, from one measurement interval to the other. The phrase "evolution by natural selection" can coherently refer to evolution *described* by natural selection, but not to evolution caused by natural selection. It may be coherent to think of natural selection as an effect, and it may do no harm to call it a process, understanding that this is shorthand for a set of interacting ecological and genetic dynamics. But it does serious harm to cling to the metaphysical world view of the science of 200 years ago, employing it now to buttress our understanding of evolution by interpreting selection as a causal force. Directional selection, which is often said to be a "force" that "produces" evolutionary change, cannot produce anything in the sense of forcing or causing, because forces acting on physical bodies produce change of motion; whereas, to quote Swenson, "natural selection is a *constraint on motion already produced*" (1991b, p. 47, emphasis in the original). If we want to find forces, mechanisms, or causes for evolutionary change, we shall have to look to the dynamical complex systems whose interacting forces *enable* evolutionary change to occur and, thus, to be measured as natural selection.[10]

If genic natural selection is not a causal force and some evolution can occur without allelic substitutions (by way of "jumping genes"), then some relief is afforded from the oft-exaggerated claims of the genic selection explanation of evolution favored by some reductionists in the population-genetic tradition. The tendency of this tradition to explain evolution as so much genetic bookkeeping, along with its tendency to reduce complexity to simplicity, is clearly inadequate for the explanation of any systems that deviate from linearity or that are sensitive to changes in initial conditions. Almost any interesting evolutionary system does deviate or is sensitive, sooner or later, unless one chooses to dismiss such peculiar properties as so much noise. For the case of human sociocultural systems, one can't. In what attitude does this place us here?

We shall assume that all the foundations of biological evolution are relevant to sociocultural change as that topic materializes but that none is over-arching, and that even if there were a unified biological theory of evolution with all the appropriate isomorphisms specified, this could not be over-arching or monolithic. Instead, we shall assume that the different foundations for biological evolution are touchstones for distinct evolutionary processes whose full interaction and interpretation to human systems requires an allowance for nonlinearities in complex, self-organizing systems whose evolutionary forces, which maintain the systems far from thermodynamic equilibrium, are not yet fully specified. Evolutionary change for such systems entails processes that the Darwinian traditions in biology have thought necessary to exclude. Among these are internal system processes whose structural and functional changes enable evolutionary change but do not yield to explanation and description in classical terms—that is, in terms of the specification of causal force laws which, in conjunction with initial conditions, enable some future state of a system to be predicted.

This commitment, we shall see in Chapter 6, creates some breaks with biological accounts of evolution, but there already are breaks in the biological accounts. It is possible the breaks are there because there is more than one process of biological evolution (cf. Endler and McLellan

1988). If there is, in any event we could hardly expect evolutionary accounts of culture and society to yield isomorphisms with the biological foundations. But clearly, with culture and society there is something to be accounted for, in terms that have to be related to biological foundations in one way or another. If we forsake the wish for a complete and unified theory of evolution, with biological and sociocultural elements all integrated in a metaphysical framework of causal-force mechanisms, able to provide us with total explanations, perhaps we can identify at least some of the evolutionary connections to human ecology. Certainly we can use natural selection in a very general way to get a foothold on the connections. Humans did, after all, evolve by natural selection, and it seems prudent to make what use we can of this.

NOTES

1. Two disclaimers apply to the remainder of this chapter, and by generalization to every other topic in this volume and in Part B, for which there exists a vast literature that is not given its full due. First, as should be obvious, a much more complete source than the present treatment provides of theory and facts about evolution and selection can be found in numerous biology texts. Other than choosing to write an encyclopedia, there is no alternative but to selectively simplify presentations of concepts, data, and interpretive issues that arise in connection with the full range of human ecology. The hope, of course, is to simplify concisely without distorting so much that the purpose of raising the subject is undermined.

Yet, even when one aims for fidelity to a subject in which one is not an authority, there always arise questions of interpretation. Here, the danger is twofold. One is that the choice of interpretive frames is slanted by an insensitivity to nuances of theory, measurement, or data—a hazard inherent to any interdisciplinary project. Another, ever-present even with the sensitivity we expect from well-versed authorities, is that fundamental world views are implicit and may be read into a treatment even when not expressly discussed. In this volume and in Part B, at times I will expressly state interpretive angles that derive from my own perhaps unexpressed world views, upon which I intend to build; at other times, I am not seeking to build any interpretive angle of my own but am implicitly accepting without critical analysis the interpretive angles provided by others. I should think it will be clear when I am doing one or the other. In the present chapter, until its conclusion I intend to take no positions on the many issues that have been raised with respect to tacit commitments about evolution and selection that intensive analyses of the subjects reveal are possible. But we have to adopt some vision of evolution and selection for framing the rest of this work. In all cases where interpretive commitments are made, the purpose is to locate theory fragments and points of departure for the future development of a general science of human ecology.

Summarized, the disclaimers are these: (1) I do not intend this or any other discussion in this work to be full and complete in its presentation of theory, data, or interpretation;

and (2) I do not intend to articulate any full and coherent philosophy of science, ethics, or politics, pertaining to human ecology or its related subjects. Any such intentions would really be pretensions.

2. Herbert Spencer, a man with little formal education, had his own ideas about evolution, some incompatible and some complementary with Darwin's. They appeared in many works on biology, moral philosophy, and sociology. In 1857, Spencer propounded a universal law of evolutionary change, with intended application to physical, biological, and cultural phenomena. It expressed the idea of increasing differentiation, an idea often associated with evolution and natural selection. Spencer's law could not compete in the struggle for survival against Darwin's theory, as developments would have it, but the times were ripe for evolutionary thinking, and Spencer was adaptable.

Eventually, Spencer would be stained with the label Social Darwinist, an ideology that interpreted natural selection as a moral imperative for the organization of human political economies. Spencer's views on this have often been misrepresented, perhaps because now we forget the tendency then was to equate evolution with moral progress— a tendency that Spencer himself furthered in his effort to develop an evolutionary basis for ethics. Spencer's ideology was laissez-faire, but he himself did not advocate survival of the fittest as the moral imperative that the fit *should* get fitter at the expense of the less fit (see Bowler 1984; Kaye 1986).

Spencer finally settled on an ecological view of the determinants of social evolution, which he tried to document with massive comparative data on numerous societies and which certainly marks him as ahead of his time. Spencer's role in evolutionary theory has been discussed by many writers, including Mayr (1982) with reference to natural selection and Sanderson (1990) with reference to social evolution. Long buried in the history of sociological theory, which he helped to found, Herbert Spencer—his work, talent, and influence far-ranging—is occasionally exhumed (Turner 1985). Apart from whatever other significance Spencer may have, however, he will always be associated with the theory of evolution by natural selection because of that historic phrase, survival of the fittest, which Darwin adopted to explain to critics what natural selection was all about.

3. Like evolution, the idea of natural selection had forerunners. Wallace's construal was just one, perhaps second only to Darwin's in significance (see Mayr 1982, pp. 498-501).

4. The role of competition in natural selection may depend entirely on the object of that competition and the type of selection at issue. Competition for reproductive opportunities may be necessary for *directional* selection (see discussion below) to occur, which is the kind Darwin was mostly talking about. Cooperation may be more important for stabilizing selection. For directional selection to operate, there does not have to be some sort of ecological competition for limited resources. Yet, that is what Darwin, Wallace, and Spencer thought. The poetic metaphor about nature being red in tooth and claw turned both ideas, cooperation and competition, into ecological simplifications. Whether competition is commonplace in nature or whether cooperation is more often the natural order of things probably depends upon choice of species, biogeographic conditions, and time frames. For instance, under a condition of rapid and substantial population migration, indeed there might ensue some intense competition for resources that directional or disruptive selection eventually would sort

into stable, cooperative arrangements. See Williams (1966) and Grant (1991) for general treatments, and several of the initial papers in Strong, Simberloff, Abele, and Thistle (1984), in which evidence from a variety of studies suggests that concepts of the role of competition in natural communities have to be seriously tempered.

5. The elements of this system were not all in place at the beginning. The concept of a gene pool, for instance, was not introduced until 1950, by Dobzhansky.

6. The Hardy-Weinberg equilibrium, sometimes called the Hardy-Weinberg Law, can be traced to 1908. Allow two alleles, A and a, to have relative frequencies p and q in the population, where $p + q = 1$. Now, if the total frequencies are unity and there are just two alleles that are randomly crossed in populations of large size, in the next generation there should be obtained the homozygote AA with frequency p^2, the heterozygote Aa with frequency $2pq$, and the homozygote aa with frequency q^2.

This represents an expansion of the binomial expression $(p + q)^2$, which when multiplied becomes $p^2 + 2pq + q^2$, which at unity becomes the Hardy-Weinberg Law:

$$p^2 + 2pq + q^2 = 1.$$

This equilibrium model can be extended for use with more than two alleles, provided appropriate algebraic expansions. Departures from random mating quickly disturb the equilibrium, as does the presence of evolutionary change.

7. This is a favorite textbook example of directional selection partly because it was so well documented. There even survives film footage of the selective predation to which the unfavored phenotype was subjected. During the 1930s and 1940s, a common form of a species of moth, the peppered moth, of Great Britain, began to disappear and a rare form, with a darker (melanic) pigment, became more common because industrial pollution destroyed the lichen cover of the trees, by chance protecting the darker form from predators but now exposing the mottled form, which heretofore had blended well with the lichen. The darker form was thus favored now to survive in greater numbers and so was selected, in the sense that this genetic variant became more common because its phenotype became more common: It survived and reproduced in greater proportion than previously, compared to the mottled form. The mean for pigmentation shifted as one tail of the distribution got lopped off.

In fact, the direction for which selection occurs can revert depending upon the trait at issue and the habitat in which its phenotype is expressed. In this case, it did. When, in the 1950s, Great Britain got serious about controlling air pollution, there came to be less soot to cover the trees, less protection for the melanic form, more protection for the mottled form and, lo and behold, the mottled form made a comeback—the direction reverted. The interpretation of evolution by directional selection applies in either direction. In the countryside, where the effects of the original pollution were less, the distribution of the forms there also coincided with the coloring of the trees.

8. In some cases, a very small number of nucleotide substitutions can enable rapid and dramatic evolution on a macroscopic scale. For instance, there is now evidence that changes in only five key alleles brought corn as we know it from its ancestor, which does not look much like corn, in only one thousand years (Culotta 1991).

9. Numerous biologists seem to think so more or less, but there is a wide range to their opinions. Stebbins and Ayala (1981), at one extreme, state that microevolution

and macroevolution are decoupled in an *epistemological* sense. Grant (1991, p. 15) does not go that far and he affirms that evolution is a unified process, but he also affirms that there are different levels of evolutionary phenomena whose processes are not entirely identical. The idea of hierarchical levels of evolution, championed by Mayr (1988), seems to be a crutch useful for those who wish to preserve the Modern Synthesis in its current form. But for others, such as Eldredge (1985, 1989), the notion of biological hierarchies is a key to describing evolutionary processes that suggest a fundamental restructuring of evolutionary theory.

10.   Among biologists, Endler (1986, pp. 29-33) has shown how, at the very least, it is confusing and misleading to think of natural selection as a causal force. It takes a philosopher to show how the idea can be made to be coherent, and coherence lies in speaking of evolutionary, not selection, forces (see Ghiselin 1981; Sober 1984a; Sober and Lewontin 1984).

Chapter 3

The Natural Selection of Humans

Because human ecology has its origins in human evolution, it is desirable to consider how the theory of natural selection brings human phenotypes specifically into view. Of course, so many phenotypes are thus brought into view that we can not possibly do justice to the vast subject of human evolutionary analysis—but that is not our goal. We shall be content just to indicate the evolutionary characteristics of a very few of the major human phenotypes that have deep significance for human ecology—deep in the sense that they have ecological origins, and significant for their ecological impacts. In this chapter, we consider sociality in the selection of humans; in the next, culture and symbols. Each constitutes a large class of phenotypes, and they interact. By first isolating them, it should be possible to get some idea of how human evolutionary fitness may have been enhanced by their development.

Unfortunately, for any discussion of human evolutionary origins in ecological context, facts are lean and speculation is rife. The truth may be forever undecidable. But even if we can not establish the phyletic bases of the inheritance of sociality or culture, we might uncover enough clues about each to reason about the initial conditions of human ecological dynamics. Current conditions of human ecology can not be comprehended without knowing the dynamics of where we came from, how we got here, and why. We got here by way of changes in human society and culture. But from where, and why?

There are today nearly 200 primate species, most of them monkeys, some of them prosimians, a few of them apes, and us. There used to be more of us. We and our immediate human ancestors apparently got started in Africa, though whether uniquely in Africa or simultaneously elsewhere is nowadays debated. As things stand, we are considered to be members of the superfamily *Hominoidea*, or hominoids, a status we share with the gibbon and siamang (*Hylobates*), the organutan (*Pongo*), the gorilla (*Gorilla*), and the chimpanzee (*Pan*). But we are the only species remaining, of the only remaining hominid genus (*Homo*). We need not get into the complicated and oft-disputed tracing of lineages, classifications, and datings of the various extinct hominid ancestors of *Homo*.[1] Suffice it to say that molecular data now indicate that the hominids and chimpanzees diverged from some common evolutionary ancestor five to eight million years ago. We are considered now to be a degenerate line, which is to say nothing is expected to come of us (evolutionarily speaking, of course).

INTERPRETING EVOLUTIONARY ORIGINS AND SOCIALITY

To get some sense of the ecology of human sociality, it should help to get some sense of the sort of primate humans evolved apparently to be.[2] But our sense will be clouded without circumspect interpretations of the concepts of evolutionary origins and sociality.

Human origins are inherently obscure. To locate the first human phenotypes or the conditions that may have encouraged particular adaptations is like looking for the Golden Gate Bridge through the San Francisco fog. One has to know where it is before one can find it. The secret to interpreting what we might stumble upon in the fog surrounding human origins is this: *There were no exact human origins*—at least no exact points of origin—for any particular phenotypes or the collection of them. Behavioral, social, and cultural traits that we now take to be distinctive of humans are extensions of the capacities of other primates, developed more fully in us, and realized and elaborated over a process during which the traits became distinct. The same observation, of course, applies to the primates as a group, who bear evolutionary continuities with other mammals through descent from common ancestors. There were no exact markers for beginnings. Gradual evolutionary modification eventually produces distinct entities but, just because it is gradual and long term, it belies the idea of original creation. We could no more find definite boundaries, with all the fine details engraved within, than we could find the exact spot on that marvelous red bridge where my maternal grandfather claimed to have once engraved his initials. The concept of evolutionary origins is almost, though not quite, a contradiction in terms. It encourages us to register a false psychological sense of singularity and event-centered closure for what, in fact and theory, is a process that materializes from multiple strands.

The term sociality can also be misleading. It may conceal two wholly different concepts. One is the concept of social behavior; the other, the concept of social organization. Social behavior is the general term; social organization, a refinement. Now, the explanation of the evolutionary origins of animal social behavior by means of natural selection is sometimes undertaken without much regard for anything ecological; at other times, when ecological factors are taken into account, the evident interest in patterns of social behavior turns out not to reflect the social scientists' concept of *organized* social behavior. I shall say more about the differences later as they come into view, as they must, for sociality consists of the graded organization of social behavior. The logical starting point is to relate evolution to social behavior with undefined organization and to consider the gradations and their significance in subsequent discussions.

Our question for the moment is: How could social behavior ever have evolved in the human ancestral train, and why should it have? A satisfactory answer provides an entree into matters of evolutionary human ecology but, we should be aware, only just.

EVOLUTION AND SOCIAL BEHAVIOR, WITH UNDEFINED ORGANIZATION

We assume that human social behavior was an ecological adaptation to the conditions that proto-humans confronted, and that it was continued in the *Homo* genus. The proof for such an assumption, if not impossible, would be extraordinarily complicated, not least by the fact that at present too many necessary data are missing. We do know that the hominids of Africa who preceded us evolved when African forests were contracting, savannas expanding, and climates turning seasonal. The evidence of changing environments suggests the hypothesis that social behavior would be selectively favored, but there is no way to confirm this empirically since social behavior leaves no fossils. Still, some plausible explanation of how human social behavior may have evolved by natural selection has been constructed, and this will do for our purposes.

The Problem of Cooperation

Any attempt to explain the origins of social behavior, in *Homo sapiens* or any other social animals, must explain how social behavior could get an evolutionary foothold. Is there some selective advantage conferred upon populations that organize socially, as opposed to populations of the same species that do not? Given some selective advantage for that population for sufficient periods of time, the species' social characteristics would become fixed throughout the population due to the enhanced fitness of individuals who behaved in a social way. Most species are not social, but some are, and for some others it is hard to say. Why the differences?

The differences turn on the selective advantage of one of the defining criteria for sociality. Whatever else it may take to be social, at a minimum it takes cooperation in some sense or other. So, to analyze the origins of social behavior requires us to analyze why the individual members of some species would ever cooperate. What is the evolutionary advantage to that? How could cooperation evolve? Its evolution implies the organization of individual behavior into social forms or at least proto-social forms. Presuming there is some selective advantage, of course, the ground is established for further social evolution of the species. There is a way to go about analyzing this.

The Concept of an Evolutionarily Stable Strategy

One way to conceive the problem of cooperation, given we are asking an evolutionary question, is game-theoretic. That is, we can ask whether cooperation might be a strategy employed by individuals that becomes stable over evolutionary time. With sufficient time, competing selection pressures for alternative forms of a trait, or for alternative traits, may tend to move from a dynamic to a stabilized state—to a temporary condition in which the population comes to rest with an evolved distribution of the traits or forms that represent the optimum that could be gotten from the opposing selective pressures. Traits under selection are sometimes caught in push-pull dynamics that can produce evolutionary compromises. Should these stabilize, this can prevent the invasion of the population by mutants. When an adaptation is immune to invasion by mutants it is said to be an evolutionarily stable strategy. Rooted in the work of Robert MacArthur and William D. Hamilton, this line of analysis matured with the work of John Maynard Smith (1974, 1978, 1982).

The game-theoretic part comes in this way. Given we want to explain how social behavior in the form of cooperation could evolve in populations of noncooperating individuals, the choice to cooperate or not represents a strategy that ought to have, evolutionarily speaking, greater or lesser payoff. Is there any reason for an individual to cooperate when noncooperative behavior is already effective? Cooperative behavior and, therefore, social behavior should not be selected for unless they confer a fitness advantage, compared to alternatives, and should not become fixed in a population unless they are optimal for maximizing the fitness of the population. How, therefore, could, and under what conditions should, cooperation become an evolutionarily stable strategy? If we knew, we would have a hook on the origins of social behavior.

Since social behavior evolved before anyone kept records of such affairs, we are restricted in the conclusions and inferences we may draw about evolved phenotypes that leave no tell-tale evidence. But we can theorize, and we can check our theories indirectly with suggestive evidence and computer simulations. This has been done, and a political scientist, Robert Axelrod, has done a lot of it (Axelrod 1984; Axelrod and Dion 1988).

Axelrod's idea is that cooperation is based on reciprocity. If reciprocal alliances form, under certain conditions they will gain an evolutionary foothold because they will confer a selective advantage. Not only that, but under some conditions reciprocal alliances will be immune to invasion by individuals that do not form reciprocal alliances. In that case, cooperation in the form of reciprocal alliances has become evolutionarily stable. How could the cooperating members of some population gain a selective advantage over its noncooperating members?

It is disarmingly simple. Assume a game in which two players can cooperate or not (called cheating or defecting) and receive payoffs for behaving one way or the other. Assume, further, that the players prefer benefits to costs for payoffs. Allow players repeatedly to interact, with some payoff each time, without knowing for sure when the interaction will terminate. What is the optimal strategy for each player to adopt— optimal in the sense that it provides for them the best long-term expected gain? Here comes the hook.

It turns out to be a cooperative response on the first trial and a response in kind ever after. This strategy is called TIT FOR TAT by its creator, Anatol Rapaport, because it describes reciprocal behavior beyond the first move. It was developed as a simulation strategy for iterated Prisoners' Dilemma games, long a subject of theoretical investigation and game-theoretic simulation. Now it was given an evolutionary component: Alternative strategies were permitted to compete with TIT FOR TAT by allowing them to be represented in a population of paired interactants, in proportion to the success the alternative strategies had in previous well-defined periods of interaction. This was an analog to the reproductive generation. Would one or another strategy prevail over well-defined periods of time—in effect, be selected as optimal? It would, and it was TIT FOR TAT, which is to say, this became the most common strategy, the one that took hold and gradually replaced the alternatives.

This cannot happen in a population of noncooperating individuals if just one decides to cooperate. However, a small cluster that does reciprocate cooperative behavior can establish itself and, once it does, will predominate in a noncooperative population to the point where eventually it can withstand invasion by mutants. That is to say, for the case at hand, noncooperators cannot regain a foothold. This is why Axelrod says there is a ratchet effect in the evolution of cooperation. Not only can cooperation easily evolve but its evolution endures as a superior adaptation, becoming an evolutionarily stable strategy that is not replaced by its earlier form.

This depends upon there being some social structure in the population to begin with—some cluster of individuals who cooperate reciprocally and invade noncooperative clusters. This requirement can be relaxed as certain mathematical parameters are changed, as frequently they have been in the numerous attempts, following Axelrod's initial work, to explore alternative conditions for the evolution of cooperation. Simulations have the great virtue of enabling quick assessments of the different effects that come with changing the initial parameters provided for system behavior. Principles regarding the evolution of cooperation will accordingly be qualified, as theoretical details are added. Many have been added.

Evidence for this theory, we should note, is not based entirely on simulations. There are observations for an assorted variety of animals to suggest the basic framework is sound (Axelrod and Dion 1988). There is, as you might expect, some interest in applying this to the human case in general, and for certain human particulars.

Machalek and Cohen (1991) suggest the framework may be used to interpret and explain facets of human social cooperation as this condition may be affected by the incidence of criminal behavior. Criminal behavior they interpret as a form of cheating (noncooperation), in analogy to game-theoretic analyses, the existence of which at tolerable levels renders cooperators *less* vulnerable to invasion and replacement by cheaters, who would have a competitive advantage in a population of cooperators unaccustomed to strategies of cheating. Machalek and Cohen hypothesize, in line with a classic sociological analysis (by E. Durkheim), that crime and its punishment in human societies promote greater stability in patterns of social cooperation than would be present if crime and punishment did not exist at all. The implication is that crime and punishment in tandem in human societies represent a superior adaptation for the society—an optimal social condition itself resistant to replacement.

Notwithstanding such interpretive applications, which can be debated, the elementary explanation of the evolution of cooperation may appeal as a theoretical explanation if only for its simplicity. But the general evolutionary game-based theory of cooperation contains some limitations of scope that are rather important.

Limits to Generalizing the Play of Evolutionary Games

The game-based evolutionary theory of cooperation requires that cooperators be able to recognize each other as unique individuals and as having a particular history of interaction. The cooperators, after all, are responding to that history and developing their patterns of social behavior accordingly. This condition excludes the eusocial insects from the explanatory scope of the theory, inasmuch as they can recognize members of their kind but not specific individuals as unique. Thus, we do not have here an evolutionary theory of cooperation that applies to all social species. The theory would, however, seem to apply to primates. If not, something like it would have to be developed in order to explain how social behavior could become fixed in primates. In their case, it might seem easy to explain the presence of social clusters that could invade noncooperators: Primates have a zero expectation for survival if infants are not cared for in groups that resemble families.

But how shall we interpret an application to primates, given that cooperation already is a fixed behavior pattern for them. Its evolution was a long-term process. We may not even think of supposing that the evolution of social behavior in primates proceeded historically with quite the simple order that game-theoretic simulations of evolutionary cooperation reflect. Simulations, by definition, simplify a system enough to enable a linear programming language to issue nested binary commands. Evolution does not proceed accordingly. It would be absurd to think that, biologically, primates had somehow biologically evolved as noncooperators and *then* some cluster of cooperators invaded, survived, and prospered. Social evolution doesn't happen that way. Cooperation evolves *as* organisms evolve, social phenotypes *with* biological phenotypes.

The play of evolutionary games, as a metaphor for theorizing about the evolution of cooperation, is also conditioned by how one interprets the genetic component implied in any application of evolutionary selection theory. How shall we interpret it here?

Social behavior is a phenotype—thus, a candidate for evolution past and present—and whatever living forms evolve it, and in whatever forms it evolves, there are genotypes to keep it company—and genotypes and phenotypes are hardly independent. The evolution of cooperation ought therefore to be understood to have a genetic component. However, there are multiple gene-gene, gene-phenotype, and phenotype-habitat interactions, some sequential and some simultaneous, that intervene, in contingent and stochastic ways, between the action of molecular genes and their expression as Mendelian phenotypes. This is what is meant by saying that the relations are many-many. Any whispering within the substratum of the mind that suggests there may literally be "genes for cooperative behavior" that could be located in the genome ought, therefore, to be disregarded. Evolutionary biologists know it is too simplistic to imagine specific genes *for* some behavior pattern *x*, just as it is simplistic to imagine specific genes for specific body parts. (By contrast, mutations on specific genes can cause developmental programs to go awry such that specific body parts may show up in the wrong places or not at all.) Genes are for making proteins and whatnot, insofar as they make anything at all. There is no evidence that genes *generate* any human behavior pattern, let alone complex social forms, nor should we expect to find any such evidence, because genes are not generators of behavior. It is wishful thinking to believe human social behavior is independent of genic selection, but simple-minded to believe it is caused by it. We must, to be realistic, think in terms of a vast array of simultaneous, multiply scaled, temporally dispersed causal forces, when we are thinking of causal forces at all, that form an integrated system. To ask about genetic components is to ask about one set of functions in the system.

In what sense does the evolution of cooperation have a genetic component? Cooperation among kin is a requisite for survival in social species, and can be assumed to have evolved because reciprocal altruism among kin promotes individuals' inclusive fitness. This concept—its development is traceable from Darwin through J.B.S. Haldane and R.A. Fisher to William D. Hamilton (1964), who made the most of it—refers to the probability that the carrier of an allele will have genetic descendants (kin) who also express the allele, regardless of the carrier's own reproductive success. The idea is that natural selection will favor traits of behavior that enable an individual's genes to be perpetuated even when the individual may not actually be a direct ancestor. Hamilton proposed a formula, one of whose terms included a coefficient for genetic relatedness, to enable a calculation of when it is in the genetic interest of an individual to act altruistically toward kin, who share one's genes, for one's own Darwinian fitness[3] is served when one's genes are passed along by kin to future generations. Behavior that maximizes inclusive fitness stands to be favored by natural selection, and cooperation among kin does. That's why, according to many sociobiologists, it is a fixed trait in social species.

Once cooperation among kin has evolved, we could further suppose that generalized cooperation is selected for, that is, that reciprocal alliances are evolutionarily stable strategies in populations with very little, or very distant, or unknown, genetic relatedness. Trivers (1971) proposed this. Passing for reciprocal altruism, this theory tells us that selection will favor the cooperation of genetically diverse individuals when the inclusive fitness of the cooperators is enhanced. Mathematically, it can be shown that a genetic trait which contributes (by pathways unspecified, in the complex manner in which genes "contribute" to phenotypes) to the formation of reciprocal alliances will increase in a population when the gains to altruism exceed the costs (Aoki 1985). Thus, Axelrod's theory of the evolution of cooperation builds upon the theory of kin selection, which contains a genetic calculus in its formula, and the theory of reciprocal altruism, which by its very conditions of scope contains no such calculus.

If we could say the natural selection of cooperative behavior applies beyond the case of kin—beyond genetic relatedness—we could also say that such simple forms of social behavior as queuing or such complex forms as bureaucracies are selected for. The difficulty with this line of reasoning is that, once we pass beyond kin, we no longer have a common currency: the genes. The evolution of cooperation can be said to have a genetic component insofar as the genetic lineage can be traced through kin. We are warranted to infer this much: Once reciprocal altruism among kin evolves, there does, probably did, and should evolve reciprocal cooperation by natural selection. We are not warranted to generalize this beyond kin. In going that far, we leave behind the metric of the theory that would permit us to generalize so. If, therefore, it is said that complex forms of human social behavior have been naturally selected for, this has to be an allusion to undeveloped theory and data that go beyond the logic of genic selection.

Perhaps a prudent metaphor to locate the true status of the game-theoretic explanation of the evolution of cooperation is to evoke a comparison of a starting motor and an engine for an internal combustion vehicle. Just as nothing happens without that starting motor but not much happens because of it, so the evolution of cooperation is necessary for sociality but is hardly sufficient. While it may be necessary in this case to begin with simple models in order to go complex, the analysis of social behavior as cooperative behavior conceals way too much. In particular, it conceals the extent to which forms of cooperative behavior are organized. A colony of invertebrates, though its organization may be self-functional, can hardly compete with the extent of social organization of which *Homo sapiens* is capable. With different species, we admit phylogenetic gradations that introduce all sorts of complications and implications. Not the least of these is the likelihood that some social behavior evolves, in species with little or no learning capability, as a purely gratuitous effect of genic selection for fitness and takes the form of cooperation and little else, while other social behavior is organized, in those species with high learning capability, into many forms as a matter of deliberate design or undeliberate adaptation to circumstances, sometimes perhaps in spite of genic selection for fitness. In the latter case, the evolution of social behavior could hardly be said to be gratuitous, but it also could not be said to be naturally selected.

Some social behavior is organized, some of it very intricately and some hardly at all or at least not much. The more the organization, the more difficult gene-selection explanations become. The difficulties arise in part because some forms of sociality change due to short-term, culturally based learning rather than long-term evolutionary adaptation (see Chapter 6). There should be no question that cooperation evolved because it was and is a superior adaptation. Cooperative behavior is a definitive phenotype of human evolution—but it is just a starter for the phenotypic array of human sociality and the organizational structures and processes that go with the array. As is, the concept of cooperation by itself is insensitive to mutualism, commensalism, and parasitism—all of which are forms of social behavior within and between species. Social parasitism, or the expropriation of the resources of others in a social network, is a cost imposed on human sociality, and Machalek (1995, 1996) has shown how widespread and fundamental are its forms in many species. Comparable sophisticated analyses of mutualism and commensalism should be no less revealing for the concept of cooperation, which is known to take many organizational forms. An elementary theory of the evolution of cooperation with degrees of social organization undefined has to be substantially supplemented as those degrees are added.

SOCIAL BEHAVIOR IN HUMANS AND NONHUMAN PRIMATES

We have considered how, hypothetically, social behavior with undefined degrees of organization might have evolved by natural selection. But we should strive to be more pointed and empirical—if no less speculative—than that. Evolutionary theory and data may be employed without whipping up gene selectionism and basing the argument on the maximization of individual inclusive fitness. To get some insight into the core of human sociality as it evolved in groups of kin, all we need to assume is populations of humans with the minimum social organization that humans are known to possess and, knowing that humans evolved from other species in a genetic train, then try to compare human sociality with the sociality of our primate ancestors. The relevant evolutionary principles are not controversial once we are clear on the meaning of the claim that humans evolved by natural selection. What does it mean, and what are the relevant principles?

First, most important, and most obvious, it means that humans descended with modification from one or another of the creatures resting phylogenetically near, or that the bunch of us (depending upon which are bunched) descended from some earlier perhaps now extinct creature. In either case, it means that a genetic lineage having diminishing shared gene proportions in principle existed and could be inferred if we could figure out which species preceded which and along which lines.

Second, by implication, and perhaps still obvious, this means that we share with our ancestors some derived traits or characters. That is to say, there ought to be—and, in fact, are—common molecular, anatomical, physiological, behavioral, and social characteristics, the inheritance of which reflects systematic not random patterns of derived characters. This includes social characters that could be evolutionarily derived by humans, since the assorted hominids from whom we descended were, in fact, social (they left evidence of that) and, therefore, must have been somewhat like us; or, put more accurately, since they came first and we derived from them, our sociality must be somewhat like theirs.

Third, we and this motley crew of which we are part and from which we derived have to have had a common evolutionary ancestor. Otherwise, we could not talk at all about descent with modification or a shared genetic inheritance. Now, it isn't just any old common ancestor that we should care about here. After all, since humans are mammals, which descended from reptiles, we could always wonder just what sort of slimy creature in the vasty deep was the common ancestor of all the mammals and hence of us. But it does us no purpose to contemplate that we may have a Loch Ness monster for an ancestral parent. For our purposes, we need to know what was our *last* common ancestor. That would be whatever species preceded our own plus the others that we group together with ourselves for the purpose of comparison. We might not be able even to say what that last common ancestor was, because the paleontological record might obscure it.[4] But if we could find a way to reason about it, using evolutionary principles and known data, with a comparative method, we might be able to draw some provisional inferences about ourselves. It turns out we can.

Last Common Ancestors

The idea of a last common ancestor, sometimes given the acronym LCA, is a theoretical method useful for evolutionary analyses of social behavior and organization. Our question now is, what can we infer about the organization of human sociality as it was evolutionarily derived from a LCA?

The method is not the usual one. Usually, some extinct hominid species is selected from the paleontological remains, which are few and incomplete, and is compared to a living primate species (usually chimpanzees), whose behavior is then proposed as a model for the LCA. From presumed or inferred attributes of the LCA, subsequent hominid adaptations are inferred. Using extant primate species as models for extinct hominids is dangerous because those long gone souls, if souls they had, were morphologically much different and, therefore, should have had different behavioral adaptations than their descendants who are still around.[5] However, we are not much interested here in accounting for evolutionary divergence; rather, it is evidence of derivation that we seek.

There are some facts to go on, provided by state-of-the-art theory, proven methods, and established data. It is known in theory that humans and the other apes share a common hominoid ancestor.[6] It is also known from observation that nonhuman primates form social relationships and attachments to particular individuals, not to conspecifics in general, and these relationships can be measured. Not all relationships are symmetrical, but affective affiliations tend to be, as well they would have to be if psychological theories of mutual reinforcement have any application or validity. Social ties representing affective attachments between group members can be estimated by observing to what extent, how long, and with what intensity group members groom, embrace, and protect each other, share food, form alliances, and otherwise cooperate. These social ties can be ordinally scaled as strong, moderate, weak, or absent, so as to display the network of relations existing within a group, and that can be done with some confidence because of clear-cut patterns of behavior already known to break according to age and sex. The point of this is to enable the sociality of the group to be characterized according to the relative strength of its network ties. The point of that is to compare the sociality of different species by arraying the species on a cladogram.

A brief diversionary explanation may be in order here, since among the social scientists, only physical anthropologists are familiar with cladistic analysis.[7] Its purpose is to trace common ancestors, based on common characters assumed to be derived, so that macroevolutionary change can be represented. Common characters may be inferred from paleontological, molecular, or other relevant data that establish structural similarities between species. Taxonomic groups called clades, which it is the point of the cladogram to depict, may be constructed from dichotomous branchings in the cladogram that represent evolutionary divergence from common ancestors. Clades, as befits a taxonomic procedure, are arrayed according to relative magnitudes of homologous derived characters. In Figure 3.1, evolutionary relationships are shown for six hypothetical species, with each branching point representing divergence from a common ancestor. Species A through F have a common ancestor and contain all the descendants of it. They, therefore, form a clade, as do species A through

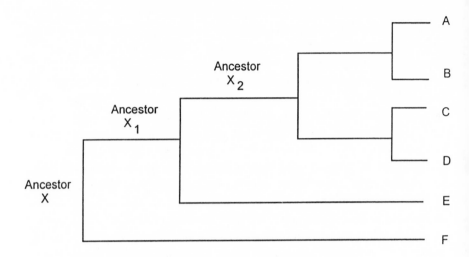

Figure 3.1. Hypothetical Cladogram for Species A-F

D, though with a different common ancestor and descendant species, and this clade represents a different taxonomic rank. Species C through F do not form a clade, however, because they do not include all the descendants of a common ancestor.

The frequency and distribution of shared characters in a clade is assumed, in accord with evolutionary theory, to be an inverse function of the distance of a chosen common ancestor. Now, humans and their ancestors, and their cousins, and anything else, can be cladistically arrayed, for the purpose of depicting the extent to which characters were biologically derived from a last common ancestor. Although we do not know what the last common ancestor for the hominoids was, we are sure on evidential grounds that phylogenetically humans are close to chimpanzees, are far from monkeys, and very far from prosimians. Fortunately, all these creatures are still with us.

We can forget the prosimians for our purposes, but let us consider the Old World monkeys (*Cercopithecoidea*), which are the closest extant creatures to the hominoids that are not themselves hominoids. Suppose we observe the monkeys' social behavior and characterize it according to its networks of affiliative ties—remembering that the monkeys, too, had a last common ancestor in the cercopithecoid taxon. This "outgroup population" gives us a baseline.

Our taxon of interest is the hominoids. Now suppose we take the apes, which we put on the cladogram with ourselves because we and they once shared a last common ancestor distinct from the LCA of the monkeys. We may measure the apes' networks of social affiliations the same way we measured the monkeys'. We may now compare the cladograms to see if there are differences. We assume that if the same social character is present in most or all apes but not in the monkeys, then the character was derived from that unknown last common ancestor that doesn't include the monkeys. The only alternative is to assume that each hominoid character evolved independently (which could be true, but which dumps most human evolutionary findings into the tank). The social characters we find present in the apes but not in the monkeys give us a reasonable hypothesis about general social features of the LCA to the apes and ourselves, which puts us in a position to reason about general social features of *Homo sapiens* that should have been present at the time the first hominid diverged from the apes. Because hominids, and especially we, did not diverge very long ago as evolutionary time is reckoned, whatever conclusions are drawn ought to apply to the present. There hasn't been time enough in human biological evolution for the general outlines of human social behavior to have changed very much. (The particulars are another matter.) Whatever general features we inherited from the last common hominoid ancestor ought to be still present and reflected (if at times suppressed and other times elaborated) in the social behavior of the various species that still represent the line.

We are not here going to do all this modeling because Alexandra Maryanski (1992; Maryanski and Turner 1992) has already done it for us. Maryanski employed just this line of theoretical reasoning[8] to analyze data for social network ties among gibbons, orangutans, gorillas, and chimpanzees, and for the social networks of baboons and of gelada, patas, and macaque monkeys. Maryanski examined data on the strength of ties for kinship or voluntary relations among adults, comparing sex differences, on the strength of ties between parents and their offspring, also comparing sex differences, and some other data as well. Then she compared the differences between the cladograms. The results are interesting, to say the least.

Cercopithecoids are known to be highly social creatures, and it is the females who are the center of this sociality. Mothers have strong ties with both their male and female dependent offspring, for instance, but fathers do not. Adult females also have strong ties with each other, but adult males do not. Females who are linked as mother and daughter, in all the species observed, maintain strong social ties as adults. Female-centered sociality is the distinguishing feature of cercopithecoid social networks.

In comparison, the social networks of the hominoids appear to have almost no strong ties. There are strong ties between mothers and their dependent offspring, and most of the other ties are weak or absent (except for adult male and female gibbons and gorillas.) For any primates, strong affiliative ties, at least for a time, have to hold between caregivers and their dependent offspring, or there would be no Order of Primates. So, the existence of strong ties between mothers and their dependent offspring cannot be generally attributed to just the hominoid LCA and, therefore, it does not tell us anything unique about the sociality of *Homo sapiens*. What does?

Maryanski's analysis shows that, compared to the closest evolutionary cousins we have that are not directly in our line, the monkeys and their friends, the hominoids are not very social at all. If the hominoids are not, the extinct hominids were not, because their last common ancestor was not—and therefore neither are we. The social behavior of *Homo sapiens* is distinguished evolutionarily by the fact that biologically, its forms are not as extensive or deep as our nearest phylogenetic relatives, suggesting we are not as affiliative or gregarious as some of our cultural myths would have it. In other words, we are not as social as we think we are. It is true, as a matter of fact, that humans have developed a massive and complex veneer of social organization that reflects a very intricate division of labor that is highly significant for its environmental impacts. But this veneer must have been superimposed if humans evolved biologically to be highly autonomous.[9] Complex, intricate, and extensive social behavior does not appear to have been an evolutionary derivation from the hominoid LCA. It appears to have been a product of culture and social organization.

One horn of Rappaport's Dilemma is beginning to come into focus.

DEGREES OF SOCIAL ORGANIZATION, HUMANS' AND OTHERS'

The foregoing analysis—speculative for its hypothetical flavor but, if valid, no less valid for that—suggests that the first human societies had to have had a rather weak social organization. By weak we refer to the degree of social organization present, which may be gauged by the degree of social organization we know humans to be capable of. Hunter-gatherer societies are "weak" by that measure. (There should be no thought that weak social organization is necessarily fragile or incohesive.) But, to make the point another way, we may turn to another comparison that yields the same result, and it is neither hypothetical nor speculative.

Some animals that live in small groups appear to be more social than some humans who live in small groups, if we consider the extent to which their potential for sociality has been realized given their organismic constraints and ecological conditions. Let us briefly consider the social behavior of African lions which, compared to some human societies that are weakly organized, is anything but.

Much is known of African lion prides, thanks to Packer (1986) and others. Permanent pride members are mostly female. Unlike the males, whose residence is temporary, the females are not nomadic. Like tribes of human foragers, which often decompose into smaller bands, lion prides often decompose into smaller groups within the hunting range of the pride. Hunting for prey is a cooperative affair undertaken by the females, and it is they who defend the range. The males defend them and claim them, but not the range. Males, in their solitary days, may traverse many ranges, until they are able to invade a pride (often there is a coalition of males cooperating in a takeover), oust the few reigning males, kill their young cubs, and sire their own—although the communal raising of cubs can sometimes obviate male-invader infanticide. In any case, this, too, is a socially organized affair. Sometimes lions appear to cooperate in defending a kill from scavengers and freeloaders from other prides. Perhaps most interesting, from a sociological point of view, is that the social organization of African lion prides can continue in perpetuity: Some prides endure within the same range past the time when all of the members, male and female, have been replaced. Socially organized cooperation among the African lions—in the hunting of prey, the raising of offspring, the defense of territory, the defense of kills, and the changing of the male guard—is almost unique among the wild cats. Mark the point that these animals have no language and nothing else resembling even the rudiments of culture.

There is, unfortunately, no way yet developed that would enable us to directly compare the African lions with hominoids in terms of network data of the kind that Maryanski developed. But in view of

Maryanski's evidence about the relative asociality of humans and of what we know of the sociality of lions, it seems justified to infer that, biologically, the lions are more social than we.

Since modern humans appear very late on the evolutionary clock, if our current repertoire of social traits exceeds the repertoire of 30,000 or 40,000 years ago, the difference has to have been provided by our own initiative and innovation. Social institutions are one form of social organization humans have initiated and innovated. These provide a way for social relationships to be continued in perpetuity and to remain pretty much the same, even though the persons who perpetuate them eventually are replaced. Institutionalized social behavior, whether weakly or strongly organized, can be a means of successful adaptation by humans to their environments.

And so it has been with African lions. Lions' social roles, which change according to age and sex and are kinship centered, are made evident by observing lion behavior and are passed to the young from the elders during the course of social attachments. When the founding members are eventually replaced, the social relations of the members remain pretty much the same. African lions are the bearers of a social structure that is perpetuated. The transgenerational perpetuity of a pride clearly mandates the conclusion that their group living, like much human group life, is institutionalized.

Lion social organization evolved biologically, when natural selection favored the cooperation of what students of lion socioecology presume were noncooperating ancestral individuals. We have seen that, theoretically, if cooperation is advantageous (in species capable of learning), it should gain a foothold with a ratchet effect. Lions and humans, though very different, both evolved socially organized behavior in response to very similar habitat conditions (they occupied some of the same habitats), and they hit upon some similar forms. The communality and social structure of lions is about what can be found in a (cross-culturally uncontaminated) tribe of human hunters and gatherers. But the hunter-gatherers are weakly organized, compared to what humans are capable of; the lions are strongly organized, compared to what they (and other wild cat species) are capable of.

What we see of lion sociality is the most we are going to get from them. That isn't true of us. The difference is that the lions are well organized by nature. We are by culture, and this enables us to become much more social in ways that the lions cannot. But, biologically, lions evolved to be not as autonomous, not as individualistic, and not as asocial as we. With culture, we can add much more social organization to our biological endowments than they, but they start with more in the dowry. The key difference is our unmatched ability to complicate things.

NOTES

1. Any current review of the status of findings and interpretations on this subject is never current for long because of rapid advances in techniques and newly acquired data. Simons (1989) provides a not-too-dated, but no longer fully current, tracing and review of human evolutionary origins, organized from an "out-of-Africa" hypothesis now disputed by some. Some socioecological aspects of human evolution are discussed in Foley and Lee (1989). As this manuscript goes to press, the oldest known hominid fossil (*A. ramidus*) is dated at 4.4 million years (Edgar 1995), out of Africa.

2. The Primate Order was named 250 years ago by Carl Linnaeus and refers to the primary order of mammals—primary, it would seem, because it includes us. But there is nothing "primary" about this order among the mammals, which go back 225 million years.

Primates have always been attractive species for study just because of what they might tell us about ourselves. We have tended to use them to tell us what we wanted to hear. Consequently, the study of primates has had a sordid history. For a long time, much of the world view of primatology was infused with, and some of its purported facts conditioned by, sexism, speciesism, and racism, and residues of all that remain. For a brilliant treatment of that angle on the study of primates, tilted though it is, see Donna Haraway's *Primate Visions* (1989) and the first five chapters of her *Simians, Cyborgs, and Women* (1991). Primates nevertheless may be good object lessons for humans if the lesson of the object is altered to demystify cultural illusions about human uniqueness, virtue, dominance, and rights of exploitation. There is no reason, in other words, that the study of primates cannot be turned against its own history. Apart from that matter, however, we might as well pay no attention to human evolution at all if we are not going to pay attention to primates. We are, after all, one of them.

3. Darwinian fitness has several interpretations, as befits the development of this concept since Darwin's time. For Darwin, fitness was a matter of phenotypic match to habitats. This can be interpreted in terms of potential fitness (as adaptability) or realized fitness (adaptedness), sometimes known as absolute fitness. Relative fitness, also known as classical fitness, is a quantitative measure of the selective value of a phenotype for mating, fecundity, fertility, or survivorship. This phenotypic fitness is algebraically connected to genetic fitness, which is a mathematical quantity that measures the relative fitness of an allele in order to gauge the rate at which selection proceeds. See Dawkins (1982, chap. 10) and Endler (1986, pp. 33-51) for discussions of the various fitnesses.

4. Paleoanthropologists are pushing ever closer to the last common ancestor of the hominids. The most likely current candidate—touted, as these discoveries often are, as a "missing link" between hominids and apes—is *Ardipithecus ramidus*, known to be one-half million years older than the earliest known Australopithecines (*A. afarensis*).

Unlike its hominid descendants, this species lived in closed forests. Species intermediate to *A. ramidus* and *A. afarensis* have since been found (Edgar 1995).

5.   See Tooby and DeVore (1987) for a discussion of the problems of inference encountered with the modeling of hominid behavioral evolution. In the same volume, an anthology edited by Kinzey (1987), Potts discusses the difficulties of constructing comparative primate models.

6.   That has to be true, or evolution is not true. For that matter, humans, nonhuman apes, and monkeys share a common ancestor in the form of anthropoids, whose divergence can be traced back at least to the pint-sized Shoshonious that swung in Wyoming trees fifty million years ago.

7.   The presentation here is much oversimplified. For an in-depth treatment of the intricate evolutionary logic required for and made possible by cladistic analysis, see Brooks and McLennan (1991). They characterize this work—of general comparative biology, not primates or humans—as historical ecology because it attempts to evaluate phylogenetic hypotheses in terms of known or presumed ecological constraints operating during periods of selection.

8.   Methods similar to Maryanski's, but with alternative assumptions and somewhat different results, owing in part to the measurement of different variables and the observation of different subjects, can be found in Wrangham (1987) and Foley (1989).

9.   Maryanski and Turner (1992) develop the implications of this conclusion for classical social theory, which has always regarded humans as the epitome on the social scale. The implications, to put it mildly, are serious. They do not square with long-standing liberal ideals and intellectual prejudices, especially the prejudices of sociologists. That aside, the hypothesis that humans evolved to be something like lone rangers adds even more force to Rappaport's Dilemma. It suggests that, indeed, there is substantial discontinuity between human bological and cultural evolution.

Chapter 4

The Natural Selection of Acculturated Humans

In this chapter, we consider the natural selection of humans insofar as culture has interacted with the process. We do not much consider the natural selection *of* culture but rather how culture may have been implicated in the natural selection of humans. The possession of culture is presumed to have conferred selective advantages under conditions of hominid environments. Culture, like sociality, is a fixed phenotype of the human species. And, presuming the biological evolution of minimal sociality in humans, we have, therefore, to begin to consider the evolution of culture and its associated symbols to find any basis by which human sociality could be developed so as to take the form of modern complex macrosocieties.

The first human societies were nothing like that although, apart from the necessary kinship, we do not know *specifically* how they were organized. Assorted hypotheses have been put forward about their organization.[1] One is Man, the Hunter (not easily sustained—some hominids themselves were hunted—but not entirely refutable). Another is Homo, the Scavenger (questionable, as a major subsistence pattern— the *Homo* genus is too high in the food chain for such a specialized niche—but still viable). Another is Homo, the Seed Eater (no longer credible—the first established hominid was not a seed eater). Another is Man, the Monogamous and Caring Father (not currently well received or widely believed). Another is Woman, the Gatherer (currently favored, in view of comparative data on chimpanzee behavior and the diets of modern hunters and gatherers, which consist mostly of food gathered not hunted). Whichever hypothesis may hold sway in the light of evidence or contemporary fashion, any of these evolutionary scenarios imply some sort of adaptive social behavior that would have, or would soon get, cultural content that could be passed along the generations.

Populations that are capable of learning and of transmitting to descendants what they learn have a selective advantage, other things being equal, compared to those not so capable. The advantage is that the adaptations ancestors evolved do not have to be rediscovered anew. For primates in general and hominoids in particular, there is a long maturational period during which parental care of the young enables behavior patterns, functional for species in their habitats, to be transmitted by observational learning or by reinforcement. Primates possess considerable behavioral plasticity, which is an advantage when habitat conditions change because then they can modify the adaptations they have learned. It's an advantage they need. Their organic constitution limits the range of their adaptability to far fewer kinds of habitat conditions than, for example, the insects. If primates could not learn and *relearn*, they could not evolutionarily compete. For humans, this is facilitated by the use of complex symbolization most often wrapped in language. There can not be much culture without much symbolization. Symbolization is key to the development of effective tools and other aspects of complex culture that humans use to extend our otherwise rather narrow range of habitats and to create entirely new habitats to which we may not be biologically well adapted but can become culturally well adapted.

Culture and its associated symbols are phenotypes that we share as part of an evolutionary heritage with other genera and species. We can better comprehend the eventual ecological significance these phenotypes took on for ourselves if we know that their evolution was not unique to ourselves. More generally, we can better comprehend the evolutionary connections of human ecology if we disabuse ourselves of assorted myths of human uniqueness. But for the time being, let us concentrate on culture and symbols.

CULTURE AND HUMAN UNIQUENESS

A prime axiom of anthropology is that culture is an adaptation to environments. But of what is this axiom true, and how shall we decide?

In the matter of culture, there has been a long-standing intellectual tradition, only recently breached, in which theory and evidence have provided a line of reasoning to support the ancient dogma that humans are unique. Social scientists in particular have defended this view. Only *we* have culture. Only we also, supposedly, have symbolic capacities. In comparison to the rest of species, we often describe ourselves as unparalleled, unmatched, and unprecedented for this, that, or the other desirable attribute. The adjectives give away the game plan, which is to preserve the special status ordained for us, among other places, in the Biblical Book of Genesis and the archives of Western philosophy. The trump card in the play of this game has always been mind and its correlate idea, self, and its necessary adjunct, language. The capability to think, and to think reflectively, about oneself; to view oneself as other people do and to see the world from their point of view; and to derive personal identities from interactions with others, all symbolized through language, are attributes that correlate directly with the capacity for acculturation. Every creeping thing that creepeth upon the earth was not endowed with these. We have minds, selves, and linguistic symbols, which give us the principal evolutionary attributes from which we get our technical name: thinking beings. With thought and its practical applications, after a time we get advanced technology, which provides the physical artifacts by which we measure complex acculturation. We, therefore, are the crown jewels in evolution. What more could you want?

For starters, an appreciation of the different kinds of errors that one may be thoughtlessly committing to by accepting these anthropocentric judgments of self-designated worth. Two sorts of errors are possible. One is to attribute to other animals qualities they don't have. Apart from being wrong, however, it isn't clear what sort of damage such an error could cause. At best, the result could be comforting myths. At worst, one could get the worship of animals, and when that occurs, and it does at times, one may get their overpopulation—but one often gets that as a matter of course, anyhow. The other error is to attribute to humans a uniqueness we do not have and to endow ourselves with assorted deific attributes and derived rights of exploitation. This attitude has been paramount in Western cultures, often with a theological blessing to subdue and dominate every living thing that moveth upon the earth. As if theological blessing were not enough, Descartes provided another from philosophy (in support of the dominant culture's theology) that claimed animals have no minds or souls. For the moment, we shall pass on the damage this error has caused and continues to cause—the suffering and destruction of untold millions of animals—simply to note that Western prejudices of human uniqueness and superiority are wholly out of touch with the modern sciences of ethology and primatology (see Heltne and Marquardt 1989; Wrangham, McGrew, de Waal, and Heltne 1994).

Humans are, of course, unique in their degree of *development* of cultural and symbolic capacities. That should draw no argument. What we can argue about is what this implies. It most certainly does not imply the subtext usually understood to go with the dogma that humans are unique, namely, that humans are superior and have a right to act like it. Besides there being so many, many ways in which humans are not superior to so many, many other animal species, any fundamental criteria for culture that we may adopt to establish our uniqueness turn out to be faulty.

CULTURE AND SYMBOLS AS EVOLUTIONARY PHENOTYPES

The uniqueness of human culture, its underlying symbol systems, and their significance for human ecology can be found in the heterogeneity and complexity of both. Heterogeneous and complex culture and symbolization seem to be additional adaptive developments that humans added to the bases—because, we may assume, increasing heterogeneity and complexity proved to be functional for survival. But so have these phenotypes been for other genera and species, up to a point, for other species provided the bases.

Culture and Its Criteria

To judge whether some interacting population possesses culture is to tacitly employ criteria for the judgment. Plainly, if we invoked all the criteria applicable to human culture, we would find perforce that no other creatures have culture, for we already know that none of them has it to the degree that we have. Therefore, to use humans as the standard for culture solves the matter by fiat. Of course, if one wanted to prove that only humans have culture, this would be the tack to take. But fiats are not persuasive means of proof. On the other hand, if the possession of culture is a matter of degree and humans have just complicated what for other animals is more simple, then we need criteria that reflect just the fundamentals. Fundamental criteria would be multispecific not unispecific. This would be the way to prove that animals other than humans have culture, if in fact they do. Let us consider several nested criteria for culture and follow with some illustrative facts pertaining to its appearance in the evolutionary record.

One criterion for culture is whether information pertaining to behavior is passed around the members of a population, especially from adults to their offspring, as a matter of imitation or learning and not genetic inheritance. Another is whether animals learn to be tool users, by which I mean they use unmodified objects in their environment to alter some aspect of their habitat. A third is whether they learn to be tool makers—whether they *modify* objects in their environment to alter other aspects of it. A fourth, applicable to all the above, is whether anything resembling a tradition develops, in which the content of culture accumulates in a generation and is passed down the generations. A fifth is whether the body of culture observed is capable of evolving—whether it can be adapted to changing habitat conditions. This last brings human culture clearly in view, although anthropologists may have good reason to wish to improve upon it for their purposes. For our purposes, the set taken as a whole can be applied to multiple species. Then, there is clear evidence of multifaceted cultural behavior in a wide range of nonhuman animals according to one criterion or another.[2]

The Cultural Behavior of Nonhuman Animals

Consider the minimum criterion, the transfer of information by behavioral means. Birds do this, and so do many other animals, for example, by warning each other of the approach of predators. Sometimes their warnings are directed at the predators. Some animal herds employ sentries to warn of approaching danger. There is no doubting that many species communicate information through behavior, some of it learned, such as the song dialects of some birds, and the list is way too long even to bother with.

Birds also use tools. For example, the Galapagos finches grasp thorns in their beaks to remove grubs from trees. Some birds use stones to break open the shells of other birds' eggs, which they wish to purloin. One of them, an Egyptian vulture, even throws stones to break open the eggs. Some sea otters use stones (to break open mussels). So do baboons. Even a wasp. They are all tool users. Are any of them tool makers? Many are not, but the making of sophisticated tools by a small number of crows that live in New Caledonia's rain forests was recently reported (Hunt 1996). Of course, if nests are considered to be tools, then most birds make tools.

There is no doubt chimpanzees have made tools. Jane Goodall pioneered these discoveries. Observations of tool use by chimps in captivity date back to the 1920s, but Goodall's observations of *Pan troglodytes* in the wild were extensive, and included evidence of tool construction in addition to tool use. Since then numerous investigators have established considerable diversity in this adaptation. McGrew (1992) reported 32 populations of wild African chimps known to have used tools, and later updated the count to thirty-six (McGrew 1994). Some chimps contrive tools to forage for termites and ants, the tool being a branch of a tree, which they modify by stripping the leaves. Some chimps also use sticks as levers and contrive from leaves something resembling a sponge, which they use to accumulate water and also to groom themselves and their offspring. Some of them use unmodified stones as hammers and rocks as anvils, and sometimes rocks as weapons. Leaf-groomers, ant-dippers, termite-fishers, nut-smashers, missile-throwers—chimp tool-use is so varied it lends itself to stereotyping! Not all chimps use all of these tools, and some use none of them. Some chimps preserve the tools they use or make. Sometimes the use of a tool by one chimp is observed and then imitated by another. Whether chimps ever use *made* tools to make more is unclear (see McGrew 1989).

One could conclude those are all primitive tools in service of a primitive tool user. Well, primitive compared to what? They are perfectly effective and efficient tools that enable the chimps to be adapted to their habitats. There is nothing primitive about that. Primitive with respect to humans, perhaps, but chimps did not evolve with respect to humans. We did evolve with respect to a common ancestor. The question is not how much they are like us, but how much we are like them. We cannot understand them with respect to our adaptations. We might understand ourselves better with respect for theirs. Theirs are the rudiments of ours.

In captivity the capacity of chimps for tool using and tool making, without training by humans, shows virtuosity and ingenuity beyond what is observed in the wild. Generalizations about nonhuman primates in captivity have to be interpreted with caution, because of the changed habitat conditions. Orangutans, for instance, have been observed to use tools in captivity but not in the wild. However, the very changed conditions themselves afford a glimpse into the adaptability of species as conditions for survival are adjusted. Chimps in the wild, eating their fill of termites, may be very happy campers. If so, they have no incentive to develop other possible tools that their natural habitat and their own ingenuity make available. In captivity sometimes they do, and the result is a tool-using and tool-making capacity not otherwise seen.

Is any of this passed on as a matter of tradition? Yes, in various species, and this provides another example of the evolutionary convergence in different species of culture-bearing adaptations. Most species, including those that use tools, have no traditions. We can say we are observing a tradition when we observe behavior that is acquired by some members of a population, through experience; is learned by others and incorporated into theirs; and is passed down the generations.

Some birds do this with their choice of migration routes and breeding grounds, and some have done it with feeding habits, which can spread from local to more diffuse populations and become perpetuated. That's a tradition. Cats teach their young how to hunt, who later teach their own young how to hunt. That's a tradition, too. It is learned, moreover, by the mother teaching the skill in successive and recursive stages. Goodall (1986) and others (see Heltne and Marquardt 1989; Wrangham, McGrew, de Waal, and Heltne 1994) report that chimps have assorted cultural traditions, which are known to be variable (in tool kits, for instance) in different, and sometimes nearby, locales.

Is there true cultural inheritance in the traditions of animals? One example is the inheritance of kinship dominance—a competitive ranking that female offspring acquire, with assistance from their kin, in permanent groups of female Old World monkeys. Another example—remarkable for its similarity with human cultural traditions—is afforded by the famous macaque monkey, Imo, responsible for the behavioral innovation of washing sweet potatoes. Other macaques in her troop copied the habit but, and here is the remarkable part, just the macaques of Imo's age and younger. The older ones for the most part did not.

Many mammals other than primates have traditions. And why would they not? Given an ongoing functional problem in a predictable habitat and a population of social organisms capable of learning by imitation, some traditions should have survival value. Once set in train, a tradition should continue as long as the problem persists, the solution is the optimal one available, and there is continuity in the population. As a practical matter, this often depends very much on the imitation by the young of the behavior of the adults. Learning by imitation, incidentally, is not a phenomenon restricted to conspecifics—a point made by Mainardi (1980). Nor is it restricted to social animals, nor even to vertebrates, as Fiorito and Scotto (1992) found clear evidence of observational learning in a species of octupus (*Octupus vulgaris*). But the development of a tradition probably is restricted to conspecific social (or quasi-social) vertebrates.

Can the cultural traditions of animals evolve? In theory, absolutely. In fact, uncommonly, although there are documented cases. Perhaps the best example is the Japanese macaque monkeys. (Imo was one of these.) Initially wild, they came under the care, protection, and manipulation of scientists, and when one colony got too large, it was split, with one troop carted across the Pacific to Oregon. There came then an opportunity for the near-perfect experiment: two groups with the same genes but different physical environments. Not much change was observed in the Japanese troop that served as a control. They, for instance, retained their female-based dominance ranks, where mothers win fights for their young sons in groups where adult males are excluded. The Oregon troopers relaxed this and other behavior patterns of the Japanese colony and produced assorted behavioral innovations (Eaton 1976; Modahl and Eaton 1977). Some of the founder population was also broken into different troops scattered in Japan and subjected to different habitat conditions. The result was commensurable: changed behavior, more functional for the changed conditions, that was passed along to descendants.

Some elephants are known to have done this. Generations ago, most of the members of a tame and docile group of African elephants were mercilessly destroyed by rifle fire. The survivors became, and their descendants today remain, aggressive and dangerous toward humans and do not make themselves known in daytime, although none of the original victims of the shooting could now be alive. The survivors adapted quickly and passed along their adaptation.[3] The loss of tameness in animals is something that the loser can teach.

The Symbolic Behavior of Nonhuman Animals

Clearly, some animals exhibit cultural behavior, some with traditions of it, some of which in principle can evolve. But can nonhuman animals think? The culture they have is very rudimentary. Is this because they lack symbolic capabilities?

No.

First, to connect to our preceding discussion of tools, it is not the case that tool use correlates (except in a spurious way) with brain size and, thus, with the capability to learn. True, only the brainiest of animals, we, have developed complex tool kits to adapt to our habitat contingencies. And apparently no others, having different constitutions and facing different habitat contingencies, make tools *with* tools. Trivially, it takes intelligence to make the tool kit humans today possess. But because most mammalian species don't make or even use tools, and because those that do have very little culture, it does not follow that they have no intelligence. A correct assessment cannot be had by using humans as a standard, for one has to take into account the adaptedness of a species population to its habitat. Is there any reason to suppose that the intelligence (whatever that may mean) that other animals have evolved is somehow inferior, as a habitat adaptation, to the intelligence that humans have evolved? For specific cases, there may be, but generally speaking, there is not.

Human intelligence (such as it is) and the complex culture it enables in no small measure are due to the greater proportion, compared to nonhuman primates, of neocortical brain mass. With this, especially with a greater mass of association cortex, much more information can be processed, greater cognitive differentiation is possible, and abstract symbol systems such as language can be devised. There are reasons that humans are the only animals that use language on a regular basis, and one reason is how much wiring we have. Brains made language possible, conditions made it useful, ancestors evolved it, speech facilitated its development and, on Bickerton's (1990) analysis, the protolanguages of early hominids should have opened ecological niches for adaptive radiation that would not be available to other primates. In other words, as Box (1984) and others have observed, language increases the carrying capacity of a habitat, especially by enabling tool construction and cultural development. Language also provides symbols with which to think abstractly about things, including ourselves, and there is some question whether any other animals have any comparable abstract self-referential capacity—a capacity that would amplify the chance to develop complex social organization as an adaptation to environments. We shall consider some of these questions momentarily.

First, I digress to remark there is an even greater question of how to measure all this, for we know enough to say that inferences of incapacity from actual behavioral performance (or failure of performance) may be invalid. Animals may be inattentive to humanly contrived experimental conditions, which may be inappropriate for them; or responses may show delayed effects; or test subjects may not exhibit the expected behavioral changes except under peculiar and uncommon conditions; or there could be cognitive changes not reflected in test subjects' behavior in the manner in which human experimenters suppose it should be reflected. When test subjects are captive, as opposed to "wild," animals, a further complication may be introduced if the subjects have been raised with significant socialization influences from humans.

Questions of measurement aside, inferences regarding linguistic, cognitive, and symbolic capacities are conditioned, and may be limited, by our concepts of language, thought, and symbol. Professional opinion varies as to what qualifies and should qualify as language, thought, and symbol and on how all these interact to enhance each other. Professional opinion does not vary on two points: Primates other than humans, in the wild or in contrived experimental settings, do not utilize *speech*,[4] for they lack either the necessary vocal apparatus or the inclination to use the physical apparatus they do have; and non-chemically based communication, by way of signs that convey information, is routine in many species of animals, humans included.

For functional, patterned, repeated responses to the same environmental stimuli in organisms capable of imitative learning, there has to be some sort of cognitive organization to perceptual categories: To learn is to use the brain, and to use the brain is to organize its pathways. But a classic mistake, Walker (1983) emphasized, is to array existing species in some neat phylogenetic order representing a linear scale of brain excellence. It may be useful to order brain capacities for gross classifications of higher and lower invertebrates. To assign cognitive superiority to different species within genera, however, becomes very messy. One has to take into account their specialized ways of living. One has to ask how good they are at what they do, and the answer is that many of them are very good. This does not grade on a scale that puts humans at top. Human neocortical size, acculturation, social organization, and the products of those, may incline us to put ourselves at the top. But the differences between the brains of humans and our closest ancestors, the chimps and bonobos, by evolutionary standards are strictly penny ante. The rather small differences have simply had rather large ramifications. Abstract thought linguistically framed and symbolic social interaction are principal among them.

Language, Symbols, and Signs

There is no doubt—for the moment at least—that hominids are the only animals ever to have *evolved* linguistic symbols. There is some reason to believe that apes can learn to use linguistic symbols (arbitrary abstractions that have referential significance) in contrived circumstances, and some authorities are now prepared to state unequivocally that "language, in its basic dimensions, may no longer rationally be held as the characteristic that separates humans from animals" (Rumbaugh, Savage-Rumbaugh, and Sevick 1994, p. 332).[5] But can apes learn to use linguistic symbols for reflective purposes, especially for self-reflective purposes, even in contrived circumstances? Can they use nonlinguistic signs for self-reflective purposes in any circumstances? This all depends on our concept of self-reflection, which in turn depends on our concepts of symbol and sign and the theories we employ about them, which will condition our interpretation of the facts of the matter. In overview, I tend to follow Peirce (1958) and Sebiok (1991) (sometimes with lamentable fidelity).

All linguistic symbols are signs of a sort. Linguistic symbols are abstract representations of objects, events, or relationships that enable information about a referent to be stored, and transmitted to others who share the symbol and can respond to it even when the referent may be displaced in time or space. Linguistic symbols are stand-ins or placeholders for referents, real (or imagined) things in the world, and they do not stand alone. The use of linguistic symbols to refer presumes a grammar (or protogrammar).

While linguistic symbols are signs that are given arbitrary, culturally shared meanings, nonlinguistic signs are organically "wired in" so that they provide indicators of some behavioral response or other reaction appropriate to an experiential configuration. A configuration of signs organizes the immediate conditions of experience for any animal that is sign-cognizant. In Peirce's dictum, knowledge of a sign carries with it knowledge of something else, because it is a relation that connects some object to the field of experience (including the cognition, if applicable) of an interpretant. Nonlinguistic signs can, but do not always, convey symbolic meaning.

Penetrating no farther than this, into a subject of extraordinarily delicate complications, what can we say about symbolic interaction among nonhuman animals?[6]

Symbolic Interaction Among Nonhuman Animals

There is no scientific justification for the dogma that self-reference can be undertaken only with linguistic symbols. Animals that can differentiate themselves and other social relationships by means of nonlinguistic signs are animals that have self-awareness and can, with the aid of signs, refer to themselves in relation to others. Many animals can not do that, but some primates can.

It is known that nonhuman primates, just like humans, sustain relationships to particular individuals, and can adjust their behavior according to histories of interaction with them. They not only recognize each other, but they appear somehow to *define* each other—usually within the context of age, sex, kinship, rank, and accumulated interaction history. Cheney, Seyfarth, and Smuts (1986), in reviewing assorted evidence, mention their own findings on this point: Vervet monkey mothers, upon hearing the tape-recorded screams of one of their offspring, were able to associate the offspring with its mother before the mother herself had, suggesting that the others recognized this unique and distinct social relationship formed of differentiated, individual identities. Since the monkeys have no language, they must have organized this with nonlinguistic signs.

This is not to say other animals can contemplate themselves as humans might, but there is no reason to demand that cognitive references to self- and other-relationships should require *contemplation* (which among humans is the pastime of mostly a small fraction of them anyhow: intellectuals). We are talking here about creatures whose knowledge is conveyed by nonlinguistic signs. If their cognitive organization enables them to identify themselves, others, and their social relationships in terms of signs, we have some reason to conclude that their cognitive capacities involve the use of nonlinguistic symbols.

Among the scientists, none have devoted to these matters more print than the sociologists, and most of them would disagree. Sociologists usually insist that symbolization requires language. The putative godfather of this doctrine, George Herbert Mead, himself was not so doctrinaire. Mead emphasized the importance of language but also averred, in his words, that "language simply lifts out of the social process a situation which is logically or implicitly there already" (1934, p. 79). For Mead, linguistic symbolization was a complication of the basic social process of signification. With language one could, whereas with other signs one could not, consciously call forth to oneself the same meaning that a social gesture or set of signs had for somebody else. When meanings are conveyed with words, one can take the role of the other, or see the world from another's point of view. By doing that often enough in the context of social interaction, conducted symbolically, humans would develop a sense of self and be able to reflect on it, and without symbolic social interaction, they would not because they could not. The development of language, self, and society is relational, evolutionary, and unique to humans, said Mead, and his analysis at times had ecological overtones (Mead 1936).

The sociological descendants of Mead drew their wagons in a circle, evidently fearing wild beasts might penetrate the enclave reserved just for humans that Mead was thought to have defined. The beasts broke in anyway. The chimpanzee, an embarrassing nuisance always, can organize and coordinate information independently acquired from different sense organs, as befits a creature with its neocortical development; can learn memory sequences the behavioral correlates of which require it to displace events in time, which that same neocortex ought again to enable; can ordinally scale classes of objects; and may be able to learn to refer abstractly to classes of objects and relationships by using linguistic symbols it has been taught to combine, a talent for which the wild chimp has no practical use whatever. With this, the chimp appears to learn to refer to itself (cf. Meddin 1979; Goodall 1986; van Hoof 1994). Povinelli (1994) drove the nail into the sociologists' coffin with his report of clear evidence of role reversal, a condition that forces one to take the role of the other. Such is supposedly a condition for having a self to reflect upon. Can chimps really reflect upon themselves?

A straightforward answer depends upon the resolution of a number of unsettled theoretical arguments, for instance, regarding whether language should be taken as a precondition for symbolizing, and on further empirical evidence and improved measurement techniques. For our purposes, there are questions more to the point: *Do* chimps reflect upon themselves, and what might occasion them to? For the most part, they probably do not, at least not very much or in ways that we might easily recognize. They don't need to.

With language, humans can do all sorts of things that chimps or any other nonhuman primate would never want to bother with. Humans have to bother with that vast veneer of social organization that cultures have piled upon our genetic inheritance. For that, we need language, symbols, and self-concepts to make sense of it all and to negotiate it. For us, it is a matter of survival. The chimps have it easy in comparison. If they have little sense of self, it is not necessarily because they lack the capability. It is more likely because their environmental context has never required them to develop it. As a general rule, if some adaptation is needed, that doesn't imply it will be forthcoming; necessary, even vital, adaptations often are not. But if some adaptation is not needed, or if it is not fitness-enhancing, it is not likely to evolve or be selected. We were selected as our ability to think evolved. Chimps were not selected as their ability to think *like us* evolved. Because they don't think like us, however, doesn't mean they don't think—including about themselves.

In thinking about themselves, there is some evidence that chimps are able to include us in the formation of their identities. Normally, of course, they would not, because normally they do not interact with us. But domesticated chimps have long provided evidence of including humans in their own identity formation: "Viki Hayes," as she came to be called, placed her own photograph, which she had learned to identify, together with photographs of other humans *instead of* sorting it into the pile of animal photographs in which she had included the family pets (Hayes and Hayes 1952). Apparently, Viki thought she belonged with the humans, which was a reasonable identification on her part considering how they had treated her like one of them. Such anecdotal evidence, of course, is not conclusive, but it does suggest the rudiments of a personal identification process on the part of an ape, derived in this case from interspecific social interaction.[7]

But one can not take inferences about ape identity formation and self-concept too far with too little, and there has been a tendency of primatologists to do this. For instance, the fact that chimpanzees can recognize themselves in mirrors is sometimes taken as evidence that they possess a self-concept. While this experimental procedure has provided valuable clarification of issues in primatological research, such an inference diminishes and trivializes the whole idea of self-concept by reducing it thus: Any animal with the visual apparatus to see its own reflection in a mirror (many animals do not have the apparatus) plus the capacity to differentiate itself from any other thing ipso facto would have a self-concept. Such a feeble interpretation of self-concept has no explanatory value whatever. This criticism, however, does not argue for the maintenance of a strictly human standard. The standard has to derive from the relationships of species to environments.

If apes in the wild are endowed with anything like identities or self-concepts, there is no reason to suppose they would be much like ours. The habitat conditions of nonhuman apes and the fit of their biological constitution and social organization to those conditions have never been much like ours except way back, when we were just like them. The habitat conditions to which they must adapt, except for extensive range compression, have not changed much. Ours did, as we changed from them. We don't live in forests or savannas anymore. Increasingly, we live in cities. They don't. They have both cultural and symbolic capacities, and hardly any use for them. We, it seems, need more and more. While their adaptations to home environments have not changed much, ours have changed substantially with the development of culture and social organization. These basic phenotypes we share with them as part of a common evolutionary heritage. If we are distinguished from them and are unique because of that, it is because of how we expanded the bases.

HUMAN CULTURE IN EVOLUTIONARY CONTEXT

There can be no doubt that the natural selection of modern humans was facilitated by the development of culture—that, broadly speaking, culture and its associated symbolization were fitness-enhancing. But for just whom, when, and how? We shall use the term human to designate the entire *Homo* genus for otherwise it could be hopelessly vague. We use the term modern humans for ourselves, the *Homo sapiens sapiens*, just the last of several known to be in the genus. Although again we conceive of origins as a process not an initial state of being, there are some tantalizing suggestions of time-specific, if broadly bracketed, points of origin for setting the trajectory and enhancing the rate of the coevolution of culture, language, and modern humans.

Jumps and Starts in the Human Evolutionary Record

The first primates, the prosimians (pre-monkeys), evolved feeding patterns that, in most instances, were adapted for a nocturnal existence. The later ones, the anthropoids (human-like), by contrast, became diurnal. A larger array of ecological niches becomes available for creatures able to walk in the sun. Thus, the anthropoids underwent a very successful evolutionary radiation, while there are not so many prosimians left anymore. With the anthropoids came the extensive development of central nervous systems, coordinated hands, and (eventually) social ties. Creatures with these traits have a selective advantage: They can create even more niches of their own. How did this happen to result in humans that eventually became acculturated? There is a standard story anthropologists have frequently told, of what is sometimes called sapienization, and it goes roughly as follows.

The evolution of bipedal walking, considered to be the first hominid adaptation, was a watershed. Bipedalism freed the hands and enabled human ancestors to leave the trees. The incentive for them to do that most probably was to find more food. Better shelter and protection from predators could not have been incentives, for these pre-human pioneers gradually left the forests and took to the grassy, but unpredictable and sometimes dangerous, savannas. Here, different adaptations were required, and the most significant the migrants developed was the use of tools. These, together with larger brains, would be selectively favored in a predatory environment for an organism with bipedal, and rather slow, locomotion. And they were favored. With the increased cortical capacity of larger brains, the daughters and sons of these pioneers could now organize the sounds made by their vocal chords into grammars for protolanguages, soon to be refined. Then, they really had something: a capacity to pass information down the generations, especially information about their tool kits, and a capacity to organize their behavior for social living and to pass this along. Some social organization would be an effective adaptation several ways. It would afford protection against predators, for there were some large carnivores back then and way out there; it might maximize investments in foraging, which could eventually take the form of hunting for meat and its protein (and with evolved dentition and digestive tract would then permit meat consumption and processing); it would promote male and female bonding, which would increase reproductive success; and, derivative of that, it would enable the care of infants who had biologically evolved to be altricial (born helpless and requiring extended care). To support all of this, a nomadic lifestyle would be effective, for the savanna has its seasons, but home bases of operation from which to forage out could be developed—another adaptation effective in a changing environment.

All of this happened at different times and places. Not all of it, of course, is supposed to have happened at once or in the same place. The pioneers who left the forests just set in motion what far later descendants, of different genus and species, would finish with language and culture. Some traits that evolved along the way would set the conditions for the evolution of others, while some adaptations would play off each other—feed and strengthen each other—and would coevolve. It all took two to four million years, and by two million years ago the transition from nonhumans to the first humans was complete (*Homo* appeared about 2.5 million years back). Or so goes the standard story, begun by Darwin and extended by many modern anthropologists.

It is a nice story and not without its foundations, but Potts (1991) told us it is a bit too cute for the evidence. And some additional evidence is mounting of which we should take note.

Twists of Culture in the Human Evolutionary Record

The earliest hominids apparently did live close to forests, and the earliest known (*A. ramidus*) perhaps within them (Edgar 1995), but this allows that the evolution of bipedalism may have been an adaptation to preserve living in patchy forests and not to venturing into open savannas. The selection pressure for bipedalism is not known for sure. Stone tools did appear (other types would not have been preserved) about two and one-half million years ago, as the story has it. Larger cranial capacity appeared then, too, with the first species of *Homo*. But brain size continued to increase—in fact kept doing that until modern humans appeared—while stone tools—the principal indicator of early hominid culture—were left unimproved for periods that lasted several hundred thousand years. Though a prime factor in sapienization, increased brain size did not correlate well with acculturation, which is to say these two adaptations were not tightly coupled. Altricial birth, which does correlate with increased cranial capacity (which affects the organic logistics of infant delivery), and prolonged infant development also appeared around the time of *Homo*, but this is much later than was thought by writers of the standard story. Home bases for foraging, a telltale characteristic of hunters and gatherers and clear evidence of the existence of social organization, is placed two million years back in the standard story. But recent evidence from some of the supposed home bases suggests they may have served as actual refuges for human groups only much later. The point is debatable. Less debatable is when humans began on a regular and exclusive basis to use tools for hunting as opposed to mere scavenging at food dumps. It may have been just one hundred thousand years ago when hunting was added to gathering—and maybe even more recently than that. The earliest evidence of tool heterogeneity begins to show about that time, and flowered around 40 to 50 thousand years ago with the unambiguous appearance of modern humans. Tool heterogeneity would imply cultural innovation, but the inverse implication also holds: With tool homogeneity, which covers most of the human record prior to *Homo sapiens sapiens*, there couldn't, wouldn't, and shouldn't be much language or culture. As to language, just *when* it began to be developed and used in ernest is not at all clear, but some authorities take its flowering to be quite recent—perhaps only in the last 40 thousand years and perhaps only in modern humans. Until that time, there is no evidence of art in the archaeological record, including in the record of *Homo sapiens neanderthalensis*, with whom modern humans shared some cultural traditions (having coexisted with them for millennia). Art—like language, a form of symbolic interaction—begins to appear with highly diversified stone tools, around forty to thirty thousand years ago, when the Neandertals begin to disappear. But another interpretation, for which there is evidence, is that some earlier hominids (especially *Homo habilis*) had language (or protolanguage) but not speech. Speech would promote linguistic development and, if novel with modern humans, would help to account for their apparently greater acculturation.

The real bullet that threatens to shatter the shield of the standard story comes from molecular genetics, specifically, from studies of the mitochondrial DNA of modern humans and comparisons with paleontological remains. Some of this evidence suggests that quite late in human evolution—perhaps within the last two hundred thousand years—there occurred rapid genetic, anatomical, and behavioral changes in a bottleneck human population (in sub-Saharan Africa) from which modern humans descended (Cann, Stoneking, and Wilson 1987). This—the Eve Hypothesis—is quite controversial. But, if it (or some refined version of it) turns out to be sound, many of the links in the standard story will have to be decoupled and the story of sapienization rewritten.[8] It may have to be rewritten anyway on account of another hypothesis debate on which has yet fully to flower, namely, that sapienization did not occur just once, out of Africa, but simultaneously in other parts of the world. If that is true, the original Eve Hypothesis is false, and would have to give way to a hypothesis of multiple human radiations from founder populations in geographically dispersed bottlenecks.

The conclusion? The genus *Homo* could be quite a bit different from other hominids, and modern humans quite a bit different from other extinct species in the genus. Their culture certainly is. For large periods in the human record, organic change can be observed but, except for a few bursts, significant cultural development can not be observed until the modern humans appear. By measures of organic evolution, there is no clear line of demarcation that sets off humans from nonhumans in the distant past—no main event. There may have been one to set off modern humans in the recent past—that proposed bottleneck. But if so, it produced the last of the humans, not the first of them. If there is an evolutionary "main event" of ecological significance, it is the cultural development of modern humans.

Regardless of the exact lineage of modern humans, a couple of matters are clear. What we take to be principal phenotypes of *Homo sapiens sapiens* evolved in numerous species, not all within the genus *Homo*, at different times and places, and have now converged in us. We are an evolutionary compromise built of competing selection pressures some of which overlapped and some of which were disjoint in time and space. This includes modern culture. It was both cause and effect in the natural selection of modern humans, but in no linear sense. Our hominid ancestors and cultural forbears can not be arrayed as chronospecies that terminated in us, and their protoculture did not develop into some linear "chronoculture" inherited by us.

Culture is a phenotype found in many species of many genera. But *heterogeneous* culture is not. Only the *Homo sapiens sapiens* provide much evidence of that. Other recent human types, such as the Neandertals, at times give evidence of social organization. However exactly we displaced the Neandertals, the relative proportions and interactive mix of culture and social organization must have provided the selective advantage. The Neandertals were more physically robust than we. But habitat conditions were then in process of being reshuffled by the climate of the Pleistocene, so there easily could have been directional selection for heterogenous tool use that would have had survival value as climate and biota changed; and selection for the other aspects of culture that go with technological innovation, especially any social organization that promoted it. There would not be much change in human biology after that, but in human culture and social organization there certainly would be.

NOTES

1. Evidence for these hypotheses and others is discussed in Kinzey (1987).

2. Box (1984) reviews some evidence about primates; for chimpanzees in particular, see Goodall (1986, 1990), Heltne and Marquardt (1989), and Wrangham, McGrew, de Waal, and Heltne (1994). Regarding traditions and their social transmission in a variety of species, see Mainardi (1980). Bonner's (1980) and Wilson's (1975) illustrations and analyses for a wider range of phyla are extensive. For examples, I have drawn from all of these.

3. This was reported in a study by I. Douglas-Hamilton in 1975, cited in Bonner (1980). Social animals transmit information to conspecifics in ways that are not well understood, but given that they do, it should not surprise us that the short-term adaptations of one generation may become the long-term adaptations of descendants.

4. Chimpanzees can be taught table manners, signs, photographic recognition, and even sexual arousal at the sight of pornography—but not speech. However, Rumbaugh, Savage-Rumbaugh, and Sevick (1994), summarizing their own research findings, flatly claim that "the chimpanzee and the bonobo are, indeed, capable of acquiring a range of language skills" (p. 319).

5. This line of research has a history of controversy in its methods, and the heat of the argument has been oppressive. For a prudent and cautious approach, and a now somewhat dated review of some of the evidence for this and related questions, see Walker (1983, chap. 9). Bickerton (1990) provides an education in the tangled difficulties that beset questions of language, species, species' linguistic capabilities, and the coevolution of these.

6. Inorganic objects or conditions can be sources of signs, and the interpretants of signs may or may not be evolutionarily (or culturally) endowed with symbolic capacities. Sebiok (1991) emphasizes, as he has for some time now, that semiosis— the exchange of messages—is pandemic among terrestrial life forms. In his Chapter 2, Sebiok describes the type of semiosis discussed by G.H. Mead under the label "intelligent gestures" as better considered as falling within biosemiotics—the more general sign theory—based on the assumption that "the life science and the sign science thus imply one another" (p. 65).

7. See Goodall (1986) for a variety of observed behaviors in domesticated chimps as well as a consideration of evidence pertaining to their mental and symbolic capacities.

8. mtDNA, inherited exclusively by females, accumulates mutations 10 times faster than nuclear DNA, thus providing more points for comparing ancestral relationships. However, determining exact chronologies from mtDNA calibrations is subject to sampling error, which is the basis some authorities cite for doubting the Eve Hypothesis (see Templeton 1992; Hedges et al. 1992; Barinaga 1992). Cann, Stoneking, and Wilson (1987) suggested that a single African female population may have been the source of all modern humans (see also Cann's 1988 initial review). But the whole idea of a bottleneck population radiating so (an idea owing to Welsey Brown) struck many who were familiar with the paleoanthropological record as unlikely. The hypothesis is clouded by the species status of the Neandertals, which is currently under debate. Assessing the evidence, Wolpoff and Radovic (1992) doubt their species' distinctiveness, and there is some evidence of the interbreeding of modern humans with Neandertals. No one can say for sure why the Neandertals are no more, or what became of them (see Trinkaus and Shipman 1993). Moreover, it is not certain that modern humans radiated out of one place. So the Eve Hypothesis is technically undecidable on the evidence to date.

Chapter 5

Human Evolutionary Cultural Ecology

When humans appeared in the African savanna, they were without much social organization or culture and were not much different from some other primates. Yet, we know humans did not stay there, did became acculturated and remarkably social, and do behave quite differently now from these other creatures. How did we get from the savanna to the culture and social organization of the twenty-first century? If Rappaport's Dilemma is to come into clear focus, it is time to begin a human ecological accounting of this. It will take the rest of the book to finish it.

One way to simplify (before we complicate) the accounting is to observe that culture-specific adaptations are the dynamic product of two variable, environmentally based conditions that cultures themselves act upon to change: resource potential and mortality. Both conditions exert a push and pull, and their distribution has changed over the course of human history. It would be nice if we could plot general curves to show how these variables have behaved in tandem, but unfortunately they don't always behave in tandem. The shape of the curves depends upon, first, the time frame chosen for analysis and, second, the units analyzed.

Having said that, we can note a general trend in the curve of resource potential for modern humans as they became socially organized and acculturated: The curve has moved generally upward. This is so if we compare the increasing numbers of humans with the sheer variety and quantity of resources they have contrived to extract from biophysical habitats. More people have found more ways of squeezing more resources out of more natural processes and systems. The finding of more ways is a sociocultural affair. The concept of resource potential is intended to cover the biophysical resources that a habitat in its given organization makes *available*—an ecological affair—but also the *conversion* of biophysical resources by means of technology and social organization into derivative resources the habitat itself has not otherwise made available. Natural systems may provide trees or bauxite; only sociocultural organization provides boards and aluminum.

The curve for mortality has moved generally, but not smoothly, lower if we measure in terms of average life expectancies and the number of natural enemies that in theory can lay waste to humans. In fact, the mortality curve has moved sharply upward at times in human history, down at other times and places, mostly in the recent past, and is high today in some places while quite low in others. The difference is due in no small measure to the development and realization of resource potential, which has been specifically applied for the purpose of reducing mortality.

Human ecological dynamics as we now understand them are substantially, though not fully, definable by the interactions generated from the push-pull effects of resource potential, as it comes to be realized, and mortality. We consider these interactions in detail in later chapters and in Part B. First, we shall have to build an argument to the effect that these two processes taken together, and their derivatives, define the principal class of human ecological adaptations. In this chapter, we begin to examine the concept of resource potential by focusing just on the dynamics set going by the availability of resources in a given habitat; and we illustrate the cultural-ecological interplay of population mortality, for the purpose of highlighting the evolutionary connections of each. First, a caveat.

Julian H. Steward, the anthropologist and titular founder of cultural ecology, early on made a vital point about the subject, namely, that biophysical environments and human cultures are implicated in reciprocal causal interactions. They are not separate spheres with independent processes or asymmetric causation. To describe culture as an environmental adaptation can sound, but ought not to be interpreted, as if culture and environment are separate, with the one dependent upon and prior to the other. In just one vital sense is that true.

In an ontological sense, biophysical environments are certainly "prior" to human cultures, because there were such environments before there were such cultures, and there couldn't be any such cultures without such environments. Human cultural evolution and development took place, and still do, within biophysical parameters, and the effects of the parameters on human culture are far greater than the effects of cultures on their habitats. There are two exceptions to that generalization. One is the sporadic and common occurrence of too many humans taking too many resources in too short a time from some limited habitat, which can degrade the habitat and increase population mortality, and thereby force cultural adjustments. The other is the development and use by modern industrial societies of habitat-destructive technologies, which permit many more humans to degrade many more habitats much quicker. In *theory*, we have to adapt to nature more than nature has to adapt to us. In fact, nowadays it has come to be the other way round (for the time being). It wasn't always that way.

Throughout most of human history, most people who ever lived have been directly involved in intimate interactions with their biophysical habitats as a necessary condition of survival. When the ancestors of modern humans appeared on the African savannas and wherever else ancestors may have appeared, the local habitats dictated the ecological conditions for human behavioral and cultural adaptations. As humans spread into different habitats, of course, they had to adapt differently to survive. But in some general respects, the original given conditions for human survival are unchanged: All human cultural groups must adapt to abiotic conditions of climate and geography, to supplies of food and water, and to conditions of predation, parasitism, and disease, which is to say to other members of the biotic community in their habitats. This is a roundabout way of affirming that all cultures must adapt to conditions of resource availability and mortality. To say that humans adapted differently to survive in different habitats is a roundabout way of saying that cultures acted to change their available resources so as to augment or diminish their resource potential.[1]

RESOURCE AVAILABILITY: MICROSCOPIC DYNAMICS ILLUSTRATED

The spatial and temporal distribution of resources, of competitors, and of predators, if any, and the relative abundance or scarcity of these, can all be shown to sharply affect numerous social species of diverse taxa in the extent to which the species congregate, defend territory, mate, and maintain different population densities. Wiens (1984) suggested that the availability of resources, which may be patchily distributed, is more central to understanding these dynamics than is the abundance of resources. His suggestion applied to studies of evolutionary ecology in general.

Meanwhile, Smith and Winterhalder (1992) and others have argued that general evolutionary ecology has certain applications to the understanding of human ecological interactions in particular. Sometimes called Darwinian ecological anthropology, the application of principles of general evolutionary ecology to humans provides a basis for evolutionary human ecology.

Evolutionary Ecology

Evolutionary ecology, a discipline that was given great impetus by David Lack in the 1940s, emerged in the 1960s out of evolutionary theory and population biology. This happened when it was given mathematical rigor, and something of a school of ecology formed, by the influential theoretical contributions of the young Robert MacArthur, soon to be deceased.[2]

Generally speaking, evolutionary ecology takes a microscopic view of ecological processes by focussing on the behavior of individual organisms.[3] The point is to gain some understanding of adaptations in process. Evolutionary ecological models attempt to describe how habitat contingencies pose adaptive problems for animals and how they, in turn, are capable of flexible behavioral responses that have survival value and evolutionary import. To deduce testable hypotheses, basic principles of neo-Darwinian selection are used, sometimes in combination with ideas borrowed from microeconomic theory. Genetic models are not necessarily employed. Rather, models for behavior, representing ecological adaptations for individual organisms in the context of their habitat, tend to be front and center. Typically, some problem of adaptation to a habitat is defined for the members of a population, followed by some analysis of the benefits and costs to individual organisms of alternative strategies available to them—short term adaptive strategies presumed or analyzed to correlate with Darwinian fitness. Normally, but not always, a mathematical model is employed to specify an optimal adaptive solution, together with the habitat constraints that limit optimal behavior, in terms of which benefits and costs can be compared. With optimal parameters deduced from a model, observed behavior patterns can be compared to expected values. This methodology has been used, for example, to model optimal foraging, one of the earliest and more prominent bodies of theory in evolutionary ecology.

Optimal Foraging

Most animal species, humans not excluded, have to forage for food. Foraging itself is assumed to have a heritable component, which is to say it is a form of behavior that can evolve by selection. Its relation to fitness is assumed to be knowable by calculating some habitat-relevant currency, such as energy capture in the form of caloric intake. Optimal foragers, it stands to reason, can survive and reproduce more than foragers that are not so optimal. They therefore have a selective advantage. The theory applies whether foraging behavior is innate or learned, and this enables genetic models to take a back seat and ecological models to come more to the fore. Without pretending to fully characterize the assumptions of optimal foraging theory, we may nevertheless consider what, in broad overview, these models are about.

If one wants to know how it is that populations feed themselves and how their members alter their subsistence activities according to varying habitat conditions, optimal foraging theory may come into play. It may play because we have asked a question about subsistence strategies, and foraging is the behavior of finding food. Optimal foraging theory, as the name suggests, asks questions about optimal foraging behavior— about the choice of alternative prey for predators, the size of a foraging group, the allocation of time to search for food, and whatnot. It is about what animals do, and don't do, while they are foraging (Pyke 1984).

For instance, it is known by observing their behavior that various predators prefer some prey to others, but in difficult times they will take what they can get. Assuming a normal distribution of what they can get, how do they decide what to take? Assume that a forager's goal is to maximize the total expected benefit per unit of foraging time, which includes time to search, capture, process, and consume the prey. (Its fitness would be diminished if it didn't act as if that were a goal.) Assume, further, that foragers search for all prey types simultaneously and encounter them randomly. Then it can be mathematically shown that two opposing cost curves are generated, one involving search time and the other involving the rest. Where the curves cross is the point at which the forager attains the optimal benefit-cost ratio per unit of foraging time. At that point, the forager minimizes the cost associated by choosing prey lower on its preference scale but maximizes the benefit obtained by spending less time searching for its more preferred diet. The behavior of the forager, therefore, other things equal, ought to be within a reasonable deviation of that optimal point.

Sometimes it is, but the forager's benefits and costs can be rather more complicated than mere calories expended and captured. The costs may include risk of predation, loss of offspring, intrusion into its territory by invaders, time spent searching for resources that are patchily distributed, and many others. Developments of the theory suggest that assorted benefit-cost parameters may be analyzed in terms of a central place, or home base of operations, when such is employed for foraging. Models for central place foraging, choice of patches, diet breadth, and others not yet conceived are needed to tell just how organisms manage the multiple interactions that figure into their total benefits and costs, and their overall fitness as this may be affected by foraging.

Applications of evolutionary ecology have been developed not just for the subject of foraging, as did R. MacArthur and Eric R. Pianka in the early and well-known diet breadth model I have just summarized. Applications have also been developed to understand how the behavior of a population is spatially organized—how it defends its turf, competes for scarce resources, and limits its reproduction. Take turf—more pretentiously, territorialty.

Territoriality

Many species of animals go to great lengths to communicate to others, with marvelous warning signs and intricate actions, their sense that there are spatial boundaries that extend around them past which others ought not to stray. Called—originally by a British ornithologist, Elliot Howard—territorial behavior, one can wonder whether there is any selective advantage to it. Put another way, if territoriality is a behavioral strategy in which the result is nonrandom spacing of animals in their range, which is often observed, how and when does the strategy pay off?

Apparently when the benefits derived from exclusive use of the territory are greater than the costs of defending it, but this condition applies usually when resources critical to the population are predictable and are neither very scarce nor very abundant. When they are scarce, the strategy doesn't pay, and when they are excessive, it doesn't matter. Why analyze territorial behavior in terms of its payoffs? Because territory is a portion of a habitat used especially by animals for the purposes of foraging and reproduction. Territorial behavior, therefore, is a contributor to fitness. A population that does not defend predictable resources in a restricted habitat is at a competitive disadvantage for the same reason that a population with unpredictable food resources patchily distributed over a wider area is at a disadvantage should it choose to defend them: In the former case, the population will show a net gain in caloric energy by successfully protecting the exploitation of its territory against encroachment, while in the latter case, the population will expend more energy from defending its territory than it will gain by exploiting it. So, populations that do not behave accordingly stand to have lower average fitnesses. Those whose adaptations incorporate such an implicit benefit-cost calculus stand to be more fit on average and, therefore, should differentially survive, reproduce, and prosper.

Evolutionary Human Ecology

Foraging and territorial defense clearly affect the resources available to foragers and territory defenders in various animal species studied by evolutionary ecologists. But does the general theory, together with problematics such as foraging and territoriality, modeled on some benefit-cost calculus interpreted to individuals in populations, apply to humans, and if so, which humans? Let us address the general question, with reference to foraging.

In principle, the theory and problematics apply because it may be fairly assumed, in accord with evidence, that individual animals function to procure limited resources distributed unevenly in time and space. It may also be assumed that resource procurement activities have some "rational" quality to it—rational in that the individuals are guided by economy of effort in their circumstances. Humans fit those assumptions hand in glove and have designed all sorts of complicated social structures and cultural relations to prove the fit. We have even produced a science which employs some of the same tenets to describe the fit— the microeconomics of human decision making, utility, and rational choice. Ecological behavior that appears to be governed by economic-like decisions made by individuals during momentary contingencies are the heart and soul of evolutionary ecology. In human applications of optimal foraging theory, a prime relevant utility has been taken to be net rate of energy return per unit of foraging time. Energy returned for energy expended is an ecological matter of the first order.

In particular, it would seem that the theory and its problematics apply to explain some facets of the behavior of those humans who exemplify rather weak forms of social organization—in other words, hunter-gatherers. Hunters and gatherers are weakly organized if we measure their social organization against the possible number and combination of dimensions available to human social organization. Even if we follow Binford's (1980) continuum by which hunter-gatherers are organized—from foragers organized to procure resources by tracking their availability hither and yon, to collectors organized to sally forth and retrieve them to a central place with stores—there is still not much organization anywhere there to complicate the analysis of human ecological behavior as economy-minded. Since, by definition, individual hunters and gatherers directly forage in their habitats for food, it is to them that optimal foraging models have been most often applied, though with some difficulty.

Bettinger (1991), who has reviewed the status of the application of optimal foraging models to humans (see also Kaplan and Hill 1992), concludes they may be useful for comparative studies of hunters and gatherers because the models employ a standard measure of caloric efficiency. With this for calibration, changes in the diets, nomadic habits, settlement and subsistence patterns, and behavioral traditions, induced by technological acquisition of foragers, in principle can be traced. One especially interesting implication apropos to survival, selection, and cultural evolution is that sedentary foragers who extensively process low-quality, broadly based resources for intensive use, have a competitive advantage over those nomads who depend upon high-quality resources, narrowly based, that they selectively use (Bettinger and Baumhoff 1982).

Unfortunately, obtaining dependable estimates for the parameters of optimal foraging models is dicey even with a standardized measure of caloric efficiency. This is especially a problem if archaeological applications are intended, for just how is one to estimate values of variables from the foraging of extirpated human groups whose behavior can no longer be observed? Even for contemporary groups, the net rate of caloric intake per unit of foraging time is not so easy to calculate simply because such an exact measure presumes exact measurement classes into which specific foraging behavior itself can be sorted for inferential purposes. When it comes to measuring human behavior of any kind, exact measurement classes are difficult to come by and, when they can not be had, we can not be sure that our specific operational measures are valid and reliable. Measurement problems aside, humans forage for more than just food, and the benefits and costs and the ratios of benefits to costs change with the invention, diffusion, and improvement of tool kits. Technological innovations together with the survival advantages conferred by sedentarism are just two reasons there are not so many optimal food-foragers left anymore.

Evolutionary human ecology has now progressed beyond the narrow range of problems and models initially bequeathed to it by biologists (see Smith and Winterhalder 1992). Many problems and models for their solution nevertheless continue to employ optimality assumptions, and most models are unabashedly economic because what they address is economic. This may be convenient for the analysis of hunter-gatherers, whom Bettinger calls "the quintessential anthropological topic" (1991, p. v). What of quintessential sociological topics—for instance, the development of societies of very large scale and organizational complexity?

Initial Considerations for the Ecological Explanation of Macrosocieties

Richard Machalek (1992) has shown how evolutionary ecology can be applied to the problem of scale. Machalek's question concerned the evolution of macrosocieties—that is, societies containing hundreds of thousands, or millions, or even tens of millions of members. Machalek observed that the appearance of macrosocieties has been quite rare in the history of biological evolution, and they can be found in species as distinct as ants and people. Why, he asked, is this adaptation so rare and why did such distinct creatures happen upon it?

We found before that social behavior is assumed to evolve because it confers superior fitness on individuals that come to cooperate, and under certain conditions its evolution should be expected. In the cases of ants and people, Machalek observes that both are organismically ill adapted to functioning without social groups. Yet for both, ecological reasons can be invoked, along with others, to explain why an adaptation for living in macrosocieties evolved. In the case of ants, one can point to the fitness advantages conferred by having a chemically based collective defense of their nests against predators, which increases survival rates, plus the increased food resources available from collective foraging and food retrieval. In the case of humans, some comparable (but far more complex) ecological conditions apply, but humans are socially organized more by culture than by chemistry. Since ants and humans have no recent common ancestor, having phylogenetically diverged long ago, Machalek argues that ants and humans independently converged upon the same evolutionary adaptation. The confluence of ecological, organismic, cost-benefit, and sociological constraints that would normally prevent the evolution of macrosocieties here rather conspired to promote their evolution in each case. Consider one of Machalek's constraints.

A sociological constraint against the evolution of a macrosociety is the ability, possessed by very few creatures, to interact and cooperate in an impersonal way. Ants have to; they can recognize each other only as members of common social categories. Humans, by contrast, have devised complex cultural forms to enable impersonal interaction. When interaction can be conducted in terms of social categories and does not depend upon individual recognition, a necessary condition for the evolution of large societies is met. Combined with right values for the other conditions, which Machalek has analyzed in detail, macrosocieties may be optimal adaptations for the individuals that evolve them. Ants (and other social insects) and people did—a rare evolutionary event.

The sociality of almost all other social species is based in kinship groups, in which interaction is conducted on the basis of individual recognition. There is, other things equal, a much greater probability that individuals will cooperate when they are genetically related. Kinship, combined with interaction keyed on individual recognition, inherently restricts the size of any cooperating group. Ants in colonies are kin; people in macrosocieties are not; yet, some convergences appear between the social organization of people and of the ants. Ant societies are highly structured, with a hierarchical ordering and a rigid division of labor with compartmentalized roles. And so it is of human macrosocieties and many of the social structures within them, notwithstanding cultural variation in the forms the structuring takes. One precondition for a human macrosociety, we shall see in due course, is the adoption of agriculture as a mode of subsistence. Ever since humans did that, there has been an increasing cultural tendency to formalize the social organization of human behavior into bureaucratic formats. In bureaucracies, impersonal interaction is a desideratum and criterion for effective functioning, and no human social structures are more fully organized than these. As human social organization has become more formal, it has become structurally similar to the colony and the hive. Human cooperation leading to formal social organization is a culturally based pattern of evolutionary convergence toward the hereditary patterns of the eusocial insects—ants, termites, and the rest.

The macrosocieties of the ants as well as of the humans are fully organized and, of some of the humans, fully acculturated. Machalek's explanation does not reach to human organization or acculturation, but it does reach to size. Size is a precondition for understanding the significance of full organization and acculturation. The significance inheres in the added resource potential that fully organized and acculturated societies possess. That will occupy us for a couple of chapters thither. It is not easily explained with the conceptual repertoire available from the theory of evolutionary ecology.

Initial Considerations for the Ecological Explanation of Complex Social Organization

The weaker the social organization of humans, other things equal, the more that human behavior, ecological included, can be attributed to the variable behavior of individuals—there being not much else to attribute it to. In general, evolutionary ecological models apply to individuals who behave in populations defined by species demography and the occupation of a territory, but not necessarily to the members of organized societies with complex cultures. The models are more obviously applicable to humans the less social organization and acculturation there are, because most models are developed for the behavior of individuals and not their organization. Evolutionary human ecology strains to take much human social organization or acculturation into account because, normally, it takes a microscopic view of microscopic problems. In this view, populations and societies are not always distinguished, and social behavior is sometimes conflated with the organization of social behavior. The result is a limited theoretical scope.[4]

A gathering of propinquitous social individuals who just happen to occupy the same territory is not an equivalence condition for organized social behavior. A demographic population that occupies a territory or forages in some habitat can be analyzed without regard to its social relations. For certain purposes, this may be useful. It may, for instance, be useful to explain the optimal behavior of the members of territorialized populations of nonhuman social animals and compare the results with humans'. But it is altogether something else to explain a social group within some territory, and the behavior of the grouped population, *with reference to* its organized social relations. Depending upon what species we may be talking about, distinctions between a population and a society, and between social behavior and its organization, can make a great deal of difference. For humans, especially, a population of them is not a society of them. The concept of population is strictly biodemographic and, in itself, implies nothing about organized social relations, which are conditions for having a human society.

From microevolutionary ecological models, taken at face value, one would not always know that. Many of these models treat social organization, when they treat it at all, as an epiphenomenal result of individuals optimizing, in which the condition of cooperation with others is an adaptive strategy.[5] This is not sufficient to analyze the ecology of a species that has social relations ranging from weakly to fully organized and, as full organization is approached, of populations that become macrosocial. The concept of social behavior as cooperation among individuals adapting to enhance their fitness simply doesn't reveal the socioecology of adaptations that require complex, fully developed social organization. There is more to human social organization than the cooperation of, and the ecological costs and benefits that accrue to, individuals. One could not, for example, possibly explain the vast hunting and gathering for fossil fuels, now undertaken by postindustrial societies, in terms of optimal foraging. That kind of "foraging," to be effective, requires too much social organization and acculturation. The microevolutionary ecological concepts we have mentioned here, to be applicable to humans, thus need to be substantially expanded, especially with concepts that enable macroscopic analyses of the social organization of acculturated populations.

Initial Considerations for the Ecological Explanation
of Complex Acculturation

If we consider the grading of human social organization to be ecologically significant, we must also consider the grading of human cultures to be ecologically significant (or otherwise acculturation does not matter much). But how shall we conceive the grading of human cultures? John Bodley (1994) offers a simple solution that will serve us well.

Bodley points to three long-term processes that, over the course of time, may compound: sapienization, politicization, and commercialization. *Sapienization*, in Bodley's usage, refers to the biocultural process (really, a set of interacting biological and cultural processes) by which human culture, language, and organic phenotypes coevolved to where

Homo sapiens sapiens can be observed in the paleontological and archaeological record (at least 50,000 years ago). With sapienization, one gets small-scale culture, and with just sapienization one could get little else.

But, in fact, we got much else—cultures of large-scale ranging from chiefdoms to states and empires. Bodley attributes those to the process of *politicization*, or the expansion of political authority, a cultural process that if dominant can cause small-scale cultures, which normally limit political power and wealth, to be incorporated, exploited, dominated, altered, or replaced. Politicization does not appear in the archaeological record until about 7,500 years ago, but with the fullness of time the process certainly came to dominate cultural development with different rates, scales, and chronologies around the world.

Commercialization, likewise a cultural process, is the term Bodley uses to describe the dominance of market economics as a force in cultural development. The realization of this process Bodley locates only a couple of centuries back, but its dominance over politicization—it is regarded as dominant when market exchanges determine political alliances—is such as to make possible the modern phenomenon of global-scale culture. Commercialization, in Bodley's words, "reversed the relationship between political and economic organization" (1994, p. 17) and has produced a relatively homogenous worldwide culture in which small- and large-scale cultures may be exploited, dominated, altered, or replaced.

This grading of cultures according to dominant processes that yield cultures of different scale, observed at different points in human history, has several conceptual advantages for us. First, this typology calls attention to fundamentally different conditions of human ecology that the species has confronted and still confronts. Second, it may go a long way to simplifying the description of, and providing clues to an explanation for, how cultural evolution and development fundamentally altered the conditions of human ecology in the last 10 to 12 thousand years. Third, there is with Bodley's scheme an implicit formula: Take humans and politicize them; then take politicized humans and commercialize them. One should get cultures of increasing scale and complexity (which Bodley describes in detail). But—more to the point of this chapter—one should also get an increase in environmental resources made available by cultural means, or an expanded human resource potential. Sapienized humans have comparatively few resources available from natural environments, politicized humans a lot more, commercialized humans probably as much as the species can muster. Politicization and commercialization make so many more resources available for extraction, which then increases the scale of environmental impacts.

Two chapters away we shall begin to explore all of this in more depth. Now, for the first time, we are in a position, where with microevolutionary ecology we were not, to introduce macroevolutionary ecological dynamics that behave in human cultures organized on a large or global scale. As an entree to these dynamics, we consider a prime factor for analyzing macroscopic sociocultural adaptation and change—namely, mortality—in just one of its many manifestations.

MORTALITY: MACROSCOPIC DYNAMICS ILLUSTRATED

The demographic concept of mortality is one of the most significant concepts available for understanding macroscopic human ecological dynamics. The concept also provides one angle for intersecting cultural ecology. Mortality does its cultural-ecological work especially by means of pathogenic diseases.

Cultural Ecology and Pathogenic Diseases

What we experience as infectious disease is just one class among many of the outcomes of biological interactions of humans with other living things. This fact makes human diseases of pathogenic origin a normal and natural condition of human ecology.[6] Patterns of pathogenic disease, of culture and social organization, and the genetic constitution of humans, all coevolve together. The demographic consequences of pathogenic infections of human populations can affect the trajectories of the culture and social organization of the populations, thus defining a branch of human ecology all its own.

Pathogen-Culture Coevolution

Chronic conditions of pathogen-based disease are given to all cultures to adapt to. In modern times, in societies with access to the fruits of scientific medicine, environmental toxins, unhealthy diets, and dangerous lifestyles may pose a greater threat to human mortality rates than do contagious pathogens. But for much of human sociocultural history, just the reverse was true. Infectious disease, which increased dramatically with the development of agriculture and the growth of large-scale cultures, has had far more impact on human mortality than have wars and natural disasters. It still does in cultures without the benefit of scientific medicine (often because infectious diseases are imported to them from other cultures). Pathogens that prey upon humans are the only significant natural enemies we have left. It stands to reason that their incidence should be a stimulus for variable cultural adaptations.

Disregarding all the other reasons, for reasons of sheer medical etiology one cannot expect the culture of persons living in a tropical rain forest to adapt in parallel fashion as, say, the culture of persons living in the Russian tundra. Far fewer pathogens can survive in the cold, and far fewer disease vectors; so, cultures that evolve in the cold can direct their adaptations to the conditions that matter for them. Likewise for those in the tropics and elsewhere. Different habitats provide humans with different natural competitors. When these competitors have the properties of infectious disease agents, in effect they become agents of natural selection.

Pathogenic diseases, if unchecked by cultural intervention, can limit human population growth or stabilize human population at given levels. But, the evolutionary or developmental trajectories of cultures can be changed according to how peoples adapt to pathogenic competitors, and the pathogens to them. The adaptation is often two-way. An increase in human numbers, other things being equal, can be expected to bring an increase in species populations that prosper at human expense, on what humans experience as disease, and the way we live because of it; and changes in the ways in which humans live, other things equal, can be expected to affect the populations of those pathogens that cause human disease.

Some pathogenic agents achieve stable relations with their human hosts. Increases in populations of humans and pathogenic agents can in turn become subsequent decreases as pathogen and host reach mutual quantitative accommodations. Cultural-ecological adaptations between humans and pathogens that prey upon them in some cases are of long evolutionary duration, and some co-adaptations are stabilized well enough to produce a constant toll on human mortality together with a stable set of cultural practices adapted to the toll. However, the existence of stable co-adaptations does not imply an obligate evolution to a condition in which the pathogen becomes more benign.

It had long been thought, and for generations taught, that the coevolution of human-pathogen interactions tends in the long run toward a benign condition—that is to say, the pathogen becomes less lethal because the human becomes better adapted. A corollary of this idea is that an extremely virulent pathogenic disease represents an instance of recently evolved ecological association that is still working itself out, toward a less virulent state. Ewald (1994) has shown these beliefs are not generally true. Not only is the evidence for them rather weak, but evolution to benignness does not even square with the logic of natural selection theory. As Ewald put it, "there is no reason to presume that natural selection favors what is best for the greatest number of individuals over the greatest amount of time" (1994, p. 4), and without that for reason the evolution of benign associations between pathogen and host cannot be defended nor should it be expected (although it can, of course, happen). Ewald points out that the fitness benefits of pathogenic virulence have to be measured by the maximizing of the number of genes that are represented in the next generation of pathogens, not by the number of gene carriers that are lost because their virulence is disfunctional for their hosts. It had been supposed, incorrectly it now seems, that selection would favor evolutionary change from virulence to benignness because the correlation of virulence with mortality also causes the loss of pathogens, whose long-term survival as a species would benefit were they to be less virulent. But it isn't necessarily so.

If pathogen-population coevolution does not necessarily tend to benignness, pathogen-culture coevolution certainly does not. Patterns of cultural behavior can provide more or less successful means for humans to adapt to their given circumstances of pathogenic disease, can select for or against the pathogen, and can but do not necessarily assure that any balance between the competing species will be achieved (Garnett and Holmes 1996).

Pathogen-Culture Co-adaptations

Rates of mortality from pathogen-based diseases often derive from specific cultural practices, for some disease-causing organisms become very well adapted to the cultural practices of humans.[7] The complicated life cycles of assorted parasitic worms and microparasites provide among the best examples of this cultural-ecological interplay.

For instance, the Turkana people of northern Africa have very high rates of echinococcosis, a life-threatening parasitic disease whose agent is transmitted from sheep to humans by way of dogs. Turkana cultural customs foster the completing of the life cycle of the parasite and, thus, maintain high levels of infection, by enabling the saliva and feces of dogs to come into contact with human orifices (Inhorn and Brown 1990). The introduction of artificial water control projects in certain portions of Africa is known to have caused a substantial increase in schistosomiasis, a parasitic infection you would not want, because an intermediate host for the fluke, a snail, prospered in the now-changed habitats. The larvae that are produced within the snail penetrate human skin, accessible all the more with humans working irrigated agriculture. High densities of the fluke are normally limited in the absence of irrigated agriculture because the populations of its intermediate host are limited, but with local increases in water temperature and solar radiation brought by the deforestation associated with agricultural development, plus indiscriminate urination and defecation practices, the completion of the life cycle of schistosomes is made easier (Coimbra 1991). Worldwide, 200 million people are estimated to be afflicted with schistosomiasis, and the World Health Organization has attributed its growth primarily to the economics of agricultural development, not to snails. Cultural practices that permit the cavalier disposal of feces, humans' and others', are substantial factors in the incidence of parasitic worm infections, which account for three of the top ten (in incidence) infectious diseases known in the world (Mascie-Taylor 1993). The incidence of ascariasis, the most common roundworm infection, which inflicts half or more of some populations in the Southern hemisphere, is attributed solely to the inadequate disposal of fecal matter. The worm (*Ascaris lumbricoides*) is uniquely adapted to the cultural practices of humans, or almost so, since humans are its only significant natural host (Mascie-Taylor 1993).

Agricultural practices, dietary customs, food preparation techniques, religious rituals, child care patterns, hygiene practices, migration patterns, sexual mores—all these can affect the incidence of infectious disease. Of these, authorities such as Krause (1992) consider migration to be the most important factor in the spread of microbial pathogens. With modern air transport, microbial diseases that formerly might have been localized now have the capability to become epidemic much quicker. A little known fact about the much touted AIDS viruses, reported by Krause, is that the original virus evolved perhaps one hundred years before the epidemic outbreak of the 1980s. It laid low a century, perhaps much longer.

The general point is that changes in human cultural behavior disrupt the relationships between pathogens, hosts, and conditions for pathogenicity, thus favoring or discouraging the survival and spread of certain pathogens. The very same human adaptation can discourage some pathogens while favoring others. It is conceded by virtually all medical authorities that effective sanitation is a prophylactic for a great many epidemic diseases, but there are exceptions. Poliomyelitis became epidemic in the United States in the first half of the twentieth century *because* of improved sanitation and hygiene procedures, which had the effect of postponing the onset of the virus until later childhood or early adulthood, at which point persons are much more vulnerable to its pathogenicity (Krause 1992).

One can look to human history to find populations of pathogens adapting to the human practice, itself an adaptation, of living in close quarters in large cities. As human cities gradually increased in size and number over the course of centuries, prior to modern sanitation practices or medical redress for infections, a hospitable environment for microbes of all sorts to successfully adapt to was at hand, especially many of the microbes responsible for pestilential diseases. Many of the historically lethal pestilences—bubonic plague, scarlet fever, cholera, typhus, tuberculosis, and typhoid fever—depend upon sufficiently high population densities to initiate human epidemics. To become established, they require the kind of contact that only large numbers of people gathered in restricted spaces can provide. Not only did human cities, as they grew in size and number, provide just that opportunity, but—according to evidence cited by McNeill (1976)—prior to 1900, in some cities there were temporary *declines* in population size, redressible only by in-migration, because of the increased mortality the cities inadvertently fostered through the sheer density of human numbers. More people in a restricted space mean more total contacts between them and, therefore, more opportunity for any disease that can be established by contagion.

That said, living in rural areas by means of agriculture did not afford relief from pestilences; rather, different pathogens were at work. Living in proximity with other animals, a prime spinoff of agriculture, long was a prime contributor to human mortality through infectious diseases. With the coming of agriculture, and long after, and in some quarters still, many peasants lived in the same dwellings as their domesticated animals. From some of these was spread to humans the cowpox virus from which the deadly smallpox virus is believed to have mutated

(Hopkins 1983). Measles was established in rural communities long before it could be sustained by the high population densities of cities (Dobson and Carper 1996). Wild animals, of course, will also suffice to spread epidemic disease in ecological relationships with humans. In one four-year period, the bubonic plague destroyed one-third of the inhabitants of Europe. That extensive an epidemic never happened again, in part because the Europeans, finding wood difficult to procure, changed their housing materials to stone and brick and thereby put more distance between themselves and the vectors, which were fleas carried by rats (McNeill 1976). Still, whenever bubonic plague did reappear, its mortality rate was about 60 percent until the 1940s, when antibiotics were developed and rendered it insignificant for those with access to modern medicine.

The epidemic manifestation of microbial pathogens may qualify as the primary agents of natural selection operating on humans for the past several thousand years (Inhorn and Brown 1990). Epidemics are sporadic but relentlessly reappearing conditions for human cultural adaptation. The human phenotype and human cultures can not always adapt quickly to the fast-changing and slowly stabilizing cycles that result from infection by new genetic variants of pathogens. This lag effect is compounded by another consideration: the ecological complexity in which a particular pathogen may be implicated.

Simplicity and Complexity in the Ecology of Human Diseases:
Smallpox and Malaria as Paradigm Cases

Modern physicians can only read of smallpox, which once wreaked havoc and horror in human affairs (see Hopkins 1983). This scourge dates to antiquity, but physicians shall never treat the disease again because they shall never see it again. The only surviving specimens of the virus are kept frozen in research laboratories in Atlanta and Koltsovo, Russia, and these are slated for destruction now that DNA fragments of the major and minor variants have been cloned.[8] But throughout history, tens of millions died of smallpox or were scarred or blinded by it (among its many celebrated victims are numbered Queen Elizabeth I and Abraham Lincoln). The last major epidemics in the United States occurred in the 1920s, and the last known case anywhere was reported in the 1970s.[9] Before it was brought under control, smallpox killed 40 percent of its victims. The World Health Organization undertook a concerted effort to eradicate the disease, and it succeeded—thanks partly to the very nature of the pathogens themselves. Smallpox provides a paradigm case of biochemical and ecological simplicity.

Smallpox affords unusual insights into the human control of a microbic pathogen. There were only two variants of the virus and, unlike many viral pathogens, they would not change their protein coating. All smallpox viruses carried the same antigens, which meant they all exhibited the same chemical markers. Since an antigen is a compound that triggers the production of antibodies (which are protein molecules), it was as if all smallpox specimens carried the same identification tag, which said: Here are my antigens, which prove I am smallpox, now produce your appropriate antibodies to bind to my antigens, and thus to my surface, so that I may be tagged for destruction by other cells in your immune system before I multiply and destroy you. Its biochemical simplicity gave the smallpox pathogens no room to maneuver and no place to hide once the connection of antigens to antibodies could be understood and manipulated. But matters were even more favorable, from a human point of view: The same antigens were carried by the genetically similar cowpox virus, which was not so dangerous to humans. Thus, innoculation that protected against cowpox would also protect against smallpox. And so it did. Once the innoculation procedure was developed, it became a logistical matter to track down the pathogens and a political matter to destroy the scourge.[10]

Something else was crucial. In addition to its biochemical simplicity, which a great many other pathogens do not have, smallpox was ecologically as simple as anything gets. First, there was no vector for the pathogen—no intermediate host in which a portion of a life cycle might play and ready the developing organism for transmission to a host that could be victimized. Second, humans were the only known living reservoir for the pathogen. Thus, these organisms with their simple biochemistry were also very highly specialized ecologically. From the point of view of eradicating the disease, things could not have been easier: Find all the reservoirs and shoot all the ducks, which all look alike and have no camouflage.

There is no reason to expect comparable success with a disease such as malaria. From the point of view of eradication, the characteristics of malaria could not be worse. Malaria is a paradigm case of complexity.

Malaria is believed to be the oldest surviving microbic killer and disabler of human populations (Livingstone 1971) and, to this day, remains the most significant pathogen-based health problem around the world.[11] The World Health Organization estimates that the rate of infection is increasing at about 5 percent annually worldwide (Kolberg 1994), and current estimates of annual infection are in the range of three million persons. In Africa alone, one million persons, mostly children, die of malaria each year (Krause 1992). The disease was endemic in the southern United States until the 1940s (Dobson and Carper 1996).

Malaria implicates organisms with complicated life cycles, in complicated relationships. The malarial organism is neither virus nor bacterium; it is a protozoan. There are four species of it, two of which are especially dangerous, and these behave differently, having different rates of reproduction, with different rates for the onset of symptoms.[12] The pathogens can survive in the blood of animals other than humans. They are vector-borne. Of all of the vector-borne microbic diseases, malaria is today the leading cause of mortality and morbidity worldwide.

The disease has proven to be intractable in part because of the ecological complexity in which the major vector, 60 species of Anopheles mosquito, functions. First, the vector can feed on many animals and thus can transmit the malaria plasmodium from many sources to humans. Monkeys are a prime reservoir for transmission by the vector. Second, the vector itself has a reproductive strategy that enables its populations to thrive under numerous environmental conditions. Third, humans have been changing the conditions, often in precisely those ways that would favor the success of the vector—and thus of the disease.

How do human activities affect the incidence of the disease? When iron tools—and the results of their implementation, deforestation and swidden agriculture—were introduced into West Africa, modes of food production changed in ways that increase the breeding sites of the vector (Livingstone 1958). Malaria in West Africa became endemic because of cultural changes. Now, throughout tropical Africa, 90 percent of the world's malarial infections are suffered by roughly 10 percent of the world's population (Collins and Besansky 1994). Meanwhile, in Amazonia, malaria is epidemic, where before it was endemic, again due in part to increased deforestation (Coimbra 1991). Malaria has been the most significant contributor—much more so than some well publicized homicidal atrocities—to the recent high mortality rates of the Yanomami of Brazil (13% of the population per year in the early 1990s), due to stagnant pools of water, left in the wake of mining operations, that increased the breeding grounds for the vector (Gibbons 1991). The incidence of malaria has even been shown to correlate with forms of human housing, adjusted for altitude (May 1958).

Attempts to eradicate malaria may have done more harm than good. DDT was first used for public health purposes in 1943, and it was quickly turned against Anopheles mosquitoes in their breeding grounds, with some incredible success at first. In Sri Lanka, in 1955, there were one million malaria cases; by 1963, a mere 18 (Garrett 1995, p. 51). But with the Green Revolution, begun in the 1960s, there came a much-accelerated use of insecticides and herbicides, which had the effect of simplifying the biota in areas intended for agricultural production. This *complicated* the control of insects, for now survivors of the insecticide attacks would have fewer natural predators, and any that could develop genetic resistance to DDT would proliferate. Some did, including DDT-resistant mosquito populations, which began to appear all over the world in the middle 1960s. At about the same time, genetic resistance began to appear in the malaria plasmodia to the most commonly used treatment, cloroquinine. Garrett (1995) describes the modern form of malaria as iatrogenic—in effect, a human created epidemic—created as a result of medical treatment and the ineffectual public health campaign that was undertaken in the 1950s .

Malaria is the quintessential human ecological disease of microbic origin. The parasites themselves go through complicated life cycles as they move from host to vector to new host, and within the human host. This is further complicated by the diverse ecology of the vector in its undisturbed natural environments—an ecology affected by rainfall, temperature, the size and proximity of monkey populations, altitude, and natural competitors. All this is compounded by human inteference with that ecology, especially by agriculture, which has tended to favor the vector. And, anyhow, the malaria plasmodia and the vector are themselves capable of evolving genetic resistance to chemical interference in their life cycles, which human sociocultural adaptations have encouraged.

A long train of epidemic diseases borne by air, water, insects, and rodents contributed to high human mortality rates for a long time in human history because people did not know the etiological or epidemiological basis of many contagious diseases. A scientific basis for the germ theory of disease was not established until the nineteenth century. With the increasing knowledge of disease etiology came increasing knowledge of its epidemiology. But only in the recent past has it come to be understood that human culture-human pathogen relationships are coevolutionary, involving continual (if punctuated) mutual adaptations. Humans *are* the habitats for human pathogens, so as we adapt to them, they adapt to us. Pathogens can track evolutionary changes in their environments, and most microbic pathogens can reproduce in very short order, which means they can mutate in very short order. Human attempts to intefere with microbic pathogens by means of medicine, it is now known, may provide a stimulus to accelerate evolutionary adaptations by the pathogens, for the very use of certain medicines encourages the directional selection of resistant variants.[13] The vector-borne pathogens are, in principle, the greatest threat to human mortality and morbidity because, in theory, they should be more virulent: A vector can transmit the pathogen from immobilized hosts (Ewald 1994, p. 52).

Theory aside, the demographic-ecological interplay of microbic pathogens with human cultures can be empirically traced. For one class of historical cases, which unraveled largely before the etiology and epidemiology of pestilential diseases became firmly established, the interplay was astonishing.

Pestilential Diseases and the Extirpation of Small-scale Cultures

The human soma, we know, adapts physiologically to the pathogens it encounters, and over time comes to express inherited or acquired immunities. Given that process, the most deadly combination of demographic, epidemiological, and ecological conditions is this: Take a large human population through which there has coursed quite a few pestilential epidemics against whose pathogens the survivors have developed some immunities. Then put the population in contact with another that has not been exposed—because, perhaps, of geographical, reproductive, and demographic isolation—and which, therefore, can have fewer immunities. Assume a worst-case scenario: the exposed population has a large-scale culture and the unexposed population a small-scale culture with little technology, and modern medicine is not available. We then have a formula for massive population mortality and culture extirpation.

That is precisely what happened with many of the indigenous populations of the Americas once the Europeans established permanent contact after 1492. Curiously, epidemic diseases seem not to have established themselves in the large cities (of which there were some) of the American indigenes, even though the size and density of the cities in theory could have sustained continual contagion (McNeill 1976). One reason they did not may have been the more limited domestic herds these people had available, which should have reduced interspecific contagion. Another may have been the peoples' own genetic make-up, which can affect immunological tolerances. A third may have been their diet. A fourth may have been adaptive mismatches of pathogens to geoclimate. A fifth may have been all of the above. Whatever, there were fundamental ecological differences between the Old World and the New, and these converted to epidemiological differences.

It is not established for certain when humans first migrated across Beringia (from Siberia through Alaska to the Yukon) and radiated south. Whenever exactly the migration began, the American continent's sheer expanse together with the foraging culture of the immigrants assured that, as the migration continued to radiate geographically, human population densities would have to remain low for thousands of years. The geographic isolation of the continent itself, and of the indigenous tribes themselves, assured that human-pathogen co-adaptations would be limited in comparison to other continents having peoples with higher population densities—especially the Europeans. By the time of the first contacts between Europeans and American indigenes, there were fewer epidemic pathogens to which the indigenes had been exposed and, therefore, could be immunologically adapted to. In Europe, many more epidemic pathogens had been adapting to humans, and the humans to them, for a much longer period of time. The same had been true in Africa. When cross-hemispheric population contacts were established in the late fifteenth century, the Europeans brought not only their own pathogens but also the pathogens of the African slaves they began systematically to import. The American indigenes were doomed. Most of them, or their descendants, would die because Columbus discovered the Americas.

The mixing of the European and indigenous American populations together with imported African slaves (who brought with them malaria and yellow fever) amounted to what Alfred W. Crosby (1972, 1986) aptly described as an epidemiological exchange.[14] It was, however, a rather one-sided transaction. McNeill (1976) reports that two generations after Cortez visited Mexico, the population of the Valley of Mexico and its surrounding environs had declined by 90 percent, largely because Cortez and other Spanish gold diggers had visited their pathogens upon the indigenes. Smallpox was one; measles, another. Comparable percentages—they varied from one-third to all, depending upon the particular epidemic—of indigenous peoples were later lost in South America from other bearers of heretofore unseen contagious diseases. After the initial outbreak and spread of smallpox and measles, both of which made periodic comebacks, influenza, diphtheria, mumps, cholera, scarlet fever, yellow fever, and probably typhus and some other pestilences, appeared, diffused, and killed those without resistance. Crosby (1972) estimates that from 1520 to 1600, there may have been as many as 17 epidemics in eastern North America alone.

It might seem that in those days, epidemics would have been geographically confined and localized, but many were not. In North America, many indigenous tribes suffered demographic die-offs of massive proportions due to Old World pathogens beginning early with, and precisely because of, the fur trade. Trade with indigenous tribes for animal furs began shortly after 1492, and its intensity accelerated due to an economic demand centered in Europe.[15] That enabled a pathogenic chain to form and to infect some indigenes in the continental interior long before they themselves had direct contact with white people (Sale 1990).

For four centuries thereafter, Old World epidemic pathogens hitched a ride throughout the Western hemisphere, cutting through the indigenous American populations and riding into the final American Indian Wars on the Great Plains, where the last U.S. Army mass murder of indigenes, at Wounded Knee, in South Dakota, in 1891, was made logistically simpler because of an epidemic then raging among those targeted for the killing, the Lakota Sioux (whose victims were mostly women and children). With the blessing of its highest general officers, the U.S. Army had already turned a nearly comparable ecological weapon against indigenes almost a generation earlier when, in complicity with the corporate railroads, there was undertaken the deliberate and successful extirpation of the Plains tribes' multipurpose cultural resource that so long had served them as a staple: the bison herds.

Most Anglo-Americans, who profited from all that, have believed that their indigenous predecessors were conquered by superior military force, superior technology, and superior numbers. That was only a part of it. Contagious disease, transmitted by Anglos and African slaves imported by Anglos, for which native Americans had no immunities, accounts for most of indigene mortality that derived from contact with Anglos and their slave-bearing culture. Exact population sizes are matters of some dispute—and, thus, so are total demographic losses— but the *range* of the rates of population mortality is less disputed.[16] Just before 1492, there may have been more than 80 but somewhat fewer than 120 million people ranging the entire American continent; there may have been fewer. The pre-Columbian population of North American indigenes alone may have been as high as 18 million, although again perhaps fewer. But by 1900, when the survivors had been mostly confined to reservations and the American government was now counting,[17] the total population was 500,000. The bottoming out varied with time and place. Depending upon the specific tribe and time frame at issue, demographic ratios of 20 to 1 and 25 to 1 are sometimes given to express the downsizing of populations from start to finish (McNeill 1976). The upper limits can never be known for certain, for the cultural histories of the American indigenes were mostly oral not written, and they contained nothing in the way of Anglo-European measures of time anyway. This is why some upper population estimates are speculative. It is not speculative that the populations were literally decimated. A two-thirds reduction in their total population since 1492, almost all of it due to epidemic diseases, is considered by some authorities to be conservative. Some (e.g., Stannard 1992) put the reduction at 95 percent. The mortality rates sometimes took several generations to stabilize.

The mortality of American indigenous tribes was mostly a demographic catastrophe of epidemiological origin.[18] The cultures never recovered. Entire civilizations of long duration broke like Humpty Dumpty and could not be put back together. Hundreds of small, once-flourishing indigenous tribes no longer exist, and the entire indigenous line of cultural evolution in the Western hemisphere mostly died away. Contemporary descendants in surviving tribes have abysmally high rates of unemployment, alcoholism, poverty, premature mortality, and suicide and are hardly anything at all like the cultures from which they biologically descended.[19] In its entirety, the "epidemiological exchange" initiated in 1492 resulted in what is almost certainly the largest demographical and cultural extirpation in the history of our species.

As this was coming to pass, something like the reverse was happening to the demography and culture of the extirpators. Modern scientific medicine was then getting its start. This eventually gave the population of extirpators a boost. As people came to be supplied with additional food now available from "their" New World, and with the implementation of public health measures and vaccinations developed through scientific medicine, it became possible to lower the mortality of all those unfortunate children whom, previously, pestilential diseases did not permit to survive to adulthood. Make it possible for most children to live long enough to reproduce themselves and, providing there are high enough levels of fertility in the population, one can then infer there should be an exponential increase in the affected population. And there was. The development of scientific medicine and the consequent introduction of public health measures over the course of a couple of centuries, beginning around the eighteenth century, brought cleaner water supplies, vaccinations, the sanitary disposal of fecal matter, and other cultural practices that gradually lowered the incidence of pestilential disease. As a result, human mortality in the European and Anglo-American populations began to decline just as it began to increase for the small-scale cultures of the American indigenes. This established a necessary condition for the growth, domination, and success of a culture whose eventual reach would extend to a global scale.

NOTES

1.   An overview of the variety of sociocultural adaptations to local conditions of resource availability can found in Campbell (1995). A more thorough treatment is Simmons (1989). Bamforth's (1988) study of selected historic groups on the American Great Plains illustrates the depth of analysis desirable, but not usually available, to establish connections between the availability of specific resources and culture-specific organizational responses.

2.   Kingsland (1985) and McIntosh (1985) provide instructive histories on this and much else concerning the development of the science of ecology in the twentieth century.

3.   Sometimes evolutionary ecology is distinguished from behavioral ecology using a criterion that the former addresses the evolutionary outcomes of the latter, which addresses the habitat contingencies that organisms confront in the short term (e.g., Low, Clarke, and Lockridge 1992). Using this distinction, some of our discussion here properly should be characterized as falling under behavioral ecology; however, we do not need the distinction here, for it does not really affect our discursive trajectory or conclusions. So we shall indiscriminately refer to both as evolutionary ecology, which anyhow as currently practiced has no subject if it does not subsume behavioral ecology.

Evolutionary ecology is altogether different from ecosystems ecology, with its macroscopic focus, as the evolutionary ecology texts of Pianka (1994) and Krebs and Davies (1991) transparently reveal. The index to Pianka, for instance, shows that the concept of ecosystem enters into discussion on only 8 of its 450-plus pages. The avian ecologist Gordon H. Orians, who is on record as expressing a tolerant view (Orians 1980), once averred in a private communication that the division between evolutionary and ecosystems ecologists is so wide that they do not appreciate each other's work and often do not even talk to one another.

4.   An extensive methodological critique of the explanatory limitations of Darwinian ecological anthropology—to date, the principal source for the development of evolutionary human ecology—can be found in Vayda (1995a, 1995b).

5. It is worth noting that optimization models, so often employed in evolutionary-ecological applications to humans, are taken by some biological authorities to apply with the greatest of caution and reservation to explain the behavior of ants (Oster and Wilson 1978). Yet, according to some advocates, it is precisely the optimal allocation of effort in time spent, risks taken, and calories acquired that defines the common condition that humans—their degree of acculturation notwithstanding—share with other social species and that, therefore, commends an evolutionary and behavioral approach to ecology (Low, Clarke, and Lockridge 1992). But, I think, it is precisely the fact that humans' degrees of acculturated social organization cannot be dismissed which ensures the contribution of evolutionary human ecology to the entire spectrum of human ecology can be only modest.

6. Mascie-Taylor *defines* human ecology in these terms: "Human ecology embraces the disciplines of environmental physiology, growth and nutrition, epidemiology, human genetics, and demography" (1993, p. 2). The initial volumes of the *Journal of Human Ecology*, first published in 1990, have been dedicated to just that definition.

Since the present work does not define human ecology in those terms, the placement of "disease ecology" as a subject within a chapter on evolutionary and cultural ecology may puzzle some readers. In my view, the human ecology of disease provides the major link between the theory of natural selection and cultural ecology in its demographic aspects and, in principle, could link human evolutionary ecology—not now devoted much to questions of epidemiology—to the cultural ecology of societies with complex social organization. If we allow for the circumstance that other species may be shown to have an evolutionary cultural ecology, because they may be shown to have some rudimentary culture and an ecology, both subject to evolutionary processes, then our subject in this chapter is properly called human evolutionary cultural ecology, taking disease ecology into account.

7. For reviews of the anthropology of pathogenic disease, see McElroy and Townsend (1989), Inhorn and Brown (1990), and Mascie-Taylor (1993). Interest in the ecology of human disease, predicated on the idea that humans, their pathogens, and human cultural and physical systems form an interactive system, owes much to a medical geographer of an earlier generation, J.M. May (1958).

8. All living specimens had been slated for extirpation at midnight on December 31, 1993, but a reprieve was issued, and then another in 1995, as debate continued (Maurice 1995) on whether specimens should be indefinitely preserved (Joklik et al. 1993) or totally and forever destroyed (Mahy et al. 1993). The latest word is that, pending approval of its full membership, the World Health Organization plans to destroy all specimens on June 30, 1999.

9. The last known victim of the major strain was a small girl in Bangladesh in 1975, who survived, and the last known victim of the minor strain was found two years later in Somalia. But not quite: If the terror of smallpox has at last ended, it did so in a macabre manner. In 1978, specimens supposedly under lock and key in a Birmingham, England, laboratory were somehow loosed, to cause the death of an employee working on the floor above, and the infection of her mother. There followed the suicide of the laboratory director, a well-known and respected virologist. The authoritative history of smallpox is Hopkins (1983). Also see Henderson (1976) for details of the attempt undertaken by the World Health Organization to eliminate the disease.

10. This oversimplifies the history of it all (see McNeill 1976). In fact, innoculation against smallpox was begun early in the 1700s, but not with the cowpox vaccine, not with the success that later would be achieved, and not with the public support that later immunization programs would muster. Partly, this was due to inadequate knowledge and public acceptance of the medical etiology of the disease. When Edward Jenner, an English physician, developed the cowpox vaccine in 1798, it was based on a hunch—not on knowledge of the virus and its biochemistry, which then did not exist. It took nearly two centuries to track down the pathogens and destroy the scourge.

11. Malaria is not the current leading cause of mortality from a single infectious disease. That honor, in the 1990s, belongs to tuberculosis (Bloom and Murray 1992). Over the course of history, however, malaria may have caused more human morality than any other single disease (Livingstone 1971), partly because it has been around so long.

12. Of the four *species* of *Plasmodium*, the most dangerous is *P. falciparum* because it reproduces quicker and does not take as long as the others to produce symptoms upon infection—and the symptoms must be quickly treated. The different species probably occupy different niches in their various biotic associations (Ewald 1994), suggesting that a human cultural adaptation effective for suppressing one variant might be ineffective, if not counterproductive, in suppressing another.

13. This evolutionary fact defines a continual problem for biomedicine: how to protect against the spread of virulent strains of bacteria that are resistant to antibiotics. New variants of a targeted pathogen can be expected to mutate until they are unaffected, thus creating the need for judicious use of new antibiotics. Mutations aside, a sufficiently large sample of a pathogen should show sufficient genetic variation that a small number of the population should be resistant anyway—thus providing a condition for the directional selection of the resistant group in the event antibiotics are applied. Neu (1992) charges that complacency about antibiotic development and use has now led to a crisis— a charge being made with increasing frequency.

Antimicrobial-resistant infections have increased human mortality and morbidity in the very recent past (Cohen 1992). This general problem for human health, serious enough, may be expected to interact with the increasing numbers of contacts between persons worldwide, due to increasing population density and modern rapid transport, thus increasing the chance for global epidemics, some old, some new (of which the AIDS epidemic is just one), which may exact increasing tolls on human mortality (Garnett and Holmes 1996). It is also reasonable to expect that human social and political organizations will not respond well to epidemic outbreaks, if the recent past is any guide. Ignorant politicians, corrupt bureaucrats, or other self-seekers too often intervene (see Garrett 1995).

14. The European-American epidemiological exchange is sometimes called the Columbian exchange, after the title of Crosby's earlier volume. The African-American epidemiological exchange has been studied much less, but see Kipple (1987). A much earlier study of the role of disease in the conquest of the Americas was Ashburn's (1947).

15. Around the end of the sixteenth century, trade in fur obtained especially from American beavers became significant in some European economies. Demand for fur and the supply of it continued to increase as trappers and traders penetrated from the American continental perimeter to the interior. Kirkpatrick Sale (1990) estimates that between 10 to 20 million American beavers were trapped and killed for their fur in

the seventeenth century alone, and that the beaver was mostly eliminated from the American Northeast as early as 1640. A great number of other fur-bearing species, plus old-growth forests, were also severely depleted. With increased demand for natural products came increased trade connections with indigenous tribes, and with those came increased mortality for the indigenes.

16.   For a quick survey of the issues and difficulties that surround pre-Columbian population estimates for the Americas, see Roberts (1988). Those intent on describing the depopulation of native Americans as genocide and a holocaust, as is Stannard (1992), typically adopt extreme high values in the range, and high ranges. A detailed and disdainful critique of the methods of "high counters" and of the problems of estimating depopulation ratios and the effects of epidemics, can be found in Henige (1992). A wide range of hypotheses, methods, and evidence pertaining to this passionate debate is evaluated in Ramenofsky (1987).

Although some evidence obtained from paleopathology is indisputable for diseases that leave telltale remarks on human tissue remains, some demographic inferences will always be disputed for lack of necessary data. Apart from additional data that would be desirable, perhaps the most serious problem attending any population or mortality estimate is this: Who is to count, and who in fact was counted in the historical record, as an American Indian or as belonging to a particular tribe or nation? One study of 1980 census data in which American Indians were identified concluded that, depending upon just how the category "American Indian" is defined, the modern population census may show anywhere from 1 million to nearly 7 million (Snipp 1986).

17.   But not counting with integrity or benign intent. Prior to 1980 (!), American Indians were not permitted to identify their ethnicity or tribal affiliation for census purposes. That practice, congruent with the subjegative policies of the Bureau of Indian Affairs—the bureaucratic agency that, until recent times at least, is without peer as the longest continuing disgrace in the history of the United States government—ensures that the full truth of the epidemiological depopulation of native Americans can never be known. While orders of magnitude may continue to be disputed by historians, anthropologists, and epidemiologists, the overall result—a vast extirpation—is not seriously disputed.

18.   Black (1992) argues that genetically deficient immune systems played little, if any, role in the massive mortality (which is a hypothesis sometimes suggested). Rather, Black argues, American indigenes may have been more susceptible due to a greater genetic homogeneity.

19.   In recent years, federal legislation has permitted the development of an occupational pursuit that heretofore was unknown in any of the indigenous Indian cultures and incommensurable with their former cultural means of subsistence: the extraction of surplus wealth from non-Indian gambling populations, in Indian-owned, full-fledged gaming casinos. Touted as a means to increase the material well-being of the tribes, whose history of domination by a large-scale Anglo culture left in tatters every treaty ever signed by them with the United States government, owing to the actions of the government, it would run contrary to American history if Anglo organizational and capital investment capabilities, and indifference to the Indians, did not also turn this venture into another venue for exploitation.

Chapter 6

Biosociocultural Evolution

The extirpation—whether through displacement, assimilation, or genocide—of small-scale human cultures by large-scale cultures and, in modern times, by a culture of global scale has been a seemingly inexorable trend of long standing, its momentum continuing to gather throughout the twentieth century. With reason, we may refer to evolution by natural selection in general terms to explain the adaptive success or decline of human populations as measured by their differential morbidity and mortality due to pathogenic disease. But as we train our focus on the increasing complexity of macroscopic sociocultural organization, it no longer becomes reasonable to rely on just neo-Darwinian interpretations of evolution to explain the human ecological dynamics out of which materialize increasing resource potential and declining mortality. As we saw before and should see again here, macroscopic ecological-evolutionary dynamics appear to involve much more than neo-Darwinism takes into account. So, insofar as we assume that evolution bears upon the push-pull interactions of resource potential and mortality, we shall have to consider evolution in other terms.

But what other terms are available? We do have available a long-standing history of inquiry into sociocultural evolution undertaken by social scientists. Unfortunately, this inquiry has produced nothing like the benchmark of evolutionary selection theory. Fundamental differences in relative theoretical sophistication between the biological and social sciences have produced fundamental differences in the relative sophistication of their respective evolutionary theories.

For the past 30 years or so, biologists have been engaged in some intense debates among themselves about evolution and natural selection. But all these debates concern different interpretations of, or promote different suggestions for improving upon, the same general body of theory. The theory is debated, and is sometimes said to be incomplete or faulty, but no one wants to return to the days before the Modern Synthesis, when there were as many competing evolutionary theories as there were evolutionary biologists. Whatever its faults, natural selection is sufficiently formalized and well enough anchored in data to provide evolutionary biologists with a common ground on which to fight.

With this, the social scientists cannot even begin to compete. They are still arguing over which grounds to conduct their fights on. They possess no body of theory (of any kind) that commands such wide acceptance, no theory as general and fundamental, no theory as cumulative, formal, and well tested. Various candidates for an over-arching body of core theory in the social sciences have been periodically offered up. None has prevailed. Current offerings probably will not prevail either, and there is an easy way to tell. In social science literature, compared to the biological sciences, one finds many more abstract nouns that end with "ism." Words that end like that are almost always names for doctrines, not scientific theories, and they frequently have ideological overtones. Thus, social science discourse is often conducted in terms of the doctrines of purported deep thinkers who, like the adherents of any doctrine, tend to be doctrinaire. One will find, for instance, as a normal event, a discourse about the evolutionary theory of so-and-so compared to the theory of what's-his-name, rather than a discourse on their respective contributions to evolutionary theory, as one finds in biology. It isn't likely that this state of affairs will change any time soon.

And how have sociocultural evolutionary theories connected to the biological theory? For the most part, they haven't. Social science as a whole does not accord a very significant place for evolutionary theory in its explanation schemata for culture and society. But even when some social scientists do, many agree with Hallpike that "social evolution is a very different process from biological evolution" (1992, p. 2). Looking back on the social science tradition of evolutionary thought, another anthropologist put it this way: "it is crucial to realize that 'evolution' as it has been used in the social sciences for more than a century is a fundamentally different kind of explanatory system than 'evolution' in the natural sciences" (Dunnell 1988, p. 169). Dunnell even affirmed that a different metaphysics is implied of the different theories.

We should not be too hard on social scientists for their failure to produce a benchmark account of sociocultural evolution and for failing to connect it with natural selection. It is not at all clear that such a connection could be made at the present time *even if* a benchmark account were available. There are, as we saw in Chapter 2, connections missing in the foundational accounts of biological evolution.

In this chapter, we shall briefly note some of the difficulties involved in establishing a satisfactory account of sociocultural evolution and in connecting it with accounts of biological evolution, and shall suggest some alternative theoretical attitudes and a primitive model to guide an alternative account of sociocultural evolution. We shall conclude with what, at first blush, may seem to be a paradox but which will serve us as a premise for examining ecologically based sociocultural development and change in chapters 7 and 8: There can be no such thing as sociocultural evolution on its own terms, but sociocultural systems indeed are implicated in evolutionary processes, and the description of those is necessary to comprehend sociocultural development and the appearance of macrosocieties with a global-scale culture.

COMPARING BIOLOGICAL AND SOCIOCULTURAL EVOLUTION

Descent with change is the hallmark of biological evolution, with genetic inheritance the common currency of descent, and natural selection the process that fixes inherited changes across reproductive generations. Development, as distinct from evolution, is supposed by biologists to be a pattern of changes that occurs for individuals over the course of their life cycles, within each reproductive generation, and influenced by species phylogeny, individual genotype, and interacting environmental context. With these general thoughts in mind, biologists and some interested philosophers have thought it necessary to clarify and decide exactly what evolves and what is selected, a question of units; what is to count as an adaptation, a question of interpretation; and how new species result, a series of questions that concern the relationship of natural selection to macroevolution. As things stand today, there is not general agreement on these and other matters,[1] but there is general agreement on the overall framework, general assumptions, and some of the lacunae in the current accounting of biological evolution. The disagreements turn on how to perfect the accounts.

Breaks in Biological and Sociocultural Accounts

From the time of Darwin, social scientists have paid natural selection little mind in the explanation of sociocultural evolution. While in the last two decades that circumstance has changed,[2] non-Darwinian explanations have provided the classical accounts of sociocultural evolution. Owing especially to the influence of Herbert Spencer and Lewis Henry Morgan, social scientists became accustomed to thinking of sociocultural evolution in terms of sequential stages, essentially a developmental concept. Though now considered passé, the stage theories led to the gradual adoption of some background concepts similar to biological accounts of evolution, but with some divergent foreground premises.

As with the biological accounts, for sociocultural accounts it has been assumed that evolution is gradual change involving adaptations, although absent a circumscribed interpretation, almost anything counts as one; that some unit—a culture, a society, or one or more of its structures or patterns—has to evolve; and some property or properties characteristic of the evolving unit have to be inherited. In the beginning, biologists and social scientists all agreed that evolution was progressive—that's progressive in the sense of *progress*, not just in the sense of some mathematically depictable progression, such as increasing differentiation or complexity, which is still widely accepted, but in the moral sense of improvement to perfection. Today, hardly any evolutionary biologists can be found to keep such a commitment, while social scientists still do (Dunnell 1988). Another point of departure occurred quite early: Darwin had populations evolving as they adapted to environments, a relation that deemed evolution to be an affair induced by external contingencies, while the received view in social science has had cultures or societies, or whatever the chosen unit of evolution, as adapting mostly to internal contingencies of the unit itself or other related units in a connected system. This evolutionary concept, known to biologists as orthogenesis, is beyond their pale, for it affirms some notion of developmental evolution and denies the canon by which evolution and development are distinguished. Some call the focus on internal system adaptations endogenetic evolution. In searching for the essential properties and units of inheritance for endogenetic evolution, the abject failure of classical social science accounts to establish any common currency of sociocultural inheritance like the gene should be noted.

Considering just the foregoing, we can already identify the *first* set of formidable problems that accounts of sociocultural evolution confront. Without any canon to distinguish evolution from development, social scientists are in no position to say whether the process they describe for the unit of change they choose is, in fact, a process of evolution or development. It does not help them to retreat to a concept of developmental evolution if they have no means in theory or fact to distinguish evolution and development, for then they cannot tell us what developmental evolution is either. Furthermore, lacking a clear model of evolution, they are in no position to assure us that their unit of evolution is appropriately chosen.

Again, however, we should not go too hard on them, for they must deal with the condition that cultures and societies *change* but do not reproduce themselves in any manner like individuals do, let alone make copies of themselves in any manner like genes do. In describing the changes as "evolution" and in sorting out its differences from "development," if such a canonical distinction is to be maintained, a second set of rather formidable problems has to be confronted.

1. The material of sociocultural change, and presumably therefore of inheritance, is symbolic information in terms of which the properties of cultures and societies are structurally and functionally organized, and in terms of which the structures and functions can be expected to adapt. Patterns of behavior, beliefs, systems of ideas, the production of goods and services and the means to do so, institutions, mores, norms, tools— all these things and much more are said to be culturally inherited, and for the very good reason that not every generation reinvents its culture starting from square one. This material, it has been thought, is the stuff of sociocultural evolution.

2. Symbolic information and the social structures and cultural processes that embody it do not stay constant within measurement intervals, for which anyhow there is no corresponding equivalent of the biologists' reproductive generation, but, rather, they can be expected to change through learning and its cultural transmission within generations. What the generations inherit, they add to and subtract from as they see fit. When they add, the symbolic material they acquire becomes part of the inheritance that is subsequently transmitted. In contrast to the inherited material of biological evolution, called Darwinian because acquired traits supposedly are not inherited, sociocultural inheritance is Lamarckian.

3. Sociocultural inheritance is a blending process wherein many symbol systems and their constructions do not retain their unit character as they change—insofar as they ever had any unit character. Typically, they are indefinite, with inexact boundaries, and blend one into another. This enables innovations in culture, which are not random but are purposefully constructed, to induce an unfolding process on their very own symbolic representations, potentially effecting a constitutive change in the representations. Examples are the development of technology or of ideas, which sometimes can transform the very context in which they appear as they themselves have been transformed by the successes and failures experienced with their own utilization. As symbolic material is culturally inherited in indefinite form, it can become something else. By contrast, Darwinian inheritance is particulate. The Mendelian gene, inferred from phenotypes, was conceived as a definite unit. Something either is, or is not, a Mendelian gene, and something can not be almost, but not quite, a Mendelian gene. This definite entity does not change its unit character as inherited, for it is not "blended" with other genes; rather, it is "mixed" with them in a reshuffling at reproductive intervals where it retains its identity. It does not become something else. Its arrangement and relative frequency in a distribution may change, but its constitution does not. It is the difference between the mixing of something like distinct varieties of seeds, which can be unmixed, and the blending of eggs, flour, and water, which can not be "unblended." Under some conditions, random mutations in a molecular gene may be thought of as inducing a kind of "blending" from which the gene becomes something other than what it was. However, molecular genes are units of function, insofar as they are well-individuated units at all. The tracing of biological inheritance by Mendelian genes, which are theoretically idealized as well-individuated units of structure, presumes they are particulate.

4. Finally, there is universal recognition that sociocultural change behaves at very rapid rates compared to the rates of biological evolutionary change. Depending upon the species and traits we may be talking about, some biological evolutionary change can take millions of years, while some sociocultural changes—permanent changes, acquired and transmitted by blending—can occur almost overnight.

Table 6.1 summarizes major differences of theory and perspective in classical accounts of biological and sociocultural evolution as regards the shared concepts that the different traditions use to get underway: adaptation, modified descent, and inheritance. The differences are

Table 6.1. Comparing Biological and Classical Sociocultural
Accounts of Evolution

	Biological	*Sociocultural*
Adaptation		
Unit	Population	System
Environment	External	Internal
Modified Descent		
Intervals	Definite	Indefinite
Units	Definite	Indefinite
Inheritance		
Type	Darwinian	Lamarckian
Material	Genetic Information	Symbolic Information
Process	Particulate	Blending
Rate of Change	Slow	Rapid

striking, which is why the traditions finish differently. Hallpike draws this conclusion about the lack of an interface between the traditions: "There is ... no reason to suppose that *genetic* change is linked in any significant way with social evolution" (1992, p. 1, emphasis in original). His view is the received view in social science, and it is borne out by the current status of the existing classical accounts: biological and sociocultural evolution appear to be largely incommensurable.

Culture as Selectable Social Heredity

Not everyone agrees that they are incommensurable, and one of the architects of the Modern Synthesis himself described human evolution as "the interaction of biology and culture" (Dobzhansky 1962, p. 18). Since the 1970s, there have been various attempts to employ some model of selection to describe the Dobzhansky Interaction, which ought to be unless culture and biology thoroughly disconnect. The models are still in early stages of development, and all posit analogies or homologies with natural selection. The resulting body of theory is known variously as gene-culture coevolution, dual inheritance theory, and evolutionary culture theory.

The models in this body of theory differ considerably, but the following orienting assumptions are used to frame most of the approaches: Culture, in its symbolic manifestations, represents a source of heritable variation; cultural phenotypes are heritable on their own terms, that is, by some social transmission process or processes that behave in addition to genetic transmission; the distinct cultural and genetic inheritance processes interact, meaning that gene pools and cultures change or coevolve with respect to each other; and the heritable variation in culture is retained by means of some kind of selection process that favors phenotypes that are marginally better adapted. From there, the models diverge.

Before noting a few points of divergence, let us pause to observe the apparent thought that gives rise to these efforts to find Dobzhansky's Interaction: If biology, culture, and society all evolve and all connect, there must exist some general evolutionary process (not necessarily unitary) in terms of which we can describe their evolutionary connections. But how?

Lumsden and Wilson (1981) construe the connections by attributing causal primacy to inherited genotypes. Genotypes are supposed by Lumsden and Wilson to constrain cultural phenotypes by way of "epigenetic rules" that direct the assembly of mental and symbolic capacities, and for which genes encode. Cultural traits are naturally selected by means of the presumed fitness-maximizing behavior of individuals who reflect adaptive variants. The assumption is that different genotypes enable some cultural traits in given environments to be better adapted and, therefore, the bearers of them to be more fit. On this explicitly sociobiological view, culture is something of an epiphenomenon of genetic inheritance. We are supposed to get a natural selection of culture by way of the effects of genes even as we get selection for the better adapted genotypes—a coevolution of genes and culture, but with genes defining the rules of engagement. Alexander (1979) proposed a similar model in which genetic selection and cultural traits were thought to be continually coupled by means of social reinforcement-learning processes to which individuals, the main engines of evolutionary action, are culturally subjected. Alexander's model allows for cultural change through learning to occur without genetic change but does not allow cultural change to stray far from individuals maximizing their inclusive fitness.

Some modeling efforts construe the evolution of humans in cultural context as a matter of dual inheritance. Here, cultural inheritance is not derivative of genetic inheritance. Rather, cultural selection is thought to operate along parallel lines to genetic selection, to change the relative frequencies of cultural traits by presumed laws of transmission not identical to laws of genetic transmission. Cavalli-Sforza and Feldman (1981) posit a series of evolutionary forces, in analogy to biological accounts, along with models to describe the interactions of the forces, which are supposed to contribute to the differential survival of cultural trait carriers. This differential survival is an indicator of cultural fitness that is not presumed to correlate perfectly with genetic fitness. Boyd and Richerson (1985) propose that socially transmitted learning, if it is culturally reproducible, is subject to different sorts of bias processes that may function in variable environments. Some forms of biased cultural transmission should, in the reasoning of the Boyd-Richerson models, also be selectively favored even though they do not contribute to an enhanced genetic fitness. The dual inheritance theories adopt a generalized Darwinian model for a framework—variation-selection-retention—while their concepts of cultural selection and fitness, seemingly analogous to Darwinian selection, are not genetical because learned transmission is taken to be a symbolic process that follows its own inheritance pathways by its own distinct means.

Evolutionary culture theory follows the pathways literally implied by Alfred Kroeber's (1948) hypothesis of a tree of human culture. Here, descent with modification is interpreted in Darwinian terms: the tracing of descent lineages in culture itself, in allusion to cladistic analysis, using ideational units in terms of which culture is replicated and differentially transmitted. In the formulation of its principal champion, W.H. Durham (1990, 1991), evolutionary culture theory recognizes two modes of cultural evolutionary change: transformation, or changes *within* established cultural systems; and diversification, or changes *of* some established cultural system over time until multiple distinct cultures appear. A consequence of the cladism writ into this model is that all human cultures must be related by evolutionary descent and must have derived from some single common culture. Obviously, such proposed evolutionary cultural descent must connect to the dynamics of genetic inheritance in acculturated populations. The problem is to indicate how so. The plan is to trace changes in the distributions of the units of ideational transmission—called memes, following Dawkins (1989)—systems of which define the culture of a population at a given time.

For all the models of sociocultural evolution that depart from the classical tradition in search of Dobzhansky's Interaction, natural selection and its panoply of associated ideas provide the guiding light. The problematics the models address, the theoretical methods employed, the imagery of the concepts—indeed, the entire framework of thought—take the biological accounts as anchors in terms of which to stabilize, ground, and validate the development of sociocultural accounts. This would seem to be a logical way to proceed and, even though still in their infancy, the sociocultural models of coevolution represent some very worthy efforts. However, we ought not to restrict our inquiry to developing sociocultural accounts that depend upon searching just where the light is.

Reasons to Develop Alternative Accounts

Among the modern theorists who advocate rapprochement with biological accounts, perhaps Durham deserves the prize for Bravest of the Brave. The cladistic method of tracing cultural descent faces the most formidable obstacles, not least among them being the paucity of the archaeological record whose missing (and, in some cases, irretrievably lost or never existent) data are needed for the tracing of family cultural trees. And Durham's daring "mother of all cultures" hypothesis stands to be falsified if ever the multi-regional hypothesis of human origins is established and overrides the "out of Africa" hypothesis. Second prize for bravery goes to Boyd and Richerson who say, of dual inheritance theory, that "Our goal is to account for *all* the processes by which the distribution of beliefs, attitudes, and values in a population are transmitted and modified" (1985, p. 12, emphasis added). The sheer ambition expressed in these goals should command our respect.

However, embedded within the conceptual framework and imagery of these efforts can be located numerous reasons—yet a *third* set—to adopt a radically different framework and imagery. We may list reasons that range from serious to significant to compelling.[3]

Serious on the list is the question of units. Most broadly, and I should think unarguably, it simply will not due to conflate cultures and societies into some single unit, the sociocultural system, which we take to evolve. The point has often been made: Societies, as networks of social relations, may exhibit similar patterns of change although their cultures may be different, while cultures, as distinct symbolic systems of shared meanings, may exhibit similar patterns of change in societies that are different. Although cultural and social change certainly interconnect, it does not follow that the processes of cultural evolution or social evolution should be anything like each other or that they can be conveniently combined into some unilinear process. Culture and society are just not the same stuff.

It does not even follow that we should conceive cultures or societies as units of evolution. The tendency in social science has been to think of cultures and societies as entities, even if their boundaries are inherently vague, but what gives rise to this thought? It is probably a psychological artifact of the ordinary, prescientific naming of different cultures and societies and the resulting reification of some of their presumed features for practical purposes. Because we can name, characterize, and distinguish cultures and societies in ordinary language, we have the sense that they are individuated—a sense that may be reinforced by the drawing of political boundaries where applicable. Mostly, this reification serves the aim of the same ordinary sense-making from which it derives. It is commonplace that persons perpetuate through their ordered meaning systems conceptions derived from the frameworks of ordinary languages, within which matters of ontology are resolved for practical purposes. But if the agreed-upon ontologies and their implicit individuations are then transported into scientific formulations of processes of social and cultural change, the effect is to impose a static conceptual structure on what is really a set of ongoing processes. While a psychological sense of closure may assist us in efforts to negotiate the realities of everyday life, it does not follow that entities that are conceived to establish grounds for ordinary sense-making, even if they appear to exist and change over time, should be theoretically conceived as units of social or cultural evolution.

Theoretical sense-making here fares no better. The conception of cultural or social units of change as generically identical, in analogy to the Mendelian gene, as proposed with Lumsden and Wilson's cultergens, Dawkins' memes, and other suggested units of cultural information that supposedly compete for survival and differential reproduction, is unpersuasive for two reasons. First, Mendelian genes are not homologous with molecular genes, which in context do the work of evolution and development in biological accounts. Why should we expect an *analogue* to do the work in sociocultural accounts? Second, the computation with units so conceived, while effective for computing the distributional mixing of Darwinian units of like kind, which admits of proportions, interpreted now for the measurement of the differential transmission of a blending inheritance of acquired characters, would require an arithmetic that does not exist.

Significant on the list of reasons to adopt some alternative imagery and framework for sociocultural accounts is the distortion imposed by a fundamental neo-Darwinian dogma: entities adapt to environments that select the fittest of the traits that are competing in the *taken-as-static* environment. The dogma distorts three ways. First, it is simply not true even for biological accounts that the adapting entities of the appropriate environments leave the environments unaffected. Living things seem to create and recreate the very conditions for their own further adaptations and evolution, because they gradually change whatever environments they are adapting to (see Levins and Lewontin 1985). The notion of an unchanging environment is a theoretical convenience of population genetics, not an accurate description of the real environments in which gene-bearing organisms adapt. Any realistic assessment of the relation of populations to environments cannot rest on just the notion of selection by environmental consequences, since the consequences are changing the very environments that are supposedly selecting for the consequences. Second, the dogma leads us to suppose that societies or cultures may be conceived as populations of selectable traits. But neither cultures nor societies are mere populations of traits, nor are they aggregations of trait carriers. Their distinguishing feature is their *organization* of meaning systems or of social relations, as the case may be. For both, any presumed trait has as its environment the other "traits" that interrelate and function *together or in opposition* to form the ongoing cultural or social process. The concept of population distributions of traits changing in response to the characteristics of environments artificially and falsely separates that which adapts and that which is adapted to. Third, the dogma imposes a set-theoretic concept where none belongs. It says: conceive your subject as a set of elements that can be sampled with replacement while, in fact, our subject consists of a system of functioning parts. Parts do not stand in relation to wholes as elements stand in relation to sets. Parts are not members of wholes as elements are of sets. Rather, parts and their relations are constitutive of wholes. The set-theoretically derived concept of a statistical population is simply inapplicable to define the systems of cultural and social relations that we normally take to *be* culture and society.

Compelling on the list of reasons to adopt an alternative framework is the suspicious idea that cultural or social evolution can be described as the transmission of some sort of material of inheritance. Material they may have, but cultures and societies do not replicate, their variation is not random, their numbers are not large, and they are organizationally systemic. How, then, may we conceive cultures and societies as systems of inheritance? Their "parts" are their "material." They (or it) may continue and be passed along, or may not, or may be changed with time, may diffuse, blend, develop, differentiate, disappear, and all the while turn into new and changing structures. Stability and constancy for the material, sometimes, change, yes, and for causes, too; but it is not forbidden of the cultures and societies that they might so thoroughly change as to retain *none* of the features with which we might first have identified them, and to do this in an orderly pattern. This orderly change would qualify as descent with modification, but if nothing of an original is maintained as it changes, no copies are made of it, and no common material survives, what can we coherently say is *inherited*? It no doubt sounds strange to suggest there could be descent with modification but without inheritance, but that's only because we are conditioned to biological accounts of evolution and development. These accounts have it that ontogeny recapitulates phylogeny, that development is an expression of inheritance. There is no reason to adopt such a dogma for cultures and societies. In these systemically organized processes, ontogeny and phylogeny may be indistinguishable (cf. Hallpike 1986).

AN ALTERNATIVE FRAMEWORK, IMAGERY, AND MODEL

In the remainder of this chapter, we shall sketch an alternative framework, imagery, and model to account for sociocultural change insofar as such change may be a function of the Dobzhansky Interaction. While the framework may be radical, the imagery is becoming more common. The model is unexceptional and its formulation most elemental, but at least it lends itself to development within the framework and the imagery. We do not undertake such development here. One intent of the model, as well as our introduction of it at this time, is merely to enable a coarse-grained focus on ecological patterns that correlate with sociocultural development in the past 10,000 years. The patterns will be recounted in very conventional terms in the next two chapters. The model employs some notions from the framework of the classic models, hopefully without classic deficiencies, and tunes in to some facets of Dobzhansky's Interaction for which it is necessary to account.

Assumptions for an Alternative Framework and Imagery

We employ a provisional distinction between evolution and development for the purpose of suggesting that sociocultural systems are capable of development but not evolution. By speaking of sociocultural systems, of course we may be conflating distinct developmental processes for culture and society—a theory choice that eventually might be regrettable (but not in this work). If there are different principles for the development of culture and societies, the model can be complicated when they are fairly elucidated. Should they be, we shall presume they would show that macroscopic sociocultural development does not recapitulate evolutionary phylogeny. That is to say, we shall not assume there is some inherent program that unfolds during development as modified by environment, although an unfolding there could be over time. Of course, we shall assume that sociocultural development responds to evolution. But to the evolution of what, and how? The short answer is: to the evolution of biosociocultural regimes, by system self-reorganization.

So as not to stray too far from convention, we shall continue with locutions that suggest sociocultural systems adapt to biophysical environmental parameters. However, we shall entertain no dualistic thought that sociocultural systems and biophysical systems are somehow "separate." For analytical purposes, at times each may need to be treated as its own affair. But each is known to interact and to change, organizing and reorganizing, in response to the changed conditions that the other, as environment, presents. For our analytical purposes here, it is pointless to take either environment as constant. While biophysical systems can function and change on their own, without input from sociocultural systems, the converse is not true. Sociocultural systems depend for their very continuation upon well-functioning biophysical systems and, therefore, should not be expected to evolve, however they might otherwise change, except with respect to the changing conditions of biophysical systems. Let us therefore go to the heart of the matter of evolution, insofar as sociocultural systems are implicated, and treat interacting biophysical and sociocultural assemblies as integratable complex biosociocultural systems, understanding that our reference line is the various regimes or different nonstationary states in terms of which such systems may be characterized for given periods of time. For the evolution of biosociocultural regimes we shall assume there is no "inheritance" to be characterized and no "transmission" process. But we shall assume there is descent with modification. For evolutionary descent, we allow the theoretical possibility of the total replacement of sociocultural assemblies implicated in biosociocultural regimes. That is to say, we allow that whatever there is socioculturally can be so transformed in the evolution of biosociocultural regimes that eventually it could become something unlike anything it was.

In rejecting a selection *model*, we are not thereby assuming the absence of natural selection or consigning to it an insignificant role. Rather, we are simply not assigning it to do the prime work of causal forces. However, one presumed effect of natural selection *can* do causal force work, and we shall need some principle to set in motion forces to generate biophysical-sociocultural interactions so that biosociocultural regimes can evolve. The principle we adopt was articulated by Alfred Lotka: "Natural selection will so operate as to increase the total flux through the system, so long as there is presented an unutilized residue of matter and available energy" (1922, p. 148). And, by way of explanation: "Evolution proceeds in such direction as to make the total energy flux through the system a maximum compatible with the constraints" (1956 [1924], p. 357)—the constraints in this case referring to boundary conditions imposed by the second law of thermodynamics. Interpreted in other words, the effects observable with natural selection are increases in biomass obtained from intensified system energy-and-materials flow rates. The principle asserts that intensified matter-energy cycling is a long-term consequence of evolution by natural selection. This implies that selection will tend to favor populations whose energy capture and exploitation are maximized relative to alternative populations that are competing for resources derived from the same matter-energy cycle.

Part of the process imagery that underlies Lotka's Law (as we shall rhetorically refer to it)[4]—only faintly in view in his day—is autocatalysis in systems that are able to import free energy and export entropy. The accumulation of entropy directs a closed thermodynamic system to a condition of equilibrium or heat death. An autocatalytic process is one in which some matter-energy cycle is able to incorporate the *products* of the cycle into the continuation of the cycle, often with the effect of reordering the system in such a way as to maintain it *far* from thermodynamic equilibrium. The creating or recreating of order is accomplished as new material structures emerge for reorganizing the flows of energy or as new energetic structures emerge for reorganizing the flows of matter. This restructuring of structures for order production in open systems is often said to arise spontaneously (which is not to say mysteriously or without cause). Systems that are able to function this way nowadays are said to be self-organizing. The dynamic action of self-organizing systems seems to be geared to system self-renewal through the production of autocatalytic nonlinearities. As this occurs, and it depends upon a variety of contingencies, a self-organizing system can evolve into something substantially different than it was, because it can incorporate the effects of its own interactions unto itself, thereby continually changing the initial conditions for future system behavior and for further reorganization.[5] (For further explanation see Appendix.)

Instead of assuming evolution by natural selection for biosociocultural systems, we shall here assume evolution by self-organization. We take selection to contribute to order-production by means of Lotka's Law, which we shall take as the force law that drives evolution in biosociocultural regimes. Adams (1988) adopted the same lines in an ambitious effort to characterize sociocultural evolution in terms of the self-organization of energy. The present model, although bracketed along with Adams's, is much less ambitious and purposefully more simplified. In the present case, I have thought it advisable to constrain the model with reference to the problematic with which this entire work was introduced: Rappaport's Dilemma, or the suggestion that the development of human sociocultural systems may contain the seeds of their own ecological destruction. With this explanatory constraint, and taking the framework of self-organizational dynamics as background, together with Lotka's Law in the foreground to drive the dynamics of the relevant Dobzhansky interactions, we may now turn to the minimal elements that need to be represented in the model.

A Qualitative Model for the Evolution of Biosociocultural Regimes

To portray biosociocultural interactions. it would seem we need to bring together some biophysical assembly, some sociocultural assembly, and some way to represent the interactions of the respective assemblies. When organized spatio-temporally, we call the assembled interactions a *biosociocultural regime*. Precluded are interactions *within* any biophysical or sociocultural assembly that are removed from direct or indirect interaction effects on the other assembly, taken as environment. In other words, biophysical or sociocultural features that do not connect are precluded from constituting the biosociocultural regime. We note that biophysical and sociocultural assemblies each contain their own sets of variable interaction processes, which are the focus of different respective sciences and which the model shall have to bring together if the intended portrayal of coevolution is to succeed. The full model, consisting of five connected, time-ordered, triadic assemblies of process interactions, is arrayed in Figure 6.1.

Biophysical process interactions often are identified by ecologists as behaving in the context of ecosystems—a concept that is not without its difficulties (as we shall see in Part B, Chapter 3), but we shall adopt the term. The model below is largely insensitive to the variable process interactions with which ecosystems have been described. At the most general level of analysis, however, it is clear that the model must incorporate *ecosystem energy production* as a variable process and, likewise, it must incorporate *human energy expropriation*. We could consider just the interactions of these variable processes, but there are reasons not to. One reason is that we need some baseline against which to evaluate the human ecological problem that is our reference. Rappaport's Dilemma suggests there may be ranges beyond which the development of societies and cultures can be sustained by the organization of ecosystem interactions (interpreted in the model with respect to energy production). Let us therefore conceive and incorporate as a two-state variable process, with unspecified range, *ecosystem sustainability/disorganization*. A triangular assembly of process interactions therefore needs to be portrayed: a relationship expressing variable rates of human energy expropriation to ecosystem energy production with respect to ecosystem sustainability/disorganization. Considering *nothing* else, this is a most uninteresting assembly of interacting processes. Changed rates of interaction within each variable process are not likely to affect rates of interaction in the assembly itself because of human activity, which here is unabetted by sociocultural organization. In this case, rates of interaction between human energy expropriation and ecosystem energy production are not likely to effect any change at all in a condition of sustainability or disorganization in the ecosystem from which the energy is produced and expropriated. When human energy expropriation activities become socioculturally organized, rates in the interaction process assembly should be affected. Interaction Process Assembly #1, as we shall call this, is nothing more than a system starter. It starts the necessary-for-survival process of human energy capture.

Interaction Process Assembly #2 allows for the effects of the development of sociocultural organization. First and foremost, sociocultural organization is organization for survival. Thus, *human subsistence organization* needs to be portrayed as a variable process that connects directly to human energy expropriation, since that is the point

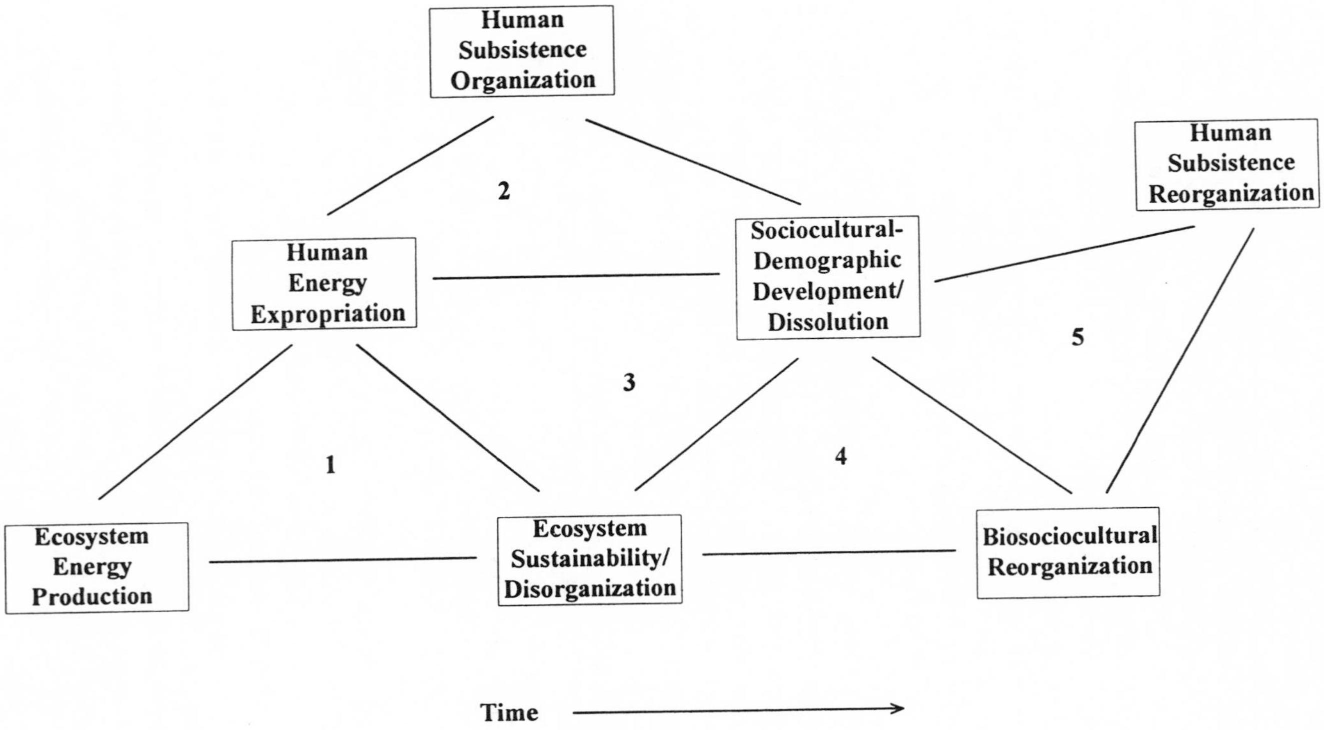

Figure 6.1. A Triadic Process Assembly Model for Biosociocultural Evolution

of human subsistence activities. A dyadic interaction between these variable processes is not very interesting in its own right either, but it becomes very interesting indeed when we consider how the interaction is changed by the combined effects of increases in technology, population, and the division of labor in society. These three interacting processes we take to constitute the internal dynamics of *sociocultural-demographic development/dissolution*, insofar as the development or dissolution of cultures or populations are implicated in biosociocultural evolutionary change—and there would be no point in bringing any of this up if they were not. Changes in rates of these variable processes, as they interact internally, most certainly change rates of interaction between human subsistence organization and human energy expropriation, as we shall see from the historical record reviewed in chapters 7 and 8. Interaction Process Assembly #2 is of special human ecological interest. Here—in the consequences of sociocultural development for subsistence—can be found the dynamics of human energy expropriation that spur the process of evolution in biosociocultural regimes. Comparable in its complexity to ecosystem energy production, this set of processes requires special models of its own to describe. Here we simplify, first, by treating development and dissolution as a two-state variable with unspecified range and, second, by being insensitive to the different dynamics of sociocultural and demographic change. For our purposes, it suffices to know the dynamics connect.

In principle, developmental change in ecosystems and sociocultural systems could continue indefinitely, limited only by their own internal processes, unless or until they reach some limiting condition from without. We assume there should not and could not be any evolutionary change in biosociocultural regimes except for the condition when interactions between sociocultural-demographic development/dissolution and human energy expropriation cross the threshold from ecosystem sustainability to disorganization. This, therefore, we portray as Interaction Assembly Process #3, which cannot really come into play until sufficient periods of time have elapsed that human energy expropriation by means of sociocultural and demographic development is able to test ecosystem limits of sustainability. The interactions between the variable processes in this assembly can conveniently be thought of as relations of carrying capacity, a subject that is treated at length in Chapter 9.

Pressed beyond sustainable limits and into ecosystem disorganization, however, something has to give. It is not just ecosystem organization that has to give. It is also the organization of sociocultural systems, whose own sustainability and organization depend upon ecosystem sustainability and organization for continued energy capture. Given sufficient disorganization in ecosystems, there has to come intensified activity by which biophysical and sociocultural interactions are reconstituted and reorganized in tandem, just to maintain Interaction Process Assembly #2. So, Interaction Process Assembly #4 also consists of a triad of process assemblies: sociocultural-demographic development/dissolution, ecosystem sustainability/disorganization, and *biosociocultural reorganization*— a process that is inevitable if sociocultural and demographic development have produced cascading effects on ecosystem disorganization. That is supposed by many, and is supposed here, to initiate cultural and demographic dissolution as energy capture for an acculturated population now becomes problematic. But, if the biosociocultural assembly itself has to be reorganized, then human subsistence organization itself has to be reorganized to conform to the changed conditions. Thus, we may define Interaction Process Assembly #5 as consisting of the triadic relations between biosociocultural reorganization, *human subsistence reorganization*, and sociocultural-demographic development/dissolution, with the emphasis now on the dissolution that should result from ecosystem disorganization. The fourth and fifth interaction process assemblies are most certainly not linear affairs. When biosociocultural interactions are characterized by Interaction Process Assembly #5, then we may speak of the evolution of a biosociocultural regime. We may proceed to analyze the new regime in the same model terms. The terms of the model, and their sequencing presume Lotka's Law as forcing.

Lacking specificity, Figure 6.1 does not express the major empirical hypotheses that guided its formulation as a sequence of triadic interaction process assemblies. The hypotheses are: that each assembly contains its own dominant process in which interactions are intensified such that rates for the other processes and their interaction fall within a range set by the dominant process; and that, as the dominant process intensifies, the entire assembly of interaction processes eventually passes some critical threshold, initiating the next assembly in the sequence, with its own dominant process that now becomes characteristic, which is itself dominant with respect to the preceding assembly in the sequence. Thus, we hypothesize a hierarchical sequence in which, for each succeeding assembly, interactions are intensified, setting new parameters for the regime. No assembly, once functioning, stops functioning, but each can be superseded in functional significance.

What is to cause the sequential replacement in the functional significance of the different assemblies? Simply, the successful expropriation of ecosystem energy sources to the point where parameters from the process of another assembly now become relevant control parameters. By assuming the operation of Lotka's Law, the model allows for evolutionary dynamics to be reflected as hierarchically ordered interaction process assemblies, each with its own supporting structures, that change the conditions for future interaction as a function of prior interactions whose cumulative effects produce perturbations in the assembly. Interaction Process Assembly #1 is changed quickly by #2 as humans acquire elemental tool kits and social organization; #2 eventually *may* be changed by #3, *if* energy expropriation approaches sustainable limits; but, #3 eventually *has* to be changed by #4 if sociocultural-demographic development initiates sufficient ecosystem disorganization. Then, #4 eventually has to give way to #5 as biosociocultural reorganization and human subsistence reorganization define a new biosociocultural regime. Lotka's Law runs from start to finish. It drives the changing hierarchical sequence of a regime over time, ordering the dominant processes in the respective assemblies as follows: (1) ecosystem energy production, (2) human subsistence organization, (3) sociocultural-demographic development, (4) ecosystem disorganization, and (5) biosociocultural reorganization. An evolutionary process that looks like this, or something very much like it, is going to have to unfold in biosociocultural regimes if Rappaport's Dilemma is real.

Three observations: First, this is no inevitable progression that we are postulating for the course of every biosociocultural regime. A given regime could indefinitely remain well within the bounds of Interaction Process Assembly #2, especially if human subsistence were organized in a foraging mode, or #3 if development were keyed to steady-state economics. Long-term stability is possible because Lotka's Law does not suppose some inherent tendency of populations to try to maximize energy capture; rather, it supposes a selective advantage for those populations that do. Those that *do*, create the eventual, and inevitable, instabilities. Second, there *is* posited an increasing inevitability in the progression toward fundamental biosociocultural reorganization with increasing ecosystem disorganization. When the adaptations of a sociocultural assembly are failing along an increasingly irreversible trajectory, this should be reflected in intensified interactions that must resolve themselves in some alternative adaptations, on pain of extirpation or extinction. Third, in this model a sociocultural assembly is not defined as equivalent to some particular, named society or culture. Multiple cultures and societies may be implicated, synchronically or diachronically, in a given sociocultural assembly. Thus, over time, many may "enter" or "leave" the regime, presumably not the same for having entered or left.

In this last observation can be found an implication especially pertinent to sociocultural change. We have interpreted such change as entirely developmental, with developmental turns and trajectories depending upon connections to changing biophysical interactions that sociocultural development itself can initiate. After sufficient periods of time, depending upon future system states that are mostly unpredictable, following trajectories that are mostly unknowable in advance, a biosociocultural system could pass through sufficiently different regimes that its sociocultural assemblies, and by implication its numerous participating cultures, could become something wholly different from anything they ever were. Indeed, as there occur increasing numbers of evolving biosociocultural regimes in which some particular sociocultural assembly is implicated, eventually participating cultures *should* become something entirely different than they were. Given a sufficiently large period of evolutionary time, eventually nothing of functional significance may be expected to survive from any *named* historical culture or society—perhaps only a partial record in an information retrieval system. If this model is at all—even grossly—an accurate depiction of the process it intends to portray, it implies that cultural genealogy after a point could not be traced because after a point there should be nothing in common—nothing to trace. Structural similarities might always be identifiable—perhaps linguistic structures that may derive ultimately from organic phenotypes represented in the organization of the human brain and vocal chords—but common contents should not be identifiable and all functional cultural inheritance eventually would be lost.

Other than this implication and the triadic structure of the model, nothing here is novel. Moreover, the utility of the model is rather limited given its broad generality and its omission to specify relations in mathematical terms. Still, it seems to me that *some* scheme for interpreting the coevolution of biophysical and sociocultural systems, in terms other than biological and classic sociocultural accounts are able to inspire, is desirable. It also seems desirable to have a model that enables a given process or assembly to amplify or recede its interaction effects in response to changing rates *between* other processes or assemblies to which the given one connects. Especially, it seems desirable for a model of biosociocultural evolution to enable autocatalytic nonlinearities to appear. Unspecified though they are, this model does.

Finally, although I have casually called this a model, really it is more of a framework for modeling. An indication of the kind of specificity needed for developing quantitative models of biosociocultural evolution can be found in Giampietro (forthcoming) and Giampietro, Bukkens, and Pimentel (forthcoming). But here we need some interpretive model-like framework for bringing together major historical patterns of human sociocultural development which, had they not appeared, would never have caused Rappaport and so many others to wonder about the sustainability of human sociocultural systems vis-à-vis their interactions with biophysical systems. While this model or framework does not even approach the standards for a benchmark account of evolution insofar as sociocultural systems are implicated, at least it enables us to proceed with a provisional accounting of the evolutionary connections to human ecology.

NOTES

1. There are disagreements on the ontological status of species (are they classes? individuals?), on the "level" of biological organization at which natural selection selects (genes, organisms, populations, demes, any or all?), on patterns of macroevolution (gradual? punctuated?), on the extent to which concepts of adaptation can be utilized for explanatory purposes (very little? very much?), on the advisability and possibility of theory reduction, and a host of technical matters. The disagreements, however, do not seem to seriously disturb, let alone threaten to rend, an otherwise cohesive community of investigators. The flavor of the discourse and the depth of the issues are reflected in numerous excellent books, including the anthologies of Sober (1984b), Depew and Weber (1985), Plotkin (1988), and Ereshefsky (1992); the historical-philosophical treatments of Mayr (1982, 1988), Bowler (1984), and Depew and Weber (1995); the analytical treatments by Dawkins (1982), Sober (1984a), Kitcher (1985), Rosenberg (1985), and Brandon (1990); the theoretical-empirical treatises of Williams (1966), Levins (1968), Gould (1977), Eldredge (1985, 1989) and Bonner (1988); the polemic of Levins and Lewontin (1985); and in much more.

2. The changes amount to, first, trying to establish some principles for biological-sociocultural coevolution, which we discuss briefly below; and, second, developing neo-Darwinian explanations for various traits of human behavior, culture, or society which, depending upon the treatment, may reach more or less into matters of macroscopic

sociocultural evolution. The books of Chagnon and Irons (1979), van den Berghe (1979), Lockhard (1980), Wiegele (1982), Lumsden and Wilson (1981), Lopreato (1984), Reynolds, Falgar, and Vine (1986), and Bell and Bell (1989) illustrate the range of neo-Darwinian penetration. Because, explicitly or implicitly, neo-Darwinian explanations of sociocultural phenomena usually invoke some variation of a principle of genic maximization of inclusive fitness and take it as bedrock, these works are often categorized as human sociobiology. In the social sciences, this mode of theorizing has many more critics than it has advocates. As to the classical accounts of sociocultural evolution, perhaps the single best critical history is Sanderson's (1990), in which he employs Stephen Toulmin's distinction between evolutionary theory and evolutionism to clarify the traditions of evolutionary thought that the social scientists have produced since the time of Darwin and Spencer.

3. Hallpike's (1986) list, from which I have here drawn, is nearly complete, and I take his refutation of the plan to model cultural evolution on biological evolution as definitive. Some reasons I do not take up here, to avoid the temptation to copy or extrapolate the theory of the biologists, were discussed in Freese (1994).

4. A law so called by some and so thought of by Lotka, but not one that is universally recognized as having the exalted status that the term law often commands. It has not gone without notice that there ought to be some specifiable transformation that relates this principle and the principle of maximizing individual inclusive fitness that some analysts take to derive from population genetics. There ought to be, perhaps, but at present there is not. Some neo-Darwinian social scientists use the trivial tactic of invoking the maximization principle willy nilly to explain virtually any sociocultural behavior pattern—and many cultural idiosyncracies—that come into view. Given that, it seems prudent to press Lotka's Law as far as possible, just to learn how exalted or minimal a status it truly deserves. We employed a variation on it last chapter without giving notice when we invoked the concept of resource potential, and notice is hereby given that it is central to the analyses presented in chapters 7 and 8.

5. Informed readers will be aware that there is much more to the imagery—to say nothing of the theory—of self-organization than this. Self-organization falls within modern evolutionary systems theory, which is described in the Appendix.

Chapter 7

The Organization of Subsistence

In Chapter 6 we asked: What variable processes have to be assembled into biophysical and sociocultural interactions, and in what order of assembly, for Rappaport's Dilemma to unfold as a consequence of biosociocultural evolution? Sociocultural and demographic development and/or dissolution was named as a variable process and was acknowledged itself to be an entire complex of interacting processes. In this chapter and the next, we briefly examine that complex; otherwise, no human ecological accounting of the emergence of a culture of global scale is possible. The gradual change of scale from small to large to global human culture can be described many ways and in many terms, but we shall select just the few that are consistent with the model presented in Chapter 6. This suggests that we should look for patterns in sociocultural and demographic development that could have and should have accelerated conditions for biosociocultural evolution by means of the changes development brought to human subsistence organization, and look for the changes that came round *to* development because of changed subsistence patterns. In contrast with the style of Chapter 6, after a time we shall adopt a pedagogical idiom for presenting some empirical sketches to provide a very coarse-grained summary of the elemental human ecological dynamics of macrosocial acculturation. If there is empirical substance to Rappaport's Dilemma, it begins in the emergence of this condition.

We shall follow some principal and well-known lines of sociocultural and demographic development with an eye cocked toward Lotka's Law: With increases in the values of a small system of variables, to be described, there occur changes in principle modes of human subsistence, documented in the sociocultural record, that represent an expansion of resource potential. And, beyond some critical threshold, increases in values of the variables initiate nonlinear system change that makes possible, if not necessary, the emergence of macrosocieties with global-scale culture once mortality drops below a critical threshold.

MODES OF SUBSISTENCE AND THE EXPANSION OF RESOURCE POTENTIAL

Changes in the modes by which humans have organized for subsistence provide a proving ground for a fundamental principle of human ecology: A variable condition of available food resources is *the* critical difference that sets the trajectories for patterns of human sociocultural adaptations and development. At one extreme, an insufficient quality or quantity of food for an extended period can so affect mortality rates that sociocultural adaptations can become tuned to the rates themselves, with the effects that development may be arrested and dissolution set in train.

A chilling illustration of the tuning of adaptations to mortality rates was reported by Turnbull (1978), following up on his famous description of the Ik—already in the process of cultural dissolution. This powerless African culture had had their hunting range compressed by administrative fiat, were forced to grow crops on marginal land to survive, were not inclined by custom or mindset to do so, and as a result were suffering massive morbidity and mortality (at times exceeding 50% per year) while Turnbull (1972) was recording their personal deprivations and cultural disintegration. Turnbull reports one observation that, considering it pertained to a starving population whose morbidity and mortality were due to nutritional deprivations, can only be called astonishing: The Ik *destroyed* food surpluses and seed grains rather than preserve them for the future. Turnbull says that the Ik legitimated this practice because a food surplus departed from the norm, so adapted to privation had the Ik become. Or adapted to their massive mortality rates, we ought to observe.

Food is not the only resource, nor its availability the only variable, to which a culture must adapt, and mortality rates (we saw in Chapter 5) are not affected just by subsistence considerations. But modes of subsistence affect the availability of food, thus survival, thus the overall capability of a population to extract energy from environmental systems, and, thus, virtually everything else of human ecological significance. The gradual change, spread about in many places over the past 10 thousand years, from small- to large- to global-scale cultures, is a change that could not have occurred without correlated changes in modes of subsistence that reduced human mortality rates and increased overall human resource potential. The adaptations of any culture have to stay tuned to its conditions and rates of morbidity, but a condition of extremely high mortality due to the insufficient availability of food sets the lower bound for a culture's adaptation trajectory.

What sets the upper bound? When mortality is low and morbidity manageable, a surplus in subsistence production enables human sociocultural activities to devise adaptations that do more than just keep people alive. Provided with a food surplus, cultural activities can turn on a trajectory by which resource potential expands and population grows. That does not always happen, in fact, but when it does, the historical record is fairly consistent: Sociocultural adaptations tune to total energy extraction rates. Food is only one form of energy extracted from natural environments. With sufficient controls on mortality and morbidity and with sufficient food surpluses, the way is open to extract other kinds of energy, the quantities and qualities of which set the upper bound.

What opens the way? Population growth and mortality rates have arithmetic relationships to each other, and the availability of food energy has an arithmetic relationship to both. Total energy extractions have an arithmetic relationship to all these. While energy that is converted into biomass may directly affect population growth rates, other kinds of energy conversions can be shown to indirectly affect them. Energy flows, when redirected through human extraction activities and converted to human ends, and population size, which is partly a function of energy extraction, can be shown to affect sociocultural development; and, these ecological variables in turn are affected by *its* critical processes. Here we shall key on two of the latter: technology and the division of labor in society.

Technology we recognize to be a combinatory sociocultural process— combined of assorted interacting cultural and economic processes—by which tools are produced. Tools may be produced in the form of hardware or software. In the form of hardware, tools are direct energy converters. In the form of software, the effect is much the same, but it is indirect and more difficult to observe. Mathematics, for example, are systems of symbolic not physical tools, and no mathematical system does energy conversions by itself. But the uses to which mathematics are put often do, the end result being increased magnitudes of energy extraction made available through the engineering uses to which these sophisticated tools are applied. A complex tool kit that includes software is no less a kit for energy conversions than a simple one with just hardware; in fact, it is more so. One consequence—if not a purpose—of increasing technological complexity, which requires software (or symbol systems) beyond a point, is the capacity for increased energy extraction.

The division of labor in society is conventionally defined in terms of the specialization of social roles that develops in an organized population. Sometimes the term is employed as a synonym for the degree of social organization present. The complexity of a division of labor may be measured by its heterogeneity. The greater the differentiation in number of kinds of roles, the more numerous are the different social functions that can be performed, and so the more complex a division of labor may be said to be. A population whose labor is increasingly differentiated into more complex, heterogenous configurations can—and must—capture more physical energy by way of its technology than a population with a comparatively simple division of labor. Depending upon the quantities and qualities of energy that humans capture, how they convert it, and what they do with the conversions; and on how many humans there are in the population, how complex the division of labor, and what environmental constraints may apply—the forms of human culture and society may be quite distinct.

Divisions of labor in society may be analyzed along lateral or hierarchical dimensions or both. The critical hierarchical dimensions are integrated by the interacting dynamics of fundamental dimensions of social organization, which we do not take up until next chapter. Those dynamics form an integral part of our subject. Social organization—which we do not here intend to be a synonym for division of labor—we shall find to be the linchpin that connects the processes whose interactions we describe this chapter.

A variable that we notice but do not analyze much (in this or the next chapter) is the growth and diffusion of information. Information development, transmission, and diffusion are clearly implicated in the growth of technology and in divisions of labor (presuming means to communicate are not restricted). The general effect of increases in the quantity and spread of information, we may assume, is to accelerate the rate of any process with which it is correlated. Certainly, such increases accelerate sociocultural development, and the loss of information may sometimes be a consequence of sociocultural development (and perhaps a cause of sociocultural dissolution). Here, we wish to focus on the complex of *socioecological* interactions that are forces for *socioecological* development. The acquisition and diffusion of information we take as a correlate of the complex, implicated in sociocultural development, but not as constitutive of socioecological development.

This gives us four critical variables whose changing values we wish to follow. We don't need sophisticated measurement for the variables (and anyhow, we haven't got it) in order to observe some elemental human ecological processes compound from their interaction. *Population size* may range from small to large; *technology* and a (lateral) *division of labor*, from simple to complex; and *energy extraction*, from less to more—in respect of the different kinds of energy that may get extracted.

While we attribute causal primacy to this system of variables, we shall not attribute causal primacy to any one of them. That has been proposed before, with mixed results, as did White (1949) with respect to energy and Durkheim (1933) to the division of labor, and Morgan (1887) and Childe (1952) to technology to enhance the surplus potential of subsistence production. Now is not the place to argue whether population growth, taken as literal demographic increase, could be a prime cause of anything. It should simply be conceded that these four variables interact. Each, as it changes, is a process, and each changes the others, singly or in tandem, depending on which are at issue, though not always simultaneously or linearly, and never without connections through social organization. The ongoing interaction of the four process variables, we call the socioecological development process. The dynamics of social organization change its parameters, but in this chapter we concentrate on how changes in the parameters affect each other. Explicitly, our focus is trained upon Interaction Process Assembly #2 from Chapter 6, with attention to the question of development, not dissolution. Implicitly, we conceive development as enabled by a condition of increasing marginal environmental returns obtained from the intensification of production for subsistence. Dissolution, set in train by a condition of decreasing marginal environmental returns, is a subject for *Environmental Connections*.

In what follows, therefore, we should be able to sketch how interactions among the four variables identified above correlate with the historical emergence of macrosocieties having a culture of global scale. A matrix of different values of the variables may be observed for the different kinds of human society, based on different modes of subsistence, that have appeared during the course of sociocultural history. Let us look at just the different types and their matrix values, and characterize from the standpoint of the human ecology why those values changed in the manner they did.[1]

Hunting and Gathering Societies

Hunting and gathering (foraging) societies have small populations, compared to the other types, often as few as 30 when they are broken up into bands, as frequently they are, though their numbers may run into several thousands when the bands are all brought together, as usually they are not. The family is the foragers' primary social unit of subsistence production. Foraging technology is no more complicated than what is required to supply the basics: food, water, shelter, clothing, and accessories. The extraction of energy by foragers is directly connected to their quest for food; most of their energy consumption is in that form, and it doesn't normally come to much. Foragers' division of labor is also comparatively simple, for there are few roles that persons can perform as members of groups that subsist in this mode. Roles break mostly according to age and gender differences, which is to say that rights and obligations are allocated according to how people sort on those statuses. There appear to be no other major bases of differentiation between the members of hunting and gathering societies (although with affluent foragers, things can get a bit more complicated). Anthropologists emphasize that a mode of subsistence based on hunting and gathering requires, in order to succeed, a somewhat communal cultural life in which there is a great deal of sharing.

The population of a hunting and gathering society *has* to stay somewhat small because the level of technology is so simple that the people would be unable, should they wish to do so, to extract very much energy from their habitats. Therefore, there can not be many foragers in a given range. The energy that foragers extract depends upon the flora and fauna in their range, and these change with the seasons, the weather, the reproductive cycles of the available game, and diseases that strike the flora and fauna. So, successful foragers often have to move about, at least periodically, to maintain their way of life.

A mode of subsistence that depends upon harvesting only what nature provides requires a low human population density in order to succeed. The maximum density may be one person per square mile, if not less, depending on local conditions. When population densities increase or habitats in the foragers' range become unstable—events that are not necessarily independent—a hunting and gathering mode of subsistence may not provide as dependable a source of food as some of the alternatives, which is probably why some of the alternatives came into being.

Pastoral and Horticultural Societies

One alternative mode of subsistence is pastoralism, or the domestication of animals, and another is horticulture, the domestication of plants. In practice, these often go together, depending upon what local flora and fauna permit. (Hunters and gatherers were not always "pure" foragers, either.) Both modes represent a change from a way of life built around the collection of food to a way of life built around the *production* of it.

Subsistence production based on domestication first appears unambiguously in the human record about 11,000 years ago, give or take, in various parts of the world; but, note that clear evidence of domesticated species at this time implies there must have been some preceding period of time, perhaps lengthy, during which domestication was incipient, while humans intervened in the reproduction of various wild species until a variety lying outside the range of the wild forms was successfully bred. When humans *first* began to do *that* is a subject of controversy (see Vasey 1992). Whenever it was, it represented the start of simple agrarian modes of subsistence that would fully take hold only with the passing of millennia.[2]

Yet, with even the beginning of the simplest of agrarian practices comes a radically different idea in the repertoire of human adaptations: Rather than go chasing after game and wild plant species, let's domesticate some animals and plants, for then we will have a more dependable food supply. In fact, things don't always work out that way, but they did work out that way often enough that such societies emerged and some prospered. And the prospering of some may be explained in part by an ecological fact that followed upon the breeding of domesticated plant species: The edible parts of domesticates tend to be larger than the edible parts of wild forms—quite probably a deliberate consideration in their selective breeding. Domesticates, as a group, and this is key, yield more food energy. So, at times and places, the radical idea was realized.

This change to a different mode of subsistence almost certainly was an adaptation to changing biophysical habitats, precipitated in part by the most significant geochemical event in the history of *Homo sapiens sapiens*: the receding Pleistocene ice. The retreat of the last glaciers brought climatological changes in which various flora and fauna were extinguished, including as many as two-thirds of the large mammal fauna—24 genera—in the Americas alone in the six-thousand-year period from 15,000 B.P. to 9000 B.P. (Simmons 1989). Notice how the timing of these extinctions, to which humans themselves are believed to have contributed by predation, coincides with the timing of domestication. Habitat changes in process may have caused serious human food deprivation. On the other hand, domestication may have begun merely as a result of new opportunities presented and seized; or perhaps both conditions obtained at different times and places— anthropologists are not sure. To add to the intrigue, there is some recent evidence suggesting that the total population of reproducing humans at one point in this period numbered a mere 10,000 (!) individuals (Gibbons 1995). In any case, a major adaptation to intensify subsistence procurement was forthcoming. The adaptation of some peoples, especially in Southwest Asia, China, and Mesoamerica, consisted of a gradual change toward an agrarian mode of subsistence. This would change forever the human ecological landscape.[3]

The domestication of plants and animals can produce a larger and more dependable food supply. With more food to eat, there can be more people to eat it, and in fact there tends to be. Horticultural and pastoral societies have larger populations, ranging into many more thousands, in part because they can feed many more thousands, than foraging societies. And they can do this in less total area. Within a few hundred years after their appearance, McNeill (1976) reports, the successful agrarian societies quickly had population densities 10 to 20 times greater than the hunters and gatherers who had used the same bioregions. And after simple agrarianism had been practiced for three thousand years, all together the human population came to five million—a remarkable increase (roughly 5.3% per generation) if the estimate of 10,000 at the outset of simple agrarianism is valid.

With even simple agrarian modes of subsistence come additional departures from a foraging mode. One is a more developed tool kit, there being more people to develop tools and more opportunity for them to do it when there are sufficient food surpluses. This enables pastoralists and horticulturalists to extract more total energy from their habitats than do hunters and gatherers.[4] With this, habitats are more affected. Pastoralists need land to graze their animals, and often they graze land until it is exhausted, whereupon they move on, eventually to return. Some horticulturalists clear areas of land, burn the vegetation, use the ashes as fertilizer to raise crops until the soil is exhausted in just a few years, and then abandon the land to repeat the process elsewhere until the land recovers. But some horticulturalists stay put.

From the archaeological record, it is not certain whether sedentism preceded domestication (current evidence suggests it did) or whether domestication preceded sedentism. It is certain that with the adoption of horticulturalism, permanent human settlement became a permanent human adaptation. Although in some variations of horticulturalism there is occasional movement around and about, permanent communities now begin to appear in the archaeological record (the Biblical Jericho existed by 10,000 B.P.). As sedentism and domestication become associated, permanent communities are a natural if not a logical consequence.

With these adaptations, a more complex division of labor becomes possible. When larger numbers of people are concentrated in one place more or less permanently, a division of labor has a chance to stabilize and expand. An increased division of labor, as it goes around, comes back around: It permits more labor to be devoted to the development of tools which, in turn, permits the intensified extraction of energy from natural sources. Additional energy extraction can be converted into a subsistence benefit, or stored as a surplus of wealth, or invested to further divide the labor in society. As various societies gradually adopted pastoral and horticultural subsistence strategies, their elevated populations, technology, and energy extraction created a condition in which there were more functions that could open up—more roles in which persons could specialize. These included such roles as craftsmen, traders, and slave holders, plus an array of status and power inequalities not normally seen in hunting and gathering societies. This division of labor would become more complex as simple agrarian societies came to be fully agricultural.

Agricultural Societies

The historical appearance and development of, first, the domestication and, second, the cultivation of plants and animals are sometimes collectively lumped under the term Agricultural Revolution or, depending upon the features to be emphasized and by whom, the Neolithic Revolution. The names refer to a series of cultural and human ecological changes that featured, in addition to the development of agriculture, technological innovations by which the stone tools of earlier Paleolithic times were improved, eventually to be replaced with bronze tools, which in turn were gradually replaced with iron tools. These interlocking developments took thousands of years to fully crystallize. The term revolution, which implies rapid change, is descriptive only when we remember that humans had lived as foragers as long as they had lived at all, but now their original mode of subsistence was rapidly displaced.

Horticultural practices, with their characteristic sedentism, domestication, and permanent settlements, diffused out of Southwest Asia into Central Asia, the Nile Valley, and eventually Europe over the course of several thousand years during which there were marginal changes in technology and social organization (to be reviewed in the next chapter) that eventually led to the development of cultures of large scale. Some of the changes had cumulative effects. When some of the early agrarian societies came to be more socially organized and technologically developed, their production for subsistence came to be further intensified to the point where eventually there appears a modified and much concentrated mode of agrarian subsistence: agriculture.[5] Once fully developed, and it was not to be for several thousand years, in comparison horticulture looks like so much ornamental gardening and pastoralism, so much herd tending. Agriculture combined the two into an intensive strategy for transforming a natural habitat into an unnatural one, the whole point of which is to get the soil to yield more edible material than it otherwise would.

The ground for a jump-start in food production was laid when around 7000 B.P., some cultures in the Middle East began using tools that resembled plows, used for churning up the soil prior to planting the seeds from domesticated plants. Heavy plows, the complete jump-start, were not in use until about 1400 B.P. There is an immediate and significant ecological consequence of tillage with a plow: It promotes the recycling of nutrients in the soil. That improves the productivity of the soil, other things being equal, and enables the same land to be cultivated annually and indefinitely (presuming it isn't degraded by overuse). As a matter of history, the plow was gradually perfected as it slowly diffused into different human cultures, not reaching the Americas until the Europeans brought it. As a matter of human ecology, the use of the plow together with other tillage devices meant that human beings could get more food more often from less land. Moreover, if someone designed a harness, and someone did, and attached it to a large domesticated animal, such as an ox or a horse, then the draft animal could pull the plow, with the result that more ground could be tilled and more food grown in the same period of time, because the draft animal could do more work than a human could. It had more energy, in the form of muscle power, which could be invested to yield even more energy in the form of food from the soil. The draft animal also left waste excrement, which was not wasted because this was discovered to be a rather efficient means of fertilizing soil and increasing its productivity even further. But the real yield from draft animals is their muscle power—the application of increased energy to transform a biophysical habitat, which was the point. The invention and improvement of tillage tools and their use with the deployment of the muscle power of domesticated animals eventually turned horticulturalism into agriculturalism.

Why some of the earlier agrarian societies began to intensify their efforts at energy extraction—punctuated, we must emphasize, by using one kind of energy, expanded muscle power, to generate another, food—we cannot be sure. The favored explanation, allowing for preferred variations on the theme, is population pressure on the food supply of local habitats (Boserup 1965; Cohen 1977; Harris 1977). If so, the adaptation worked, or so it seemed, for by farming humans had found a way to produce more food, which meant that more people could be fed.

The result was that there came into being more people to feed. The populations of agricultural societies can range into millions and even hundreds of millions. That many can live, and without agriculture that many cannot, because an agricultural subsistence strategy uses additional energy inputs, together with tools more sophisticated and better designed, to extract extraordinary energy outputs from natural habitats. This is why it is sometimes said that agricultural systems are energy traps. Success depends always on the weather, but the result can be, often was, and still is, a food surplus. A food surplus is an energy surplus available for human consumption or investment.

How does one "invest" a food surplus? With a food surplus comes a labor surplus—all those people not needed to produce food at sustenance levels but who themselves are sustained by food producers. One way to effectively employ surplus labor, so that it can command its requisite sustenance, is to intensify efforts at developing even better tools. Agriculturalists did. Technological innovation, too, had been mostly a process of marginal changes with some cumulative effects until around 6500 B.P., when there came another jump-start from the Middle East: the wheel, that marvelous contrivance that continues to provide an unparalleled test of the human imagination to find practical uses for it. Among its earliest uses was to adapt it to vehicles to be drawn by domesticated animals. Significantly, the wheel came in the Old World not the New, and because its versatility enabled so much compound technological innovation, its invention permitted a substantial difference in comparative rates of technological development in the different hemispheres. But the wheel is just *one* tool, however important, that figured into an increasingly complex set that the surplus human labor of agricultural societies undertook to produce around this time. Writing, no trivial innovation, was another, once it became employed to facilitate the spread of information. As tool kits became more sophisticated from an increasingly complex technology that developed with agricultural modes of subsistence, there was in fact—as in theory there should be—a correlative development.

Investing in technology represents a tacit commitment to another kind of "investment:" When larger numbers of people have a food surplus and, by definition, not everybody is needed to produce it, human societies have the luxury and at times the necessity of expanding their division of labor to accommodate the labor surplus. It happened that way as agricultural societies developed. In them, one finds specialized occupations for which the previous types of society that we mentioned, having simpler tools and social organization, simply provided no room. For instance, one finds many more roles associated with trade and craftsmanship, because now one finds permanent large cities with assorted individual occupations. One also finds the emergence of a true political state, with a system of taxation and military activity. One finds artists, builders, even philosophers, that one did not find before. In short, one finds a much more complex division of labor, all of it dependent upon the agricultural base, much of it possible just because of that base and some of it now *necessary* because of that base. Food surpluses have to be stored, or transported, or sometimes guarded, if the fruits of agricultural labor are not to be lost. As this came to be discovered, a division of labor developed accordingly. It is especially significant that some early agricultural societies happened upon an adaptation whose full exploitation continues still—namely, devising a more complex division of labor directed to the intensification of agricultural production itself. The earliest success, also still being exploited, was the deployment of labor to develop irrigation systems to enhance productivity.

Generally speaking, in agricultural societies more slots open up for people to do more kinds of things, in part because more kinds of things need to be done to sustain such a way of life. And, when there are more people, as here there are, the newly opened slots tend to fill. As the Agricultural Revolution proceeded, there began to be institutionalized into human culture a subsistence strategy, around which human societies came to be organized, that set the conditions for further cultural development and social organization. One of these conditions was a more complex division of labor in society; another was more complex acculturation. Anthropologically and sociologically the expanded division of labor permitted the emergence of all sorts of sociocultural traditions and institutions, many of which are still with us.

Ecologically, there are three very significant consequences to notice. One is that macrosocieties had evolved. The five million total human population of 7000 B.P. became 50 million by 3000 B.P. (just four thousand years), and would become 600 million in another 2,700 years— that is, by 300 B.P. The second consequence, alluded to above, is the substantial increased disturbance that was now visited by humans upon biophysical habitats through the domestication and cultivation of those habitats. This consequence, moreover, cannot be avoided when so many people are using so much technology to draw so much additional energy from the habitats. (Many of the early agrarian societies collapsed because of the disturbances they themselves inflicted on their biophysical resource bases.) The third consequence is that human populations, having grown so much in size with agriculturally based adaptations, had now become continually and permanently dependent upon an increasingly complex technology and division of labor for sheer survival.

More was to come. For the successes of an agricultural mode of subsistence proved to be ephemeral and fleeting. They appear to be successes only when we take a coarse-grained, long-term view. Taking a microscopic view with a fine-grained lens, an agricultural way of life is lived on the ground, by individuals, whose sociocultural existence now became more constrained by the agricultural organization of their subsistence (Maryanski and Turner 1992) and whose personal welfare was not generally improved by it.

There were numerous reasons. As a cultural adaptation to natural environments, preindustrial agriculture was and is labor-intensive. This enabled (and enables) agriculturalists to get squeezed from both ends— from one, by the organizers of agricultural labor, who made sure that the bulk of the surplus and its value, and the land on which it was produced, accrued to them and kept labor impoverished; and, from the other end, by the fact that *more* labor has to be expended per capita to farm than to hunt and gather (Harris 1977). As if to tighten the vice, farming does not necessarily produce more *nutritious* food than can be had by foraging. Agriculture produces more food on less land but, according to Harris, the fivefold increase in productivity of irrigation agriculture observed over nine thousand years may have led to a *decline* in nutrition levels compared to earlier horticultural production. The problem was this: Agriculture, which could feed more people, brought with it more people to feed. How did they fare? Ponting bluntly summarized it: "Until about the last two centuries in every part of the world nearly everyone lived on the edge of starvation (1991, p. 88)." With respect to food supplies, mortality, and biological well-being, Cohen (1989) explains:

> Neither the record of ethnography and history nor that of archaeology provide any clear indication of progressive increase in the reliability (as opposed to the total size) of human food supplies with the evolution of civilization (p. 135). Until the nineteenth or even twentieth centuries, the improvement in overall life expectancy appears to have been fairly small in any case (p. 140). At best, we see what might be called a partitioning of stress by class and location, in which the well-to-do are progressively freed from nutritional stress ... but under which the poor and urban populations, particularly the urban poor, are subjected to levels of biological stress that are rarely matched in the most primitive of human societies (p. 141).

So, agriculture did not always, or even usually, produce enough food to feed, or to preserve in a state of well-being, the people whose very lives it had made possible.

What would?

Industrial and Postindustrial Societies

The fundamental human ecological problem posed by a preindustrial mode of agricultural subsistence was this: Agriculture lowered, it did not raise, the quality of human life by producing more people, who had to perform more labor, just to subsist on the edge of starvation—along with increased habitat disturbance to boot.

Was there an upside to this adaptation? The development of an agricultural mode of subsistence also brought a substantial amplification of technology, energy extraction, division of labor, and a correlative increase in surplus wealth, but most of that was concentrated in just a few hands. Notwithstanding the fact that we are hard pressed to identify the net benefits most people living life-on-the-ground derived from this mode of subsistence, the increase in resources now available from natural systems and the *capability* of humans to further expand their resource potential by expanding their technology and socially organized divisions of labor, was amply demonstrated in the agricultural societies of preindustrial times. Then came industrialization. Setting aside population size, which now becomes a wildcard to be discussed on its own, all this amplification pales to insignificance compared to what industrial societies were to bring in the way of increases in values of the critical variables.

Perhaps an example chosen for its sheer triviality will help to make a point in the comparison of respective divisions of labor between agricultural and industrial societies. In an agricultural society, there might be someone who milks the cow (often the same person who provided it feed), someone else (although perhaps not) who delivers the milk to market, and someone else who sells it. (Add one or two other roles, as you wish.) How do industrial societies handle this function? By dividing it up interminably. Numerous persons contribute in various ways to building the machine that milks the cow, some others supply feed to the cow after some others produced the feed, somebody else delivers the milk to a processor, where somebody else pasteurizes it, after which it is packaged with the assistance of someone who supplied the containers, whereupon it is delivered to a warehouse by someone and then by someone else to the place where it is sold, passing then into the hands of someone who refrigerates it, thanks to those who built and delivered the refrigerator, after which somebody rings up the price for a consumer whose choice all the while has been influenced by someone else who advertised the brand. *That* is a division of labor. And it applies to just one trivial function found in both agricultural and industrial societies.

Now imagine differences of that magnitude multiplied for all the common functions. Then add to that imaginary quantity the division of labor for the additional functions of which industrial societies are capable but agricultural societies are not. The expected result should be roughly in view: The division of labor most certainly does not increase in a straight line, and it connects to other processes whose interaction cannot be modeled with straight lines, either. Comparing agricultural to industrial societies in terms of values of our variable processes, we are not going to get mere linear increases.

Consider technology. The conversion of energy into different forms is just the obvious principal use to which tools are put. Less obvious, but no less significant, tools can be employed for the making of more tools. Some hominids were using tools well past two million years ago and were making them well past one million years ago. Some used fire three-quarters of a million years ago. It wasn't much by modern standards. Today there is one tool that can carve a second on the clock into one billion equal parts (and we even have a name for it—nanosecond). But how does one develop a tool that can carve a second into a billion (!) equal parts? By constructing it with a slightly less sophisticated tool kit. And how did one get that? From the same operation: applying the even less sophisticated tools inherited from forebears to make tools they did not have. The process may be repeatedly indefinitely, as indeed it was. And after three-quarters of a million years of tool making to control fire, now humans can use fire to do more than just heat their caves. Now they can use it to burn up the world.

The point is, the development of technological series is a recursive process. Any given point in a connected technology depends upon all the prior points in its development. That does not say that all technological series, let alone all tools, are *preserved* by human cultures; we know many are not. It says that technological development is step-wise, not necessarily linear, involving replacement, with mostly marginal improvements. Modern tool kits could not have been constructed except with the outmoded tools of yesteryear, some of which became outmoded just because they served the end of producing better tools.

The degree of technological development is functionally related to the degree of the division of labor in society. This also has some cumulative structure, with its progression partly asymmetric and serially ordered. The performance of complex social functions cannot occur without the prior development of other, more elementary functions that make them possible. Once someone invents the internal combustion engine, *then* a whole class of social roles can be defined and performed that otherwise could not have been; and, once defined and performed, new roles can be defined and performed off of those together with newer technologies to facilitate them. The functions at the outer edges of a complex division of labor are cumulatively built of the functions at the core whenever the increasing complexity has some technological impetus.

To understand the correlation of enhanced technologies with an increasingly complex division of labor, it helps to invoke the hypothesis of the sociologist E. Durkheim (1893), who argued that competition for resources is effectively reduced and resources more efficiently utilized when a division of labor in society becomes more differentiated—a condition supposed as a natural consequence of the increased interaction that follows with increases in population density. But this, which is still the received view, will not generate a critical mass that accelerates sociocultural change into nonlinear ranges. To get that, add intensified energy extraction by means of mechanical converters.

Power is the rate at which energy flows, and *the* definitive characteristic of an industrial mode of subsistence has been the design of machines to enhance the flow rate exponentially. With the mechanical energy converters made available by industrial technology, the potential for energy extraction by humans was expanded by converting into energy sources various materials and processes that, formerly, were not usable as resources. Note that enhanced mechanical power presumes a division of labor sufficiently specialized so as to permit such highly organized functions to be undertaken. The increase in energy yield in turn can be, and often is, invested to yield greater returns in technology, with a correlative further differentiation in the division of labor.

Beyond some critical threshold, and no one knows exactly where that is, the interactive effect of increases in energy extraction, technology, and division of labor does more than generate linear increments. The interactive effect takes hold with increases in the *rates* at which energy is extracted, technology developed, and labor divided in human society. Rates of energy extraction increased slowly in preindustrial times but, as industrialization has proceeded, in effect a new energy system has been designed (Debeir, Deleage, and Hemery (1986) such that exponential curves are needed to describe the behavior of the variables that behave in this interactive cycle. The new energy system, and with it enhanced interactions in the cycle, was enabled by a bonanza that industrial technology was able to exploit to an extent that earlier technologies were not—the fossil fuels, and by an ever-increasing food supply, a condition that came to pass partly because of the application of fossil hydrocarbon (and other) technologies to agricultural production.

One effect has been startling increases in agricultural productivity. In the United States, for instance, observing from about 1930 to about 1980, the average yields of corn from American farms increased from 21.9 bushels per acre to 95.1 bushels per acre, and there were comparable gains in productivity for other crops and feed grains for livestock (Brown 1984). These increases in productivity were the result of assorted technological innovations, which included insecticides, herbicides, nitrogen fertilizers, the application of genetics to develop hybrid seeds, and the efficient extraction and extensive transport of massive quantities of water. As this happened, so efficient was it that the percentage of the American labor force employed directly or indirectly in agriculture declined from about 30 percent of the population to less than 3 percent. This was possible because the amount of labor required to produce many crops was dramatically reduced by the improved technology that was applied—reduced by 98 percent in some cases (Lenski, Lenski, and Nolan 1991). And all the while, the American population nearly doubled while food prices drew gradually lower! This marvel occurred because labor was subsidized with increased fossil hydrocarbon energy inputs, thereby reducing labor costs, increasing labor productivity, and, in effect, displacing laborers (Cleveland 1991).[6]

With industrialization, agricultural production is much less labor-intensive and the increasing labor surplus can be directed to the pursuit of other functions now made possible by the relief afforded by industrial technology. As people are relieved from making a living off the land, they will make a living other ways, often more to their liking, in the pursuit of a greater share of surplus wealth. Provided with agricultural production and labor surpluses, surplus wealth can increase as industrial technology converts natural resources into goods for increased material consumption and higher standards of living. At least that can happen for a time, for this human ecological experiment is not yet over.

What sets this exponential growth cycle in motion? Agricultural societies convert to industrial societies as they gradually replace muscle power with mechanical power.[7] The incentive to do this is irresistible.

There is simply no comparison, other things being equal, between a 350 horsepower engine and 350 real horses in terms of efficiency of transport. Whether human beings should want that much power for transport or whether mechanical transport is efficient in the long run is not the point now. The point is, if you give some individual, who does not live in the long run, a choice between an axe and a chainsaw, in the long run you will see a lot of chainsaws. One can do so much more with them so much quicker. The principal incentive for industrial technological development is to change the ratio of labor invested to the surplus wealth derived as a benefit.

And it works. Industrial technology provides a much more efficient way to harness much more energy from natural sources than any alternative, and it yields a correlative increase in surplus wealth that can be invested or consumed as a higher standard of living. This depends upon an adequate agricultural base or the existence of trade relations that ensure a stable food supply. But provided there are food surpluses for at least some social classes, there is then enough surplus labor to develop new tools. New tools are developed and adopted, or are not, according to how they enable people to more efficiently perform the same functions as before, or to perform functions heretofore unknown but now valued. As new functions are enabled by new technology, we have, by definition, an expanded division of labor. These things feed off each other.

The United States, the most successful of the industrial societies and among the first to take full advantage of the relief from agricultural poverty that industrialization afforded, has been the prototype of a postindustrial society[8]—one in which services and information, rather than industry, provide the primary means of subsistence. More American occupational roles now fall in the category of services and information than in industry. With this distinction, if that is what it is, Americans have taken the division of labor in society to absurd lengths. There is, for instance, an American occupational function, and very well compensated at that, enabling people to specialize in rushing the passer in professional football games. This sort of role can come into being only in a society with extraordinary surplus wealth, for without that there simply is no room for such a luxurious function to be performed, which is one reason it is not performed in, for example, Mozambique.

Americans also have the dubious distinction of consuming about one-third of the world's energy resources distributed among their puny 5 percent of the world's population. Such lopsided ratios of population to energy extraction are inherent in a postindustrial mode of subsistence. To satisfy its profligate demand for outlandish material consumption, a postindustrial society has to utilize proportionate quantities of energy, because surplus wealth is *energetic* wealth—energy transformed. By 1970, on average, Americans were consuming 230,000 kilocalories (kcal) per person per day (of all forms of energy), compared to the 26,000 kcal consumed by people in advanced agricultural societies (Cook 1971), who themselves consumed nearly 10 times the energy per capita that foragers had. "Consumption" includes, as it must, the increased energy inputs that are needed to power the more complex divisions of labor and associated technologies that figure into postindustrial production.

And the upside to this adaptation? With their industrialized agriculture, Americans spend only about 8 percent of their disposable income on food, far less than people in most nations of the world, which leaves Americans with much more surplus wealth per capita. When realized, the additional resource potential of a postindustrial mode of subsistence converts directly into a higher standard of living, one in which the most important ratio of all has been drastically changed: Provided with industrialized agriculture and postindustrial technology, divisions of labor, and surplus wealth, far more food is produced, or is capable of being produced, than can possibly be eaten.

So, the solution of the most fundamental human ecological problem that confronted advanced agricultural societies—the problem of feeding everyone adequately to stave off morbidity and mortality—was to industrialize.[9] The solution has been implemented only in part, owing to sociological and political relations concerning capital ownership, production, distribution, and inequality in income distribution—matters I take up in Part B. Of interest here is the sort of human ecological adaptation that industrialization represents, and the demographic result in terms of which the ratio of food resources to population came to be inverted.

The Population Wildcard

Industrialization was an adaptation compounded of agriculture. Industrialization had been incipient for hundreds of years but gained momentum only when political democracy began to take hold in some Western societies, thus creating a favorable climate for entrepreneurs and innovators. Entrepreneurial innovation was needed and should have been in demand, if agriculture was a system for perpetual poverty. Advanced agricultural societies had been able to enhance their productivity, but they did so without changing their biologically based energy systems. The resulting surplus was realized in population growth, not economic development, as output per capita remained stable. Traditional energy sources alone could do little to change the ratio of food resources to population. Only a different energy *system* could decouple demography from economy, and capital-driven industrialization provided precisely that (Debeir, Deleage, and Hemery 1986).

But if industrialization provided the means to enhance the surplus wealth of agricultural societies, reflected in the eventual inversion of the ratio of population to food resources, it is important to note that *both* terms of the ratio gradually changed: As food productivity increased, the demands made upon the increasing supply did not keep pace *even though* population increased. Demography *was* decoupled from economy, as capitalist entrepreneurs began to exploit the fossil fuels and design better mechanical energy converters, such as the steam engine. Simultaneously, scientific knowledge was developed (partly on demand) that enabled the gradual implementation of assorted mortality control measures, direct and indirect. These, in combination with other demographically relevant socioeconomic changes underway, turned the trajectory of human mortality downward, thus destabilizing the population/resources ratio.

What "other demographically relevant socioeconomic changes" were underway? An abstract, constructed around just a few basic facts listed for comparison, should suffice.

Fact 1: Prior to the implementation of public health measures, improvements in the human diet, and other mortality control measures, infant mortality rates were quite high in preindustrial societies in the West. Sometimes infant mortality rates ranged around 50 percent, which is to say only half of all children reached adulthood. Those who did, did not live long—on average, perhaps 30 to 40 years at the beginning of the Industrial Revolution (Petersen 1961; Cohen 1989).

Fact 2: Crude as it sounds, children in agricultural societies are an economic asset. They can be, and typically are, used as labor that contributes to the well-being of their families. This they do when they are young, by working on family enterprises, and when they are adults, by caring for their elderly parents, who almost always lack anything like a social security system except this.

Fact 3: Almost always, the distribution of wealth in agricultural societies has been (and continues to be) sharply skewed toward a small ruling and land-owning elite from which common farm families are excluded. To adjust to the sheer economics of survival, therefore, people in agricultural societies have tended to live in extended family households, which may contain multiple nuclear units and assorted hangers on, usually relatives but sometimes not. It is a cheaper way to live.

Facts 2 and 3 undergird the routine demographic observation of high fertility rates in agricultural societies. As a matter of cultural tradition, families in agricultural societies have tended to be larger—a tradition almost certainly born of practical economic necessity. In economies in which manual labor is an asset and families live in relative poverty, with no social security except what is provided by other family members, many of whom die young, many therefore are born. Here, high fertility makes economic sense. And, because many die, it makes reproductive sense.

In industrial societies, mortality and fertility rates decline because, gradually, the conditions of mortality and fertility change. Here, by contrast, children are an economic burden. Their labor is not as useful in a mode of subsistence in which economies are not centered in families and labor is dispersed—but children have to eat and be cared for anyway. Their families tend to have a greater surplus of wealth and, although that wealth is still unevenly distributed, it is not as grotesquely skewed toward such a small elite as it normally is in preindustrial societies. These families, therefore, can and do function as nuclear units without the extended trappings. The nuclear family is a more luxurious way to live, and people choose to live that way when economic conditions permit. In industrial societies, they permit.

With the changed conditions of subsistence in industrial societies, reflected especially in the greater economic well-being of families, fertility rates begin to drop. Women in industrial societies give birth to only about one-third as many children as women in preindustrial societies, and their children have a much lower mortality rate and a much longer life expectancy—now twice as long as compared to the start of the Industrial Revolution. As a general rule, there is an inverse correlation between economic well-being and average numbers of children per family. Poorer people tend to have more children. But—industrial societies tend to be wealthier.

This, *sans* nuance and detail, was the socioeconomic foundation of the demographic transition that took place over long periods of time as some advanced agricultural societies gradually industrialized. The transition refers to a change from high fertility and mortality rates, which are typically observed in agricultural societies, to low fertility and mortality rates, which became the trajectory for the first of the industrial societies. The size of human populations had been increasing with the different types of preindustrial society in order of their chronological appearance. But when societies industrialize, or so the historical experience has been, population size becomes something of a wildcard because the dynamics of population growth behave differently. The size of a population will not necessarily be larger in industrial (or postindustrial) societies than in agricultural societies. The potential is there but the necessity is not, and whether increases happen or not depends upon when and where one chooses to look. As a matter of historical fact, population growth was exponential in many of the industrial societies that first experienced a demographic transition because, when this first happened, scientific medicine and derivative public health measures and improved diets were gradually adopted over a long period of time. The effect was to gradually (but substantially) diminish mortality rates. The decline in mortality rates preceded the decline in fertility rates by several generations, and in the interim populations increased exponentially (they had to, by the sheer arithmetic of numbers). However, when the first industrial societies completed their demographic transitions, the exponential curve topped off and additional population increases in them now are largely a matter of built-in demographic momentum from prior increases or, in some cases, from immigration. At the present time some industrialized nations of the world are experiencing a decline in the size of their populations.

The classic demographic transition is an outcome of changes in socioeconomic organization that have repercussions for family size and cultural reproductive traditions. Whether societies that are *now* industrializing and replacing their agricultural mode of subsistence will, in fact, undergo a demographic transition cannot be predicted with any confidence because modern preindustrial nations do not face the same conditions that confronted the first industrializing nations. Among the first, mortality rates slowly dropped *as* industrialization occurred, while today mortality control measures can be, and sometimes are, immediately transported to developing nations. So, their mortality rates can drop much quicker. To complicate matters, some modern nations are now developing industrially in response to international economic conditions of competition and cooptation set by those nations that have already succeeded. The terms set by already developed nations tend to favor themselves. So, we cannot be sure that a demographic transition will always be associated with industrialization, because we cannot be sure that future industrialization will conform to its past history. Population remains a wildcard.

We can say with confidence that the interactive cycle in which increases in energy extraction, technology, and a division of labor each triggers increases in the others does not itself trigger increases in population beyond a point. That point is somewhere in the industrialization process, probably late in the process, presuming the process does not significantly depart from past practice; but, prior to that point, population size is an increasing variable in the cycle of interactive causation.

If, with industrialization, the cycle is able to kick into a nonlinear range, note that a condition for this is a substantial decline in mortality rates. Industrialization can succeed where agriculture fails only when mortality rates drop below some critical threshold long enough to permit the nonlinear ranges of the interactive cycle to produce surplus wealth that benefits ordinary families. With sufficient surplus, families can learn that their high fertility rates are no longer needed for marginal economic advantage; then, their reproductive decisions can change. With insufficient surplus, there is no incentive to change them. But, to back up, nonlinear behavior in the cycle itself depends upon an energy system which offers sufficient margin or slack to enable technology and energy extraction to be accelerated so that economic organization can generate surplus wealth. All this has to play out right. When mortality rates are in the ranges of the preindustrial societies, then none of it does; then gains in food production are offset by population growth, as families seek to reproduce all the children they lose. With mortality rates too high, industrialization, too, fails.

It could fail entirely on its own terms—with or without demographic transitions—because of its massive environmental impacts. No other mode of subsistence brings so much disturbance in its wake, in part because no other exploits so many biophysical resources so quickly. Notwithstanding the extensive environmental impacts of agrarian modes of subsistence, amply detailed by Goudie (1990), it is the cumulative impacts of industrial societies that enable Rappaport's Dilemma to be realized empirically. This subject will get considerable space in Part B.

THE ORGANIZATION OF SUBSISTENCE
AND THE SUBSISTENCE OF ORGANIZATION

When, over the long term, increases in population, technology, division of labor, and energy extraction compound above a threshold set by food surpluses, a momentum gathers from increasing values of the variables. The momentum can become exponential above a threshold for mortality reduction. The overall pattern—which is not entirely smooth, for there are many breaks in the historical record—is one in which larger numbers of people produce increasing transformations on biophysical habitats, using their socially organized divisions of labor to expand their technology for doing so, with the effect of capturing ever more energy from ever more biophysical sources. As this process continued historically, different modes for the organization of subsistence came to dominate, each having its origins in an historically prior mode. The modes often mixed, and the process, often interrupted and sometimes punctuated, gave rise to diverse cultural instances. This, in sum, is the portrait that emerges of macroscopic acculturation arising from the human ecological dynamics considered so far.

However, in theory there has to be, as in history there was, more to macrosocial acculturation than this. Specifically, there is that question of how divisions of labor get socially organized. As a matter of evolutionary and reproductive necessity, the core around which human populations first came to be socially organized was kinship. In all human societies, regardless of their mode of subsistence, kinship remains the core around which other forms of social organization may be culturally layered, but with agricultural and industrial societies the cultural overlay becomes much thicker and more significant than the core. How can we explain this just by describing the organization of *subsistence*? It is not adequate just to observe that divisions of labor expand and complexify correlative to intensified subsistence activities that promote population growth, technological innovation, and increased energy capture. One has to take a closer look—if still coarse-grained—at the *organization* of subsistence to account for the macrosocial acculturation that followed upon the adoption of the different modes of subsistence. In this organization, one finds the division of labor expanding not just laterally but hierarchically, as different dimensions of social organization appear, compound, and synergize an increase in population, technology, and energy capture—which, in turn, synergize the complexity of social organization.

Macrosocial acculturation cannot be realized without a hierarchical division of labor created by different forms of social organization— fundamental forms, interacting with each other, and ecologically rooted—that develop around kinship but eventually cascade far beyond its control. And so it was, when the first agrarian societies appeared and macrosocial acculturation was incipient, that certain forms of social organization also took root for the first time and gradually developed in symbiotic association with expanding divisions of labor and changing modes of subsistence. Three forms in particular are worthy of notice: political, economic, and urban organization. All were dimensions of the organization for subsistence, and all, themselves, have been sustained because of the subsistence activities whose very organization they molded.

NOTES

1.   A fine-grained analysis of the topics in this and the next chapter would require extensive comparisons using substantial ethnographic detail, which is the strategy often recommended—for example, by Hallpike (1986)—for studies of sociocultural evolution. But we are committed to the view that sociocultural evolution does not occur on its own terms, and all the topics in this and the next chapter can be treated on their own terms quite apart from human ecological considerations. We focus just upon the processes that seem to be, and to some extent have to be, implicated in socioecological development, which we take to occur within the context of the evolution of biosociocultural regimes. As a historical matter, the socioecological developmental patterns reviewed here provided the contemporary empirical foundation for Rapapport's Dilemma, and they are congruent with the theoretical foundation of the Dilemma, which we take up in Chapter 9.

2.   Just the naming of types of human societies and a listing of their chronological order of appearance in history runs the risk that interpreters will omit to consider that a change in subsistence patterns sufficient to justify a change in labeling of type may involve a protracted period of transition in which one or more mixed types may simultaneously flourish. For an indepth ecological analysis of just this pattern of not-so-neatly-ordered change from one impure type to another, undertaken for the transition from foraging to agrarian modes of subsistence in Neolithic Europe, see Gregg (1988).

3.   Anthropologists and geographers will notice that this brief discussion glosses over a myriad of detail some of which makes for significant differences. Simmons (1989) includes a wealth of detail on the changing landscapes wrought by agrarian activities, as do the Cowan and Watson (1992) anthology and the general treatment by Vasey (1992).

4.   It is debatable whether they extract more per capita, although in principle they could, but even if they should, it might not result in a higher standard of living. The

currently fashionable opinion among anthropologists is that foragers, with an overall lower level of energy extraction, generally have had a *higher* standard of living than horticulturalists. Here we run a risk of comparing apples with oranges, for the uncritical application of conventional economic measures suitably transformed to fit societies with different modes of subsistence overlooks a critical sociocultural process. Quantitative comparisons are complicated by the fact that, as societies develop more complex forms of divisions of labor, surplus wealth tends to be concentrated in a few hands. The unequal distribution of surplus wealth, largely a socioeconomic and political affair, impurifies the ecological measurement of the role of increased energy capture in changing modes of subsistence. Conventional economic measures, developed for industrial societies, often utilize rates of energy extraction per capita compared against some percentage of gross domestic product. Depending upon the exact measure used, there is considerable evidence that industrial societies, after a point, suffer no loss in quality of life when their energy consumption is moderated (Olsen 1992). The general point is that rates of energy extraction do not bear a linear relationship to standard of living. However, specific functions aside, there is no doubt about the general functional connection between rates of energy capture and different modes of subsistence.

5.   At this point, we have no need to make much of the difference between organic (preindustrialized) agriculture and industrialized agriculture, although later we shall. The development and application of industrial technology has transformed agriculture in modern times, but that does not gainsay how the development of agriculture itself transformed earlier times. A couple of thoughts worth bearing in mind even at this stage, however, concern the comparative efficiency of agriculture compared to other modes of subsistence and whether said "efficiency" is estimated with or without the industrial component. Critical, to clarity if nothing else, is the measure of efficiency employed. The increased output of food energy obtained by industrialized agriculture is comparatively *inefficient* when measured against its energy inputs, but when measured against labor and land in production, it is much more efficient than organic agriculture. Both kinds of agriculture can produce more food than pastoral or horticultural subsistence strategies, but that does not imply there will necessarily be more food available *per capita*. That depends on how, and to how many, it is distributed.

6.   Increased energy investments in agriculture are subject to decreasing marginal returns. Ponting (1991, p. 292) notes that between 1952 and 1972, the food production of industrialized agriculture increased by only 30 percent while energy inputs were increased by 70 percent. Statistics vary by time, place, and crop. As a follow-up to the statistic cited above regarding the productivity of the American corn crop in the twentieth century, I cite Ponting again: "Overall the *energy* efficiency of American corn production has *fallen* by half since 1915" (p. 292, emphasis added).

7.   Industrial societies were not the first to do this (water was used as a source of power to drive machinery at least 2000 B.P. in Egypt), just as they were not the first to use fossil fuels (coal had been used for hundreds of years in preindustrial Europe). What marks an industrial society is the extent to which it *displaces* muscle power and residual sources of power with machines that have a substantially enhanced capability to convert energy into other usable forms. For this to become an economical way of life requires the technological development of energy sources to power the machines, such that per capita rates of energy extraction and the surplus yield, taken together, exceed the potential available from alternative modes of subsistence.

8. Kirkpatrick Sale calls the use of the word postindustrial in this regard "an intentional misnomer, a sociologist's sleight of hand intended to direct attention away from the often unpleasant truths of the ongoing economy" (1995, p. 208). We may disregard Sale's false prejudice that leads him to impute intentions that few sociologists really have. More important and true are some of the observations that Sale takes the term postindustrial to gloss over: We have entered a second industrial revolution that can be expected to accentuate the negative results of the first and which may be expected to include the accelerated degradation of the earth and the dispossession of those—including labor of all stripes—who are marginal to the concentration of capital, now globally invested, supported by war-making institutions, and technologically driven. Some of the issues we take up in Part B, *Environmental Connections*.

9. Cohen's (1989) summary of the array of evidence on this and related points should be very discouraging for those who are inclined to think that the "march of civilization," represented in the appearance of agricultural and industrial societies, represents some sort of progress in human life chances. But the belief that that was and is progress continues to inform the world view of Western cultures and their intellectuals. Now, on that matter, a disclaimer is in order.

Changes in modes of subsistence that range from foraging to industrialization are chronological facts documentable in human sociocultural history covering the last 10,000 years. Social scientists have usually characterized the pattern of these changes, through the different types of society that can be identified, as stages in an evolutionary progression. In this chapter I have not, for a couple of reasons.

First, there arises a host of difficult theoretical issues to be addressed if one wishes to call this an evolutionary progression. Just because certain types of society appeared in a certain order in the course of human history does not, in itself, imply that these are stages in the evolution of human culture or society or, if they are stages, that they are evolutionary. They could be developmental instead, which is our interpretation here. There certainly is no empirically invariant progression (evolutionary or developmental) from one type of society to another, which anyhow are ideal types, and there is no theoretical ground to suppose there should be any progression through these ideal types, invariant or not.

Second, as we remarked in Chapter 6, the idea of evolutionary progression in social science has always been conflated with the idea of progress. Although now expunged from evolutionary biology, in which a concept of evolutionary *progression* suitably circumscribed need not carry any inherent ideological load, the idea of *progressive* evolution is highly value laden and still a routine interpretation of social scientists for the patterns they observe in sociocultural history. We have this, for instance, from an introductory sociology text by a well-known contemporary evolutionist: "The further a society advances on the evolutionary scale, the greater is its ability to overcome the limitations imposed by the biotic and physical world" (Lenski, Lenski, and Nolan 1991, p. 197). That is a reference to different modes of subsistence as progressive stages, with industrial stages representing the epitome of progress. This manner of thinking traces back to nineteenth-century evolutionists, for whom the notion of social evolution as social progress was very convenient for the politics of colonial expansion and expropriation. It remains convenient today as a smokescreen for the imperialism of economic hegemons.

There is absolutely no theoretical justification for equating the idea of an evolutionary progression with cultural, social, or historical progress. And, as Cohen (1989) has shown, there is not much empirical reason even to *think* of it.

Chapter 8

The Subsistence of Organization

Since sedentism became a permanent human adaptation, social organization has amplified from a condition so thin as kinship to a condition so thick as the bureaucratic organization of postindustrial societies. Maryanski and Turner (1992) argued that, compared to some other social primates, humans *qua* primates are not all that social. If by nature we are something like lone rangers, by culture we are something quite else. With hindsight, the reason is clear: Some principal forms of culturally provided social organization are functional adaptations to human ecological necessities. The adaptations themselves may have been contingent, but they addressed the necessities and facilitated an array of ecological and sociocultural consequences.

As an adaptation to natural environments, the prime human ecological consequences of social organization are these: (1) Depending upon the forms of social organization that are constructed beyond kinship, the integration of the forms enables a larger human population to sustain itself than could otherwise be sustained on the same resource base. (2) Depending upon the social institutions that integrate the forms, a given resource base can be expanded and resource potential amplified if the supporting institutions encourage the correlated increase of technological innovation with hierarchical differentiation in divisions of labor. A resource base can expand so, with system resource potential amplified, because energy capture is amplified.

Invariably, social organization is accompanied by, eventually to be surrounded and elaborated with, a vast array of symbolic and cultural apparatus to expand and legitimate its institutional and cultural expressions. That is a subject for the social sciences proper, and not ours. However, many of the organizational superstructures one sees in the various cultures of human society are elaborately connected to substructural ecological conditions. So, the fundamental ecological roots of human social organization are necessary subjects for this chapter. The vertical elaboration and integration of ecologically based social organization are also. Ultimately, these socioecological organizational processes are rooted in the material necessities of human survival.

The elemental material resources necessary to sustain humans are food and water. Those resources were the first on which technology and a division of labor operated as humans sought to provision themselves; they were the first to become socially organized. The most fundamental forms of social organization therefore are political, economic, and urban organization, for these forms can be shown to be adaptations to provision for the elemental necessities. Although we shall survey political, economic, and urban organization severally to exhibit their ecological roots, in fact none of these dimensions for the organization of human society behaves in isolation. None can be treated as a pure system of social organization, because none is pure. They interact with each other, sometimes simultaneously and sometimes with delayed effects, but typically as a complex.

One primary effect is that the complex gathers its own sociocultural momentum for growth—even for its own evolution, if we use the term loosely. The momentum gathers from the fact that the complex itself comes to subsist on the very conditions of human subsistence that it organizes. The elaboration into different kinds of culturally organized superstructures, some far removed from ecological necessities, can be expected in theory, as it so happened in fact, as the complex itself culturally adapts to the changes in subsistence conditions that its own activities have caused. Provided initially with social organization for successful subsistence provisioning, it then becomes possible for cultures to devise adaptive organizational superstructures that bring the environmental conditions of local habitats under greater organizational control, and, eventually, to extend those habitats and thus the cultural resource base, in effect by extending the reach of the culture's social organization into the bioregions of other cultures. Population, culture, and organization then become interactively and correspondingly large and complex. With the growth of acculturated macrosocieties, forms of macroscopic social organization begin to cascade, eventually to transform the environmental conditions that originally gave rise to them and to promote the development of a culture of global scale.

We assume that the emergence, perpetuity, and development of the political-economic-urban adaptation complex had its impetus in the changed socioecological conditions of individual persons living life-on-the-ground. If Maryanski and Turner are to be believed, humans would not have submitted to enhanced social organization had they not discovered some benefit for doing so. Apparently, they did. This microscopic angle of intersect we characterize lightly, but hopefully enough to secure the macroscopic angles of intersect. The macroscopic intersections implied by this chapter and the last may be summarized thus: Populations are socially organized into divisions of labor (and sectors of those) for the purpose of energy capture by means of technology, whose production surplus is returned to populations congruent with the populations' distribution in the hierarchical divisions of labor that social organization has provided. As the connected dimensions of social organization considered below come to set contingencies for subsistence production, they too can be seen as socioecological in character, and they give the socioecological development process a momentum sufficient for Rappaport's Dilemma to empirically unfold.

POLITICAL ORGANIZATION

The political ordering of social relations may be the most important general form of human social organization ever to have been devised, if one measures by its consequences. Disregarding for now the fact that so many of those consequences have been so deleterious for so many down the ages, it is not difficult to propose hypotheses to explain why individuals, confronted with the uncertainties of subsistence, would find some forms of political organization to their liking: Now and again, when political organization was not killing people outright, or causing them to be killed, or exploiting their labor, it was promoting their survival by promoting their subsistence production.

The rudiments of political organization sprung to life when sedentary communities first appeared. Why should this have happened? If there ever was some sedentary community with modest food surpluses but with no social organization except kinship, these people would have had some serious problems: how to protect if not defend the surplus they produced and stored, how to organize future subsistence production and distribution, and how to secure production and its surplus in perpetuity. The mere fact of a surplus of anything immediately confronts humans with a decision: What to do with it? In the case of food surpluses, humans usually decide to preserve them, for the obvious reason, presuming they are not very perishable. But then come additional matters to resolve: Who shall do the preserving, and how shall the benefits that accrue from the surpluses be distributed? Those problems were historically addressed, and continue to be, through the development, maintenance, and perpetuation of political organization in human society.

Compared to sedentary horticulturalists, foragers—of earlier times or any time—have little incentive for much political organization because their numbers are so small, their resources so few, and their habitats so sparsely occupied. But with sedentary subsistence strategies, the values of the variables change. Human numbers and densities increased with increased agrarian production but, when numbers and densities increase, it isn't just further increases in production that have to keep pace. There have to come increases in the way all this is managed and organized because, as more is produced for a greater number, there is greater potential conflict in theory and fact, for now there is something to secure. In a phrase beloved of rational choice theorists, the benefit-cost ratios are altered. It makes ecological as well as reproductive sense to defend land that can provide a regular food supply. With sedentary agrarianism, land and food come to be socially defined in terms of the changed values they now have—defined as real property. With the appearance of claims to real property, which are unknown among foragers, political organization gains momentum, proliferates, and dominates.

When subsistence surpluses are produced in sedentary communities, increasing political organization gains a competitive advantage over kinship and other less routinized means of social control and organization. The advantage is that it can effectively manage the distribution of the surplus. Political organization, traceable to when humans began to domesticate plants and animals, is a means to domesticate people. It came to pass just because humans stopped foraging about. By domesticating nature, Maryanski and Turner's lone rangers found the autonomy and communal singularity of their foraging way of life surrendered now to the control of political organization.

Political organization may take different specific forms, such as chiefdoms, regional empires, nation states, and variations on those, with different characteristics that emerge accordingly. To explain the emergence of different specific forms in different environmental circumstances requires considerable attention to cultural and ecological detail, as Harris (1977), Johnson and Earle (1987), Zeder (1991), and others have shown. It is clear, nonetheless, that the general form has some common identifiable patterns and that it has ecological roots that develop thick and deep once true political states emerge and change from pristine, to secondary and, finally, to modern nation states. The prototypes of political organization—prestate organization—began to take shape with the development of managerial functions to control the surplus resources produced as the Agricultural Revolution gained momentum. But the emergence of true states, in whatever form, is considered to be a watershed. Pristine state organization appeared in the Old World in the millennium 6000-5000 B.P. and independently in the New World around 2000 B.P. In prestate organization, control usually devolved on whoever was strong or authoritative enough to command or otherwise organize a redistribution of surplus production—chiefs or warlords, depending on where and when one looks. But after a time, as population grows, chiefs and warlords outlive their usefulness. When they were replaced with something like a culturally institutionalized polity that perpetuated itself, a point of no return was passed.

A bedrock principle of political organization is employed by any polity (or any warlord, for that matter) whose goal is the control and redistribution of vital resources. The principle is: the redistributors retain a percentage of the spoils for themselves. Governments call it taxation when they do this, extortion when anyone else does it. When warlords or gangsters do it, it is called tribute. Whatever it is called, the result is the same: Whoever or whatever can levy taxes, thereby appropriating resources unto itself, and can marshall the force or authority to do so, has given social organization a political cast and, in the process, has insured its own continued survival.

Literal castes were the result of the taxation of subsistence production by pristine states. Modern states continue the unequal distribution of surplus wealth begun by their progenitors. Once social inequality is set to going in human society, it too will gain a foothold and develop an institutional momentum of its own as favored castes or classes seek to retain the objects of their favors. The political state is a vessel for— some would say *designed* for—socially organizing and institutionalizing in human society, by means of force if not genuine authority supported by cultural values, systems of social inequality based on the control of valued resources and the means to produce, protect, and distribute them.[1] The resources at issue, in the beginning, were those associated with production for subsistence—with food, land, water, and tools for developing each, with the groups for organizing all that, and with the protection of all those. Harris could then ruefully remark: "With the rise of the state, ordinary men seeking to use nature's bounty had to get someone else's permission and had to pay for it with taxes, tribute, or extra labor" (1977, p. 102).

By subsisting on the subsistence activities of producers, state political organization creates the conditions for its own further development. Taxation forces subsistence farmers to put more land into production just to maintain their comparatively underprivileged position. And that position provides an incentive for larger family sizes, to supply additional labor. Increased population size, in turn, generates more pressure to increase the yields of subsistence production. Thus are fashioned the conditions for habitat degradation, especially in the forms of water and soil erosion, which eventually yield diminishing marginal returns for production. The state then has to act. Typically, it does so by promoting technological innovation so that subsistence production yields increasing returns per unit of labor. At other times—desperate— the state initiates war for the purpose of territorial expansion, which temporarily alleviates its untenable position. Whatever the state response, increased production along with increased population requires an increase in administrative organization, which is to say, a larger fraction of labor must now be diverted to nonproductive activities. Meanwhile, to protect its own position vis-à-vis its subjects, the state secures its own internal control capacity by means of police forces. Thus, eventually, state political organization grows by feeding on its own activities.

The development of political organization was a historical point of no return because political elites, able to marshall the needed labor, succeeded in intensifying agricultural production even further than it had been to that time; in encouraging population growth and the development of technology, to which the successful intensification of production itself contributed; in increasing the division of labor in society through elaborating administrative structures, which is a self-protective and self-enhancing adaptation typical of governments; and in expanding territory under their control, which they often did by military conquest—itself a stimulus for technological innovation that eventually produced the most important political tool ever: firearms.

The overall ecological effect of long-term, gradual political centralization was to bring more biophysical environments, and more of their conditions, under human control, domination, and exploitation—and more humans as well. One vital condition that early political administrations fostered, and on which they capitalized, was the development of agriculture by means of irrigation. Now, one does not need to move water around in order to farm the land, though if one does one can get more food out of it. However, if one wants to move very *much* water around to farm the land, one needs a substantial degree of sociopolitical organization to do it. Chiefdoms, being a rather elementary form of sociopolitical organization, can't do that to any real degree. Imperial systems can. In some imperial systems, those of the Oriental despots and perhaps some others in the Americas (Harris 1977), the centralization of political authority correlated with the development and intensification of irrigation agriculture (Wittfogel 1957). Grow more food by making more water available to more land that doesn't normally get enough, and one can grow more people—and the political organization by which one controls and accomplishes all this grows as well.

The effort to irrigate land was not the sole cause of the development of political organization, for this is one of the details that varies with historical time and place. However, at certain times and places, hydraulic developments under the control of central political authorities sharply accelerated the exploitation of biophysical habitats by elaborating the division of labor, by demanding greater technology (especially weaponry for use by its military castes), and by extracting more energy from natural systems. Historical variations aside, the human ecological significance of water resources and the intensified extraction thereof cannot be exaggerated.

Next to sunlight itself, water is the most important factor in the yields obtained, per acre and per calorie invested, in agricultural production. Its redistribution for the purpose of irrigation can provide a jump-shift in the human exploitation of biophysical habitats, which in turn can provide a jump-shift in numbers of humans. Historically it did, but the expansion of irrigation practices and the development of other water works have accelerated the growth of political organization even into the present. The choice of human settlements is entirely dependent upon water, the productivity of agriculture is a direct function of it, and the size of human populations and their forms of social organization are strictly limited by it. Industrial societies, for instance, can develop only to the extent that they can diminish the fraction of their work force devoted to agriculture, to which human-designed water works significantly contribute, and can endure only to the extent that their supplies of water, and therefore of food, are assured from whatever sources their contrived division of labor may have arranged. The productivity of a large fraction of industrial manufacturing, including some vital functions without which there would be little industry, depends directly upon the use of large quantities of water. Almost all large cities in the world are now located on or near large bodies of water. This was no accident. It is easier to move about there—to function and to live. Commerce and industry are more efficient there, and the products of agriculture are more easily distributed there. Power can be harnessed from water, plants and animals prosper near water, trade is facilitated on water routes, and fresh water can be diverted and transported for irrigation. With water, humans can do wonders, and without it they can do nothing.[2] With political organization, more of them could use more of it for more purposes.

Quite apart from intensifying subsistence production by expanding the organization of it, the emergence of political organization in state form had other consequences. One was the beginnings of what is now taken to be the formal organization of society by means of bureaucracies. These were simple at first and primitive by modern standards, but the modern versions derived from the early ones. The incentive for bureaucratic growth resides in a human social psychological frailty of which C. Northcote Parkinson (1957) took special notice, namely, that almost any functionary, to assist in the performance of his or her function, will prefer to employ two subordinates rather than one competitive peer. Thus is planted the seed for a predictable expansion in the bureaucratic *organization* of the productive functions of a society, even when (some would say, especially when) productivity shows diminishing marginal returns. The first bureaucracies appeared with the first states, and the growth of formal bureaucratic organization is inherent in the growth of state political organization: States act, in response to problems mostly of their own making, as we noted before, by reinvesting expropriated surpluses in such a way as to increase the proportion of nonfood-producing specialists. This kind of action itself entails increased costs and, to succeed, requires an increase in administrative bureaucracy.

The emergence of state political organization thus promoted the growth of a vertical division of labor in society. Zeder (1991) makes the point, although she uses a different terminology, that prestate organization was largely lateral. As political states, with their intensified economic and urban organization, are brought to bear upon subsistence production, eventually divisions of labor that formerly were lateral— and, therefore, relatively homogenous—begin to show hierarchical differentiation as well. This facilitates their further lateral differentiation, substantially increases their heterogeneity, and coincides nicely with heightened social inequalities. Once set going, the expansion of hierarchical divisions of labor eventually spreads to all the ecologically based forms of social organization, for the forms interconnect and must adapt along parallel lines to keep pace.

Political organization taken in its own right, from a human ecological point of view, originates in the intensification of production for subsistence. The historical details differ considerably, but a general pattern nonetheless is observable in cultures that developed independently and that represent historically unrelated cases. When the pattern unfolds completely, and it does not always, we find foragers diversifying to the point where they gradually adopt horticulture, then agriculture. As horticulture diversifies, villages form (they have to if horticulture is to diversify), thereby intensifying production even further. The continuing intensification of production into advanced agriculture implies a division of labor diversified now laterally and hierarchically, and this is enabled only by means of further social organization. Social organization takes a political form when leaders or bandits, if there is a difference, can organize cartels to siphon off a percentage of the surplus that is produced from subsistence activities. If that percentage is invested in the organization itself, so as to create permanent roles by which this or other forms of taxation can be regularly imposed, then the rudiments of a bureaucratic organization are in place. A bureaucracy helps to assure a regular income in the form of taxation and, thus, the continuation of a rudimentary polity. When their existence is secured by force and the intensification of production continues to expand, encouraged or mandated now by political leaders and their creeping military or policing apparatus, rudimentary polities tend to expand into regional ones and beyond as the course of events may allow. In complex forms such as nation states, polities will be underwritten by abstract law. As an operational guide, however, one gets state political organization with the appearance of some routinized form of taxation. When a piece of the action is thus set aside, the stage is then set for elaborate changes in other dimensions of the division of labor in society—changes that accentuate its lateral expansion, now hierarchically designed. A developmental trajectory for the economic organization of human society, which reacts back on the political, then can be traced.

ECONOMIC ORGANIZATION

Polities reconstruct economies, and that process further politicizes and, therefore, bureaucratizes society. We shall assiduously avoid chicken and egg arguments as to whether sociopolitical structures are the primary determinant of economic structures and processes, or if it is the other way round. It is both ways round, although current opinion holds that at different times in history one and then the other dimension has come to dominate. Generally speaking, the economic organization of human society is the complex of social and cultural relations by which humans provision themselves with the material means for survival. Economists typically isolate a portion of that complex or a subset of those relations—those pertaining to how humans organize economic transactions. For economists' analytic purposes, the properties of economies can be isolated. For human ecological purposes, they cannot be.

Economies have ecological foundations without which they cannot, and with which in terms of they must, function. Economic organization evolved to exploit material conditions for subsistence, and this implies there has to *be* material that economies can exploit. Economists and many other social scientists, for their part, usually take what there is for granted, proceeding to treat the ecological foundations of economic organization as givens. But the action of economic forces and the organization of human economies depend unilaterally on biophysical processes and conditions. Economic systems, however much their form may change through intercourse with other dimensions of social organization, derive ultimately from ecological systems as these have been exploited by the entire complex of human social organization. What makes economic structures so important is that the economy of a society is the principal channel through which ecological parameters influence social organization and by which they are influenced in turn.

The conventional wisdom of the social sciences emphasizes political connections much more than ecological connections. The conventional wisdom is that economic organization issues from a competition for scarce resources. This competition is expected to result in the unequal accrual of resources for production and the unequal distribution of income obtained from their investment, and thereby to generate among the members of a society inequalities that tend to become institutionalized. Whoever controls critical resources or access to them, especially capital, is in a position to control production and differentially distribute the income from it, and thereby to assure the continuation of their own privileged position—a position that the political organization of society typically helps to perpetuate as it, itself, comes to be influenced by the owners of capital. The owners of capital, in turn, may be heavily influenced in their production decisions and investments by the agendas of those with the power to tax and enforce other relevant laws. Inequalities in human society, therefore, issue from the economics of production around which is wrapped the political control of the means of production and the economic control of politics. Once such a state of affairs has materialized, we may speak of the existence of a political economy. Its fundamental process is the exchange of goods and services in a market. The fundamental units of this process are said to be households and firms.

Political economies became organized when families became vulnerable to the effects of political organization that complicated the lateral division of labor hierarchically into different economic spheres so as to require labor and promote transactions that extended beyond families. It is helpful to contrast political economies with subsistence economies, roughly following Johnson and Earle (1987). The unit of a subsistence economy is the household, or family, whose elemental economic behavior is the organized provision for food and shelter. This form of economic organization is considered to be more stable in theory, just because it is less politicized, is more purely economic, and is supposedly self-sufficient. Its exchange of goods and services does not contain the sorts of economic transactions that we associate with modern political economies, for the exchanges occur mostly between kin. The historical elaboration of complex political economies to the point where they and not subsistence economies dominate current affairs tends to disguise a fundamental fact: The basis of human economic organization is the production and distribution of energy in the form of food—originally a family affair in subsistence economies.

Besides being of necessity the original reproductive institution, the family was also the original economic institution. It was the primary social unit of human population organized for the purpose of extracting necessary matter and energy from biophysical habitats. The elemental economic behavior of family units becomes generalized and exaggerated as political economies gradually develop, and assorted other telltale marks of social organization, such as permanent forms of social inequality and military forces to support political states, emerge and surround economic activities. To this day, the family remains fundamentally an economic unit of social organization in all societies, although in industrial societies its role in the economic process has been drastically altered. Where once the family was first cause and prime mover in economic organization, as political economies have become more complex, the family has gone to the end of the economic process, so to speak, there to be buffeted about and shaken up like dice in a cup by economic and political forces far exceeding its reach.

Modern political economies developed with the growth of entrepreneurial capitalism in advanced agricultural and early industrial societies, but they derived from the family-based subsistence economies of societies with simpler divisions of labor. To this day, some societies with a simple division of labor still rely on a subsistence economy. Historically, subsistence economies expanded with population growth and technological development and, as they did, political organization came more into play because subsistence economies became less viable without it. Families themselves can for a time retain their viability as units of economic organization in the gradual conversion to a political economy, depending upon the systems of land tenure that political elites establish. Historically, land tenure often took the form of patronage, which was not always desirable since patrons extract obligations for their favors. But as Johnson and Earle note, the costs of not participating often outweighed the costs of cooperating. With patronage, there came the gain that political patrons would provide protection for producers. In political economies, once families were provided with land and protection, they could sustain themselves now with somewhat different arrangements and obligations (taxes and military service) imposed by political organization. Moreover, as political patrons became an elite class, individuals often had the foresight and their political organization had the necessity, to reinvest for the development of new technologies a sufficient amount of the capital that had been seized through expropriation. Technology is more capital-intensive the more developed it gets, especially the more mechanical it gets, and political organization is needed to initiate and manage its development beyond a point.

The nut in this shell is that political organization, if it consists of more than pillage and plunder, gradually converts subsistence economies into political economies. To get political economies from subsistence economies, take families, add government, and organize firms to pursue economic activities that families are incompetent to execute. This conversion process will be shifted into high gear if along the way a monetary system is introduced to provide a standardized medium for transactions. Money is remarkably efficient for facilitating and expanding the exchange of and demand for goods and services, compared to the systems of barter traditionally used in subsistence economies and surreptitiously used to this day in some industrial societies to the great consternation of revenue collectors. Faced with bureaucratized revenue collectors in political economies, families that wish to barter their labor or its product are at a competitive disadvantage.

Although families get lost, if not undermined, in the shuffle of complex political economies, the function of providing for subsistence by exploiting material conditions is unchanged, however elaborate economies may have become. The *structure* of economic organization is changed, and its environmental reach is considerably extended, when political economies emerge as complex elaborations and transformations of family-based subsistence economies, financed by surpluses taken from families. We held that political organization was ecologically based because it gained its impetus and found its function in the organization, intensification, and taxation of subsistence production. The same conclusion applies to the economic dimension of human social organization. Without control of the resources for subsistence production and distribution, there is little to be economical with respect to—and nothing much to politically organize on a macroscopic scale.

Note that one human ecological principle is continued as we add economic organization to the mix: The single most fundamental object for the development, maintenance, and change in the entire complex of human social organization is food—its production and distribution, and the intensification thereof—and, thereafter, other forms of energy extraction.

Historically, the evolution of polities and economies began with something like a dance to which each party was casually attracted; but, with time, the parties became inseparable as political economies, and now they are shockingly intimate. Modern students consider the economic control of politics to have superseded the political control of economics. A full report of proven indiscretions, consisting of the graphic degradation of human environmental conditions and processes, will occupy us in Part B.

Setting aside for now the fact that political economies developed to perform in and on ecological contexts, it is necessary to consider how changes in political and economic organization are sensitive to matters of size and density. To understand the human ecological dynamics of political economies, most authorities tell us (with good reason) that we must add another fundamental dimension of human social organization: the process of urbanization. This, too, is ecologically based, for the urban organization of human society depends upon the dance of the political economies. Eventually, it becomes a full partner, changing the tune for the dance to where commercialization, in Bodley's (1994) sense, becomes the dominant cultural process. Only when urbanization is added to the mix—it makes possible, but not inevitable, a culture of global scale—does the economic control of politics become secure. And, as urbanization proceeds, macrosocial acculturation becomes a clear and present characteristic for a species that had, comparatively, little social organization, culture, or population just 10,000 years ago.

URBAN ORGANIZATION

Urbanization[3] is the socioecological process by which cities grow in size, number, and distribution. Though population nucleation is the most obvious feature of urbanization, it is not helpful to think of the process as just a matter of demographic expansion. Cities of small size first appeared in human history when societies began to take horticultural forms. Their number and size have expanded ever since, as political economies replaced subsistence economies, and especially in the recent past as the Industrial Revolution proceeded full bore. A city itself, named and circumscribed in geographic space, is a sociopolitical entity, but the *process* of urbanization has ecological roots. We just argued that the political and economic organization of society constitute dimensions for adaptation to the problem of provisioning for material subsistence. So is urbanization. It facilitates the development of, and its own development is facilitated by, specialized economies and, thus, the provisioning for subsistence. Specialized economies are facilitated by specialized administrative hierarchies, whose imposition and coordination are prime functions of state-level political organization. So, as the world turns, political organization facilitates economic organization, which facilitates urbanization, which facilitates political organization—all of it a subsistence adaptation-complex.

Fine-grained generalizations about the process of urbanization can be tricky and the details must be qualified for particular societies because, the more fine-grained the generalization, the more exceptions to it one can find. For instance, it matters whether one is talking about postindustrial societies or not, for some of these have shown population losses in their cities in recent times. It matters whether one is talking about industrially developed nations, already rich, or not—developing nations being the term used by social scientists and politicians to describe poor, sometimes wretched, agrarian nations that are trying to industrialize and get rich. And it matters whether one is talking about societies with a market economy or an economy in which there is some kind of so-called rational redistribution. Rational redistribution is the sanitized term for nations with (typically) totalitarian governments whose economic production decisions are made by bureaucratic committees in accord with a (typically) socialist ideology, in which urbanization often is a political dictate. With the meltdown of communism and the near-disintegration of many state-socialist economies seeming to come to a boil and burst around 1990, we may direct our attention to how the process of urbanization is affected when people are left to their own devices, perhaps assisted by government instead of commanded by its arbitrary dictates, which can interfere to distort social and economic forces. The urbanization process may be characterized in summary fashion, focusing first on the received view of how it connects to economic organization.

The Economic Connection

The received view of socioeconomics tells us that in nations with market economies we may observe most clearly how the urban organization of human society interacts with its economic organization. Generically, beyond some threshold, urban organization is said to be capital-intensive, labor-dependent, and demographically sensitive, with its rate governed by the economic integration of technological innovations. Urbanization is said to have its impetus in economic activities, to be a catalyst for socioeconomic development, and to be provided further impetus by its own developmental successes. In other words, beyond some threshold, urbanization generates its own internal momentum and becomes self-reinforcing. How so?

Let us imagine, as a playful way to illustrate, how difficult it would be to build a factory on the side of a mountain. Just to build it, we would have to transport all the labor and materials to the mountain. Once it was built, we would have great difficulty producing anything in it, just for lack of labor, since not many people can live on the sides of mountains; and, if it was produced, we would be hard pressed to sell our product for the same reason, or to transport it to a market where it could be sold. Before long, we would be out of business because we were out of touch—out of touch with the other segments of human economic organization on which our production, and its distribution and consumption, and therefore our own continued economic sustenance, depended. Realizing this, we, and others like us, who all depend on each other for subsistence purposes as we adapt in an organized political economy, seek each other out just as a matter of economic efficiency. Without much aforethought, we all bring the mountainside—more exactly, the raw materials of it together with those of the river valley beneath it—to a centralized place. Raw materials in hand, then we can find the people and their associated labor, technology, and production and distribution functions that we need. So can they.

With the centralization of production activities, there normally come economies of interdependent production functions. Communication, transportation, access to labor, to refined or finished materials or technological processes needed for production, and to markets, are all facilitated when a population is concentrated in cities. The economies of production enabled by a dense population in turn enable increases in economic productivity. Productivity concerns the efficient production of a good that is in demand—from a labor point of view, output per capita per time period, relative to the market value of the product. Other things being equal, such as a reasonably free market but with constraints against monopoly formation, economic productivity is a prime force for economic growth. Economic growth refers to an increase in the value of goods and services produced. In theory, this does not necessarily imply *quantitative* increases in production and consumption, although in practice quantitative increases have been the typical path by which the generation of surplus wealth has been realized.[4] Mostly, it is thought in the received view, surplus wealth is the product of the economic activities (supported by the politics) of people in cities.

There is a significant demographic process that interacts with the economic. With the efficiencies obtained from concentrating interdependent economic activities in cities, producers can generate some return and can expand their production, thus creating a demand for more labor, thus stimulating in-migration. As a rule, people will tend to go to where they can make a living, if they cannot make much of a living where they are. They can make a living in cities, which demand their labor, so they go there. When they get there, they increase the demand for goods and services just by being there, and so stimulate further production and an even greater demand for labor. Meanwhile, agricultural economics begin to change because of something else happening there.

The increasing surplus wealth that historically accumulated in certain human societies depended substantially upon technological innovations, which also were centered in cities. Many technological innovations were put to local uses, however, as if guided by an invisible hand that would make urban organization secure, some technological innovations diffused to rural sectors. Agricultural production, not much of which can occur in cities for the obvious reasons, was substantially enhanced by the industrial technology developed in cities. On the whole, as a result, especially in the twentieth century, less labor became necessary to sustain agricultural production, which helped to send more labor into cities, where it was in demand anyhow. So, cities—more accurately, the happenings in cities—were catalytic for socioeconomic growth as they simultaneously diminished the need for labor in rural sectors. Because of the changing agricultural economics induced by urban development and technology, cities attract migrants when the diffusion of technology to rural communities makes people redundant there.

Substantial migration from rural to urban sectors, though never exactly predictable, is expected to continue in the world's developing nations. It is the latest manifestation of a long standing historical trend. For centuries in human societies there has been a pattern, occasionally broken here and there, of rural-urban migration. Back in 1800, only about 2 percent of the world's population lived in cities having 20,000 people or more (Hawley 1971), while 200 years later, more than half are expected to. Urbanization transcends nations and cultures, and it transforms them. Of the process in the United States, one demographer said: "No theme in national history is more important" (Peterson 1961, p. 179). Urbanization displaces earlier modes of subsistence and their supporting cultural norms by promoting a heretofore unavailable lateral and hierarchical expansion and integration of the division in the labor of a society.

The pattern of rural to urban migration, as we remarked earlier, has now been arrested in some postindustrial societies. In those, one may now find decision making by corporate firms, many having humongous capital assets and multiple locations, affecting the spatial distribution of employment opportunities across wide geographic latitudes. Such arrangements enable surplus wealth to be more effectively distributed across urban-rural sectors, thereby reducing the incentive for populations to concentrate in cities. In underdeveloped nations, things are rather different. There exist in these nations some rather gross inequalities in the distribution of surplus wealth. Moreover, a great deal of their indigenous wealth in the form of natural resources was expropriated by the colonial policies of Western nations and is now exploited by multinational corporations, whose penetration of developing economies tends to benefit mostly the corporations rather than the indigenous folk. Thus, urbanization in underdeveloped nations is not an independent affair. What will become of it in the short term is anyone's guess, but there is in progress in these nations an unprecedented rate of growth in their urban populations. About half of this demographers credit to high rates of fertility; the other half, to rural-urban migration.

The Ecological Connection

If the foregoing sketch of the growth of cities sounded to good to be true, that's because it is. Although cities are here to stay and some mighty metropolises are yet to come, we can say with ecological certainty that urbanization can not go too much farther on its present trajectory until it produces diminishing returns. Cities will not always be catalysts for socioeconomic growth and will not forever be able to maintain their self-reinforcing internal momentum. There is writ into this portrait, which is rather standard, a fabulous fiction.

The fiction derives from neoclassical economics where it informs a great many economic analyses, including that of the urban organization of human society. The fiction will occupy us much more in Part B, so let us concentrate now on just the particular application to urbanization.

In the case at hand, we moved to the cities with our store of materials obtained from the mountains and the valleys, but then we got caught up in our self-reinforcing internal growth momentum, forgetting about the mountains and the valleys. Our resultant theory of urbanization reflects this. It tells us that populations concentrate in urban areas because of a surplus of wealth generated by the economic activity located there and, provided there are agricultural labor surpluses, as an urban population grows, more wealth is generated there because of the demands the population makes, thus inducing migration into the city and continuing the cycle; and this goes on and on, apparently without end, because it is a function of the economic integration made possible *by* the organization of economic activity in a dense, concentrated, specialized population.

This theory, ecological economists have observed, describes a perpetual motion machine—the fabulous fiction I referred to. The theory, although not itself circular, describes a circular process that is self-contained. Here is the problem: Cities, however vast their interlocking networks, however significant the decisions made by powerful economic agents located there, however well adapted they may be for a time to the problems of providing subsistence for their populations and of generating surplus wealth that may get spread around, to all sectors of the society, which they may heavily influence, are not self-contained.

The economic well-being and perpetual functioning of cities are utterly dependent upon agricultural production from rural sectors. The converse is not true. These would be trivial remarks, except for the fact that this fundamental asymmetry is almost never acknowledged, except in a perfunctory way, in analyses of urbanization. Sometimes, thanks to the neoclassical economics from which they reason, urban theorists become so enchanted with their perpetual motion machine that they forget the foundation of urban social organization: food. Cities, which produce almost none, must import it. Before they can provide consummables for their indigenous populations, those same populations must first be provided with caloric subsistence. This demand cities supply through transactions with agricultural sectors. The sheer volume, complexity, and concentration of economic and organizational activity that cities generate, and the influence they have, make rural communities and their agricultural product, and the connection of agricultural surplus to urban functioning, look inconsequential. The *economic* influence of urban on rural communities is far greater than conversely. But the ecological influence is the other way round. Food matters more than video cameras or anything else produced in cities, and food can be grown without the benefits of modern technology, as for so long it was and in many places still is. The bedrock of urban organization, and therefore of all economic production associated with it, is agricultural surplus.

With the march of time, cities are becoming more not less dependent upon the agricultural sector. But urban ecologists sometimes get this backwards. They sometimes talk about cities and "their" ecosystems in purely sociocultural, economic, and organizational terms, as if cities were self-sustaining and agriculture a purely residual affair having little bearing upon the ecology of urban communities. In the analysis of Berry and Kasarda (1977), agriculture appears to be not only residual but irrelevant, except as a historical phase in development that gave way to urbanization. But the ecology of urban communities *is* the ecology of the food that is grown to feed their populations and the energy that is used to power their activities. Cities otherwise have no activities. Cities must import—from the mountains and the valleys, either at home or abroad—the materials to keep their economic motion machines perpetually running. The running of the urban economic machine presumes that markets will provide the material staples that cities themselves cannot. That presumes the staples, or equivalent alternatives, will always be available. And they might be if we could discount habitat degradation.

The evidence is clear,[5] however, that the urban organization of society is not just an economic machine that produces surplus wealth through the operation of markets. It is also a machine that can produce ecological ruin. As it does that more and more, it will perforce have fewer and fewer material staples that it can import to power its motion, thus assuring the motion cannot be perpetual. That is why the urbanization of human society cannot proceed without diminishing returns. All things that act to degrade the biophysical conditions upon which they depend, including forms of human social organization, eventually come to grief if they degrade fundamental conditions for subsistence—especially conditions for the growing of food. The demands that cities are placing upon ever-degrading soils and aquifers to sustain their populations, of which the populations themselves are barely aware, and the technologies being employed to do it, are causing just that effect. With the increasing economic and ecological interdependencies throughout the world at large, the entire condition is exacerbated. Urbanization has been intricately tied to quantitative economic growth, but that has been intricately tied to various forms of habitat degradation. Among the worst of these are soil erosion and water loss, which portend eventual declines in agricultural production. Should the populations in cities come to economic grief from production shortfalls in agriculture and the perpetual motion theory be remembered still, a misanthrope might say: let them eat video cameras.

The urban organization of society can sustain momentum only to the extent that the momentum itself incorporates and provides for the development of agriculture, from which cities derive fundamental life support. Urban organization has done this so far. Contrary to popular myths about family farming, agriculture in industrially urbanized societies is largely a business, and a rather significant corporate undertaking in modern political economies, that governments explicitly try to manipulate. Governments and private firms have so far enabled agriculture to continue to provide the necessary staples—at least for the well-to-do of the world—on which the momentum of urbanization depends. So, for the time being, the momentum continues.

CONTOURS FOR RAPPAPORT'S DILEMMA

From the interlocking political-economic-urban adaptation complex of so long duration now, what major differences in the human ecological condition become apparent and significant?

The gradual organization of human society into concentrated urban sectors by means of political and economic institutions was catalytic for a unique and startling development in the biological history of social species. Of the thousands of other social species, only a handful of genetically bizarre insects (the *Hymenoptera*) live in macrosocieties. But with the beginning of horticulture, for the first time in human history there began the growth of macrosocieties—without doubt, the most significant sociocultural event in the evolutionary history of humans and, it may come to pass, given the ecological significance of humans, in the evolutionary history of a great many other species. No other vertebrate species has ever exhibited societies with coordinated divisions of labor among populations some of which eventually grew into the hundreds of millions. To this demographic scale, add acculturation and genetic diversity between the members of the populations, and human social organization now becomes biologically and sociologically unique. And more than that. No such scales of population, social organization, and acculturation are possible without proportionate extractions of energy from natural habitats. The human consumption of biomass alone, and the consequences this has, makes the species environmentally unique.

All sorts of hypotheses about human uniqueness may be rejected as unworthy of consideration, on the grounds that they are false or irrelevant, but not these. The expanded potential of humans—of so many of them, so well organized and acculturated—to extract resources from biophysical systems provides a stark contrast to the past, when this large-brained primate, organized in kinship groups, was foraging about with limited environmental consequences. Now the subsistence foraging of this primate has been given over to acculturated social organization, which has turned the quest for subsistence into a much more sophisticated and intricate affair. Several results are certain. One result has been to insulate individual humans from the requirement to directly forage; another, to insulate them from the vicissitudes of it. A third has been to raise the specter of over-foraging by the very social organizations that were designed to eliminate foraging strategies: the specter of extracting too much for too many in too short a time. To that join a fourth result: The developmental trajectory of acculturated macrosocieties is irreversible.

The third and fourth results provide contours for Rapapport's Dilemma. As to the fourth, it should escape no one's notice that the expansion of interlocking political, economic and urban organization, treated as a complex with all that goes with it, introduced assorted ratchet effects as populations grew in size. Increasing, large human populations are possible if, but only if, greater quantities of energy to provision the populations can be extracted from natural sources. Once those populations appear, however, to survive and reproduce they depend on those larger quantities of energy supplied with the sophisticated technologies and complex divisions of labor that made them possible. There seems to be a general rule, though not without its exceptions, that an energy-generating technology eventually will create demands for more energy than the technology itself can supply (Bassala 1988). Increases in the demand for energy provide one major incentive for technological innovation[6] and, correlatively, for expanding divisions of labor whose specialized populations then depend for subsistence on the very existence of the specializations. The interlocking structures of technological series with divisions of labor also conspire to ratchet the human ecological condition to effectively prohibit any reversion to earlier modes of subsistence.

And there is more to consider: the *formal* organization of social behavior, most apparent in institutionalized bureaucracies. It exhibits a critical property that bears upon the ratcheting of macrosocial acculturation. Formally organized behavior permits a higher degree of behavioral specialization than can ever be gotten when social organization is based on kinship. A kinship-dependent social organization has to be comparatively small in the number of persons and roles it can accommodate and, thus, has to contain more behavior generalists. A formal social organization can be much larger and, therefore, can accommodate behavior specialists having a wider range of narrowed functions. That difference makes salient a general principle emphasized by entomologists about the macrosocieties of the eusocial insects, namely, behavior specialists are productively superior to behavior generalists (Oster and Wilson 1978). And so it is with human formal organization. Design an administrative hierarchy, a necessary definitive property of formal organizations, to coordinate and integrate the activities of behavior specialists, and more can be produced in a shorter period of whatever it is one wishes to "produce"—food, conquest, salvation, entertainment, revenue, surplus wealth, and most definitely the political, economic, and urban organization of society that enables macrosocial acculturation.

The result is irreversible. The original conditions that set in motion the processes that produced acculturated macrosocieties were so transformed by the processes themselves that the initial forms for the organization of human subsistence were gradually—sometimes pitilessly—displaced. Most human beings who have ever lived, lived in hunting and gathering societies. Few ever will again. There simply is not and can never be enough wild plants and game to support a human population of over 5.8 billion people, or any reasonable fraction of that number. Should industrial and agricultural modes of subsistence falter for any length of time, the human population will quickly decline out of sheer physical necessity. That would not return the survivors to some pristine natural state, for they would take their chainsaws with them. In the process of developing advanced technologies for massive energy capture, industrial societies adopted a subsistence strategy that in effect destroyed their origins. If the division of labor in human society were now to be substantially simplified from the fully organized form that postindustrial societies present, food production would be substantially lowered. Another effect would be to render vast numbers of people entirely redundant. Human beings have complicated the division of labor in society and expanded their social organization down the millennia to avoid just such a state of affairs. People who are not redundant are people who can make a living, which is what human subsistence adaptations are all about.

Notwithstanding the irreversibility of macrosocial industrial subsistence strategies, the case for the reality of Rapapport's Dilemma admittedly is not yet complete. What is to prevent macrosocial industrialism from succeeding for the indefinite future? Absolutely nothing except what we called "the specter of over-foraging." The reality of this condition is crucial for the reality of Rapapport's Dilemma, and in quickly attempting to tie matters together a few pages back, we glossed over the issue. Some of this, too, must be deferred to Part B, but now at least we are in a position to introduce the problem and to indicate why, in theory, the condition must not be glossed over. Quite apart from empirical developmental processes of long historical duration whose confluence may be promoting its realization in modern times, it turns out that Rappaport's Dilemma has a theoretical foundation as well.

NOTES

1.   Some theories of the state merely correlate the state with structured inequality, while others define the state in terms of inequality. Fried (1978) is one who equates the state with inequality, and he is also credited with distinguishing pristine and secondary states. State formation and change are vast subjects all their own into which we need not sojourn, but perhaps one note is in order pertaining to the explanation of these matters.

Any explanation conceived (deliberately or not) in terms of identifying necessary or sufficient macroscopic antecedents for state formation, supposing a state to be a dependent entity of autonomous local control, is doomed. The process of state formation is much too intertwined with other macroscopic processes (ecological and sociocultural) that behave in complex ways, and with microscopic processes whose connections have not been mapped, but rather speculated, and the historical facts are far too rich, to enable explanation using such a simplistic model regardless of the variables that are plugged into the model. Thus, for example, with respect to the coarse-grained explanation we are developing here, Carneiro (1970) can doubt that the enhanced surplus obtained from sedentary agricultural economies is sufficient to generate autonomous political units, or Service (1975) can doubt that hydraulic developments foster state formation.

Empirical questions aside, the doubts are justified by the very nature of the subject and the course concepts we train upon it. All explanations of state formation must necessarily be coarse-grained, however fine their empirical detail, just in virtue of the nature of the concept. What, exactly, is a state? For this there is no answer because the concept is inexact. Does it make any sense to consider the formation of modern nation states within the same explanatory framework as the formation of pristine states? Only if one disregards ecological incentives for state organization as well as the modern world economy—which can hardly be disregarded. One could go on and on, but there is little point, except this: A concept of explanation as some system of necessary and sufficient causal conditions is wholly inadequate for a general explanation of the evolution of political organization to the point where autonomous local units of state organization can be identified and shown to fit the explanation regardless of time and place. However, such a disclaimer does not gainsay the role of ecological factors regardless of time and place, if only because ecological factors operate at all times and places. But when they do, there is no reason to suppose that their operation, in conjunction with other sociocultural processes, produces results that are perfect replicas of each other. Coarse-grained explanations (of anything) present an appearance of uniformity that their own inherent conceptual limitations cannot sustain.

2. Humans can, and for millennia did, increase the size of their permanent settlements in river valleys precisely because rivers make valleys fertile. They can design those wonderful waterwheels, as they did in antiquity, and use them on swift rivers to generate power, which they did into the beginning of the Industrial Revolution until the results produced a demand for more power than the waterwheels themselves could generate. Waterwheels can be—and were—dispensed with in favor of steam engines, and steam engines, too, eventually can be relegated to museums. Antiquated technology usually gets peeled away, and with it the residual division of labor that developed around it. There is no peeling away of the need for water. Water depletion is one cause of perpetual political conflicts in the Middle East, one cause of periodic massive mortality in parts of Africa, and is expected to be a prime cause of increased internal political conflict in the American West in the twenty-first century.

3. Urbanization has long been thought to create an urban geography of sorts, in which competition for land generates different spatial patterns that contour a city's physical environment in terms of which the residents must function. For a long time, sociologists took the study of land use patterns, which falls within what is usually called urban ecology, to be *equivalent* to human ecology (about which more in Chapter 1 of Part B). Numerous papers in the Theodorson (1961) anthology present human ecology interpreted as urban geography. Wilson's (1984) later review of urban ecology, however, does not equate its subject with human ecology proper. A related interest in what has come to be called the ecology of "built environments" is reviewed by Lawrence and Low (1990).

4. The difference between quantitative and qualitative economic growth and the significance of the difference for the environmental connections of human ecology are appropriate to pursue in Part B. Ecological economists, not given to the received view of cities being characterized here, in which quantitative growth figures so substantially, devote much time to the development of models of qualitative economic growth. For instance, see Jaeger (1993).

5. The evidence and its implications are prime topics for Part B, *Environmental Connections*. Thus, I do not review and cite here what is reviewed and cited there.

6. The replacement of one technological series with another almost always involves multiple reasons, some of which may have nothing to do with increased energy capture

but may have much to do with social and cultural matters. For instance, the steam engine, so important to the early Industrial Revolution, came to be at an economic disadvantage compared to the internal combustion engine, because the Stanley steamer was a device that required a supply of public water. Eventually, the steamer was forced to comply with health ordinances intended to combat epidemics of foot-and-mouth disease, while the internal combustion engine distributed no biological pathogens.

Chapter 9

Conditions of Carrying Capacity

Macrosocial agriculturalism and industrialism, in all their glories, have contrived to place now 5.8 billion increasingly urbanized humans at the end of the food chain, and a station is reserved by demographers for twice that many in the not-too-distant future. Industrialized agriculture, quite well organized, is also contriving to feed all those people principally by shortening or substituting for natural food chains. Some elementary principles of ecology make it quite clear that to position so many large fierce animals at the end of natural food chains[1] is to strike a precarious relationship that cannot be indefinitely sustained. As ecological dynamics are sidestepped and finessed by shortening human food chains using industrialized agriculture and genetic engineering, it raises the possibility of human "over-foraging" *even if* technology permits so many people to be indefinitely fed. In this chapter, our goal is to characterize in theory, for empirical analysis in Part B, the evolutionary foundations and the ecological conditions of the problem of human carrying capacity, limits to it, and the overshooting of limits.

CARRYING CAPACITIES AND LIMITS

Put in colloquial terms, the question of humans overshooting the limits of carrying capacities is the condition of there being too many people and not enough to go around. In such a condition, it has long been thought, something has to give. Adam Smith thought this in 1776 when, regarding the question of upper population bounds, he remarked (erroneously, as it happens) that "every species of animal naturally multiplies in proportion to the means of their subsistence, and no species can ever multiply beyond it" (1964, p. 71). David Ricardo followed suit (with modifications) after the play of T.R. Malthus who, of course,

193

seized the issue in his famous essays on population.[2] All were addressing an ecological condition of evolutionary origins: the condition of a resource-limited species.

This condition, discussed below, means that the question of human overshoot is not as simply construed as the colloquial formulation might lead one lazily to think. Overshoot most definitely is not just a matter of population size, as the aforementioned founders of classical economics well knew. They thought to contend with a dynamic relation between population size and food resources, and we now know to contend with more than that, since humans consume much more than just food. We need a concept that does justice to it all.

Unfortunately, concepts of carrying capacity (to say nothing of the measurement of carrying capacity) can be elusive or misleading. Cohen (1995, chap. 12) examined no fewer than nine distinct concepts of carrying capacity from basic and applied ecology and concluded that none of them was adequate for the human case. There is not universal agreement for interpreting carrying capacity, for it is not a unitary concept. Dhondt (1988), after reviewing the concept and its confusions, concluded that any reference to the carrying capacity of an environment "should be avoided at all costs" (p. 344)—advice we shall not exactly follow (preferring instead to use it as an idealization). In Dhondt's view, the confusions arose especially after Odum (1953) equated carrying capacity, previously a concept that had been used (with little precision) by wildlife ecologists, upon the urging of the legendary Aldo Leopold (1933), with the upper asymptote of the logistic equation for animal population growth.

Carrying Capacity as a Population Limit

The logistic, as it came to be called following the work of Raymond Pearl,[3] applies to a highly simplified set of conditions, especially observable in controlled monocultures when exponential population growth is observed in a fixed environment. A "fixed" environment implies a limit to population size, or a population carrying capacity, which exponential growth eventually should reveal.

Exponential Growth

Assume a single population in a stable environment with nothing to limit population growth except the physical parameters of the environment itself. How will the population grow? This depends upon the intrinsic rate of natural increase for the population, the value for which differs from one species to the next. Symbolized as *r*, the intrinsic rate of natural increase for a given population is defined as its fecundity rate minus its theoretical mortality rate.[4] Fecundity is a theoretically possible limit of reproduction set by the rate of gamete production or cell division, depending upon the species, under ideal environmental conditions. Empirically realizable reproduction under some actual set of environmental conditions defines fertility, rates for which vary according as how there are more or less individuals in the reproductive phase of their life cycle. Likewise, there is a theoretical and a realized mortality for any species—an average natural longevity that can be expected under ideal environmental conditions, as distinct from observed mortality rates that are subject to the vicissitudes of actual environmental conditions that typically depart from the ideal. Idealized *r* is sometimes written r_{max}, with realized *r*, written as is, interpreted as the instantaneous rate of change in population size per unit time, per individual. *r* may be estimated for a population by subtracting the instantaneous death rate from the instantaneous birth rate and then adjusting for emigration and immigration. Then, with *r* taken as a constant, a specific population growth rate, dN/dt, can be calculated provided one has a value for the number, *N*, of individuals in the population at time *t* and each time interval thereafter.

At rate *r* for some species in an unlimited environment, after a time in theory we should observe the famous, and highly misleading, exponential growth curve. That is to say, the rate of population growth at time $t_n + 1$ should be an exponential function of the number of individuals at time t_n. The equation for this is:

$$\frac{dN}{dt} = rN$$

(1)

The size and density of a population whose growth fits this equation can continue to increase exponentially only until the population encounters some limit inherent in its environment, such as a biogeographical boundary, after which growth would abruptly cease for the obvious reason that there would be no more room to grow. Prior to that, growth in size might appear to be independent of density. When environmental factors affect the same proportion of the population at any density, population growth is said to be *density-independent*. Exponential growth indicates such a condition (see Figure 9.1).

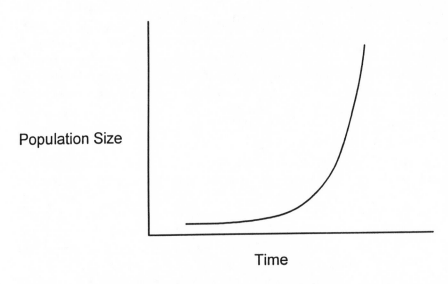

Figure 9.1. The Exponential Growth Model

If it follows an exponential growth curve, the size of a population is increasing as a multiple of the exponent (whose value will vary with the species under consideration.) For a positive exponent, this implies that the increase is proportional to the initial value of a given number from which growth proceeds. Using an arithmetic scale and permitting sufficient increments of time for a population to double in size, a curve that is initially turning slowly upward will, as time advances, turn ever more sharply upward.

The potential for exponential growth is writ into the biological fecundity of species—in their theoretical capacity to reproduce, which varies with their evolutionary history and physiological constitution; if species did not have exponential growth potential, it is likely they would become extinct. In theory, exponential growth could be observed indefinitely, but only for a population in an unlimited environment. In fact, exponential growth can be observed temporarily for environments that are temporarily unlimited—that is to say, for large and previously unexploited environments. For such environments, with exponential growth in process, the only initially effective limit is fecundity itself. But environmental limits come quickly into play. There are no unlimited environments beyond the idealized world of classic population theory (and neoclassical economic theory).

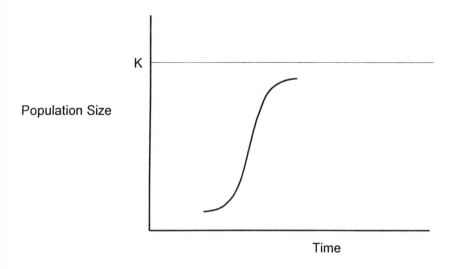

Figure 9.2. The Logistic Growth Model

Logistic Growth

The first limit to consider—from this comes the Verhulst-Pearl logistic—is the increasing density that an unchecked rate of population growth itself creates. As the density of a population increases in a given environment, the ability of the members of the population to survive and, therefore, to continue growing at rate *r* may be affected. If no dispersal is allowed for such a population, then after a time its growth rate is said to be *density-dependent* because the rate should begin to decline as the density increases beyond the point where the growing population itself creates environmental resistance. This condition gives us a sigmoid growth curve, referred to as the logistic (see Figure 9.2).

Density-dependent population growth in a limited environment, where realized *r* is always less than r_{max}, converts what otherwise would have been an exponential curve into an S-shaped curve. The turn in the vertical slope of the line occurs as the size of the population approaches the limit or carrying capacity of the environment, symbolized as *K*. The parameter *K* is an equilibrium value that will vary for each intended application. When $N = K$, $dN/dt = 0$, and when $N > K$, dN/dt is negative. The following equation, given here in differential form, generates the sigmoid or logistic curve:

$$\frac{dN}{dt} = rN\frac{K-N}{K}$$

(2)

The expression dN/dt, the derivative of N with respect to time, is the instantaneous rate of population increase expressed as a function of the number of individuals at time t. K represents the upper asymptote of the population size; it is a number the population should approach but, in theory, should never reach. Note how Equation (2) has been built from Equation (1). The formula

$$\frac{K-N}{K},$$

which incorporates K as an additional parameter, provides for growth to turn away from the exponential slope and top off the curve at the limit K. r serves as a mathematical constant that quantifies growth independent of the effects of density, but N is a variable. rN we may think of as a "growth force." With density effects in play, rN is dampened by the proportion of K not yet occupied by N at t. The growth force equals the environmental resistance at $K/2$, the inflection point on the curve. Below $K/2$, dN/dt is increasing; above, it is decreasing. As population size approaches K, population size is supposed and is sometimes observed to stabilize, with the effect that it is maintained below the level of K. But not always, for K is a mathematical not an empirical limit. In fact, some real populations at times exceed K, because population growth does not always decline with increasing density.

Population growth that approaches the mathematical asymptote does not always trigger an immediate environmental reaction to suppress further growth. Indeed, the effects can be delayed for a species such as humans, if certain conditions are met. Among the conditions are that the young utilize fewer resources per capita than mature adults and that the time interval from one generation to the next is substantially longer than the generational interval for reproduction of the resource species upon which the growing population relies for subsistence.

An observed population that grows in size beyond its theoretical K is said to overshoot the carrying capacity of its environment. Boyce (1984, p. 429) cautions that the logistic model itself does not logically imply that r and K are an inverse function of each other. Empirically, they may be, for in a condition of overshoot normally something has to give: When $N > K$, N should decline also asymptotically toward K. Observable effects of exceeding K for sufficient periods of time may include abnormal rates of morbidity (disease) and mortality, depending upon the extent of environmental degradation and the periods required for environmental recovery. When population size overshoots carrying capacity and K is fixed, the only alternative to morbidity and mortality is emigration. Depending upon the species and its immediate environmental conditions, any or all effects may be observed. When they are, the growth curve has to turn downward at least for a time, determined by however long it takes the particular environment to recover sufficiently to support those individuals that remain. Should a population exceed K too much for too long and not allow sufficient time for its environment to recover, the value for carrying capacity may be permanently lowered, notwithstanding increased mortality and emigration.

Limiting Conditions for Population Growth

Most populations of most species most of the time remain below the carrying capacities of their habitats. Their population growth rates may be limited in a variety of ways so that K is not reached or not exceeded, and for a combination of reasons not all of which are presently understood.

Some species' population growth is *self-limited* and often goes no farther than the inflection point on the sigmoid curve. Territorial behavior in some avian species is believed to be one mechanism by which a species population regulates its own rate of growth. Other mechanisms have been suggested, even the natural selection of groups whose reproductive behavior keeps their numbers well below K—a suggestion that proved to be quite controversial.[5] In other species, such as some insects or amphibians, growth rates may be limited by unfavorable geoclimatic conditions, but when their habitats heat up or moisten up, they come up. For a brief period, the exponential curve may fit their growth well, since their increase is independent of their density. *Geoclimatically limited* under normal habitat conditions, some species are evolutionarily adapted to such vicissitudes. Yet other species' population growth may be *predator-limited*—a condition that cuts two ways. Predators limit the size of the populations of their prey for the obvious reason that they eat them but, likewise, predator populations are limited in size by the availability of prey. Both populations will tend to oscillate, usually in delayed tandem as if they were tracking each other. The result cannot be fitted to an exponential or logistic curve. Rather, populations that oscillate within a stable range are observed, and early on were modeled by Lotka-Volterra equations, to describe predator-prey relationships.[6]

But, now, eliminate the predators for some species whose populations are normally limited by them. Such populations often become *resource-limited*. Even resource-limited populations may exhibit what looks like density-independent population growth so long as their numbers stay well below K. But should growth exceed $K/2$ and approach K with K fixed, resource limits must come into play because the operative environment now can provide fewer per capita resources that the individual members of the population need to sustain their well-being, their way of life, and even their lives. In such a circumstance, the overshooting of carrying capacity can lead to a permanent population crash, unlike a cyclical bloom and crash sequence, sometimes observed in simplified ecological systems, in which populations periodically recover after periodically overshooting.

A well-documented case, not involving humans except at the outset, was provided by some Arctic reindeer courtesy of the United States government. In 1944, when the U.S. Coast Guard decided to close a station on St. Matthew Island in the Arctic, authorities decided to turn loose on the island 29 young reindeer they had imported. Then everybody left. Confident the vegetation could support the reindeer population, it was 13 years before anyone returned to do a census. By then, the 29 reindeer had become 1,350 reindeer. (There were no predators on this island at the time.) Intrigued, observers came back again in 1963, just 19 years after the original colony had been turned loose. Now there were some 6,000 reindeer—an increase of over 300 percent in just the last six years. Unfortunately, this marked the beginning of the end of the reindeer. It was estimated that the vegetation on the island could support only 2,300, and with more animals than that, the vegetation could not replenish itself and, therefore, could not replenish the animals. This meant there were now 3,700 too many reindeer. A year later, true to expectation, massive starvation set in quickly. When it did, reindeer numbers dropped to well below the estimate of 2,300 that the island could theoretically have supported on a continuing basis—all the way down to just a couple of hundred. The population has made periodic comebacks since then. It has not come close to the 2,300 level it once could support, let alone the 6,000 it once did support. The reason is that, just by living there and so successfully reproducing, the reindeer so transformed the habitat—degraded it so much—that their own further reproductive success on such a scale was quite impossible for the foreseeable future. They have permanently lowered the island's carrying capacity for their kind.[7]

The operative phrase in the last sentence is "for their kind." The idea of carrying capacity as a population ceiling has no useful interpretation except with reference to some environment from which an affected population is drawing life support. But, it follows, if there is some focal population and there is some limit, K, to its growth in some environment, that limit is with respect to that population. So, to speak of the carrying capacity of an environment is simply a shorthand way of speaking about the limits to the population growth in some environment of a focal species—or better, in the case of a species such as humans that evolved or finds itself to be resource-limited, of a dominant species. The idea of carrying capacity expresses a relationship of population size to resource consumption and the continued availability of resources to sustain given patterns of consumption. There can be no population ceiling without some environmental resource limit, and the existence of some actual or potential environmental resource limit for any resource-limited species implies the possibility of overshooting that limit.

However, it must be admitted that to speak so is to run the risk of confusion that Dhondt (1988) wished to avoid. After ecologists equated carrying capacity with the equilibrium value of the logistic, it was generally forgotten that Leopold (1933) actually had introduced two related concepts: saturation density, which was a population ceiling *not* limited by resources and not applicable to all species; and carrying capacity, which was. It is a difference that, in some form or other, has to be retained for the analysis of human ecology.

Interpreting the idea of carrying capacity strictly as a population ceiling quantified by the K term of the logistic does not enable us to assess the additional complications—many of them sociocultural—that the human case poses for the relationship between population growth and ecological and evolutionary change. Evolutionarily speaking, humans like other mammals evolved to have lower intrinsic r but higher offspring survival rates. This type came to be called a K-selected species, in contrast to assorted species that evolved with high rates of reproduction but low survival rates for offspring. The latter came to be called r-selected.[8] Not adapted by evolution to survive through sheer force of fecundity, humans underwent natural selection in a K-regime. In theory, human population growth is density-dependent. But, to notice one empirical complication for the human case, population growth rates at times have shown a *positive* correlation with increasing density—the inverse of what is normally observed in resource-limited animal populations.[9] This would seem to suggest that human population growth is *independent* of its density. Exactly what is going on with humans?

HUMAN ECOLOGICAL CARRYING CAPACITY

What is going on, in the main, is that the adaptive ingenuity of human sociocultural organization often turns human ecological carrying capacity into a variable—nothing at all like the mathematical constant K.[10] The expansion of human carrying capacity figures significantly into total biospheric carrying capacity (analyzed in Part B), the sustainability of which we take to be the rationale for considering the human dimensions of carrying capacity. For the present purpose of defining the problem, it should help to consider a case in point.

The ideal case is one in which sociocultural organization is minimal and its adaptive ingenuity limited, so that it can be shown how, indeed, human societies may be vulnerable to overshooting carrying capacities; and so, as complications eventually are added, it can also be shown how inordinately complex the overshooting of human carrying capacities and their measurement figure to be for any but the simplest of cases. We shall recount the story of one paradigm case, which Catton (1993), Ponting (1991), and Bahn and Flenley (1992) all interpret for similar purposes, a case that for all the world made a society of humans look just like a colony of reindeer.

Overshoot on Easter Island

Easter Island is the location for what once was, say Bahn and Flenley, "one of the most highly evolved Neolithic societies in human history" (1992, p. 207).[11] The island got its modern name when it was discovered by European explorers on Easter Sunday in 1722. The Europeans were not the first to discover it. When they arrived, they found a human society already there. Unfortunately, the one they found was in the process of disintegrating. The process would accelerate.

The human story of Easter Island began, so far as anyone now can tell, at least 1,500 years ago (possibly earlier) when some Polynesians far to the west immigrated from the South Pacific. Nobody knows why. Nobody knows how many came, either. It is quite likely that many did not survive the journey for, although they are known to have had good open ocean transport, they had no maps and had to have traveled at least 1,400 miles across the vast South Pacific. The few who reached Easter Island were lucky to have found it. Had they missed it, it is likely they all would have died, for the nearest land beyond, Chile, is more than 2,000 miles farther from the direction the Polynesians were coming. Geographically, Easter Island rests in the middle of nowhere.

But arrive the founders did, along with their chickens, and they found a place suitable for human habitation. At that time, we know (from contemporary evidence) that the Island was heavily forested and shrubbed. There was plenty of space. The Island wasn't very large (14 miles long, 116 square kilometers), but in the beginning there were not very many people to make use of it. So, make use of it they did. Isolated from the rest of the world because of their location, the original settlers founded a society based on the Polynesian culture they brought with them. Their descendants survived and prospered for more than a millennium.

As the centuries passed, there developed a basic division of labor that turned around two principal roles. One, an obvious necessity, pertained to the gathering and cultivating of food and other accoutrements necessary for survival. The other role pertained to worship of the sacred, and in this, after a time more and more people became employed on a regular basis. Their employment consisted of constructing gigantic stone statues, monuments to their ancestors, carved out of a rock quarry in a dormant volcano. The finished statues were usually transported to the shore of the island, there to be erected facing inward from the sea. Many were placed on platforms as part of large outdoor temples, themselves sculptured monuments connected to the Easter Islanders' religious sentiments and observances. It is these statues that have fascinated so many modern people. The statues are the principal legacy of the original Easter Island society. They were also directly connected to the process by which the society and its culture came to a horrible demise.

Building the statues consumed a great deal of the resources not only of the people but also of the island itself. The finished statues stand anywhere from six to over 30 feet high, and most weigh tens of tons.

Exactly how they were transported about the island is uncertain, but it is certain that the Easter Islanders had to cut down trees, which they did, and also had to build an extensive network of roads, to transport the statues. In addition, other huge public works projects, consisting of various dwellings, platforms, and terraces, were built. Clearly, the amount of human labor represented in all this was as monumental as the statues. The human resources devoted to it increased as the centuries passed. It was to become "the most spectacular religious building compulsion known anywhere in Polynesia" (Bahn and Flenley 1992, p. 210). And it continued for 500 years.

The Islanders came to regard their massive devotion to these constructions, with all the religious significance attached to them, as vital to their culture. So, as one might expect, for it happens this way when humans value things, the Easter Islanders developed means to perpetuate and sanctify the various tasks associated with the production of the statues. They did so by organizing a priesthood, which appears to have contributed to the moral integration of the culture. The statue builders for their part appear to have developed some sophisticated methods of engineering, considering that they had no metal tools. Meanwhile, the food producers specialized in horticulture and fishing. Each role justified the other—one fed the body, the other fed the soul— and the society based on this division of labor appears to have worked very well down the centuries.[12]

The division of labor slowly began to break down, and the principal roles came to cross purposes, because the effort at statue construction slowly caused the island itself to break down. The principal cause is now reckoned to be the excessive cutting of palm forests, especially due to the demands that came from accelerated statue construction. There is, of course, no ecological mystery about deforestation on a massive scale: It decreases the ability of soil to retain moisture and minerals, which leads the soil to become less fertile and, thus, yield less food per hectare. When rich topsoil is lost to production, marginal soil must be put to use, and that also implies fewer yields. That food production and water supplies on Easter Island became more and more difficult for the people, because of the loss of moisture and nutrients in their soil, due to deforestation, is a virtual certainty: Today *there are no* trees on Easter Island—at least none worth counting and none that could make up the difference for the palm forests and shrubbery we know to have been destroyed—and there were none when the Europeans arrived. Wood had now become scarce, and no water now flowed on the windswept land. Deforestation, in the estimate of Bahn and Flenley (1992), had been completed more than 250 years before.

The conditions that eventually came together were these: The natural resources of the island were diminishing. The people had evolved an interdependent society in an isolated environment from which no one could escape, an environment they had slowly but enormously changed during the centuries they had used it. Their environment had changed because of the ways they had used it. And all the while, their population had been slowly rising. After more than a millennium, the island had become a lot smaller, not because of any change in its geography but because the population now numbered from 6,000 to 12,000 or more. That estimate range (the exact number can never be known) applies to 1680, 42 years before the Europeans arrived. And nobody was leaving, because the canoes they needed for ocean transport could no longer be built from the wood they no longer had.

With the gradual degradation of the land, the division of labor on Easter Island became more competitive because the specialized roles of statue construction and food production came more to interfere with each other. The massive construction effort interfered with food production because its indirect effect lowered the supply of fertile land; the decline in food production meant that there were fewer calories to provide the energy necessary for the people to continue the construction. The final nail in the coffin of the Easter Island culture was provided by the fact that there had formed social classes roughly corresponding to the division of labor and, as one might expect, the priests and their associates were the highest class. Higher classes tend to think of themselves as privileged and tend to assert their privileges most when the legitimacy of the privileges is called into question. We know that Easter Island's social classes became sharply distinguished, that the reigning class retained unto itself all surplus produce, and that the legitimacy of the reigning class was challenged. It is not speculating to say that the classes became competitive. When the Europeans arrived, they found these two groups facing off in the ultimate form of human competition: warfare, generally believed to have begun in 1680.

In the beginning, there was massive killing and destruction and, although it was not continual, it did not cease. It became a way of life. Croplands and other means of acquiring food were destroyed by one group of combatants, and this included substantial losses of the Islanders' main domesticated species and a food staple, their chickens. Other combatants attacked the symbols of the moral order: All the stone statues were maliciously toppled, and some were ingeniously—and with difficulty—beheaded. (All the statues now standing have been re-erected.) Sporadic warfare continued for decades until, with the assistance of later European expropriators, the statue builders and the priestly class were killed off (the last of them to be deported as slaves). During all this, the capacity of the island to support much of a population was diminished even further; it had been under great stress anyhow. Food became increasingly harder to come by. With resources diverted to war-making and the production of subsistence undermined naturally and now culturally, the division of labor that once had allowed for the sharing of food become well nigh nonoperative. Eventually, the loss of organic resources and the human-caused suffering were so great that the population conspired to destroy forever its sources of food and the division of labor by which it was produced and shared. This left surviving descendants to scatter about the island, subsisting by raiding and preying upon one another's food sources and reserves, and probably subsisting on each other. Committed now to sporadic warfare that would take a full century to wind down, the Easter Islanders dissolved their society into bands of indiscriminate warriors and, thus, disintegrated a social organization that had served them well for a thousand years.

Although the upper bound of the pre-European population is uncertain, it is certain that various European visitors added to the problem of depopulation that had been under way since before they arrived. Depopulation accelerated rapidly in the 1860s when smallpox was imported by means of a short-lived slave trade. By 1877, 200-odd years after the warfare erupted, there were only 111 indigenous people left. At that low point, the population had decreased by an order of magnitude that clearly fits an overshoot-crash curve (see Figure 9.3).

Although a few biological descendants survive, the original society that lived on Easter Island for more than a thousand years is gone forever. For a long time, what happened at Easter Island was a subject of great mystery and fable, inspired by those haunting statues that tell no tales and by romantic adventurers who told false tales.[13] But the tale of the people of Easter Island is not mysterious at all: They overshot their island's carrying capacity. One could, of course, overlook an ecological interpretation to favor instead one based on purely sociopolitical factors. Especially, one could point to that war. But how is one to explain the cause of *that*? Was this purely sociopolitical or sociocultural in origin? It could hardly have been. It is clear from the relevant archaeological and ecological evidence that the Easter Islanders had developed a way of life that was ecologically unsustainable. When unsustainable conditions develop far enough, people have a good reason to go to war: They get hungry and thirsty. The people of Easter Island evidently did.[14]

The Variables of Human Carrying Capacity and Its Overshoot

The story of Easter Island is not just a story of a human population that crashed or died off. It is also a story of a habitat that crashed with respect to the humans that were using it. Populations will crash if habitats do. Habitats will crash if they have become deficient in some critical resource for some critical period of time because of the ways in which the population uses the habitat. If the use of a habitat by a population is unsustainable, emigration is prohibited, and carrying capacity is not infinitely expandable, then a population growth curve approximately congruent with Figure 9.3 should be observed.

Figure 9.3 is a useful illustration, but a highly limited representation, of a human overshoot condition. The figure illustrates, using a declining value for K, that the carrying capacity of a habitat may be lowered by the activities of a dominant species in the habitat, as was the case with the Easter Islanders. Note that a condition of overshoot cannot be evaluated just with respect to the size of a population at a given time. Values of K may change in relation to the activities that the population, whatever its size, undertakes in using its habitat to sustain itself. There are two sorts of sustenance-relevant activities that a population will inevitably undertake with respect to habitats. One is to extract resources. The other, a natural and inevitable consequence of the first, is to deposit the waste products generated from used resources back into habitats. If the resources extracted are renewed and the wastes generated are recycled, there should be no overshoot, for the population should then be living within habitat carrying capacity. But when resources are not renewed or wastes not recycled, then we have, by definition, habitat degradation. That condition itself, if permitted to continue for sufficient time or at sufficient levels, should lower carrying capacity. But to evaluate the significance of population size, one has to know how the members of that population are living with respect to the habitats they are exploiting and know the load these habitats can tolerate. One would have to know, for instance, the critical role that the now-extinct palm forests played in the ecology and the culture of Easter Island and, then,

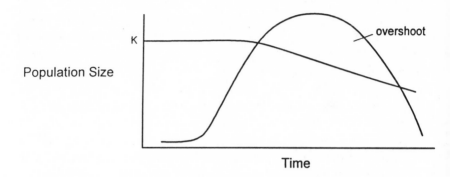

Figure 9.3. The Unidimensional Overshooting of Carrying Capacity

calculate the ripple effects that this degraded resource had on other vital resources—and the relation of them all to sociocultural organization—in order to evaluate the significance of population size. Sheer body counts are no indication of whether carrying capacity has been exceeded and cannot be used to estimate load levels, at least in the case of humans. Humans may have higher or lower standards of living, and their standards are directly tied to how much energy they extract from biophysical habitats and the impacts they have on the habitats in return. Large numbers of people who extract little energy may be well within carrying capacity, while small numbers who extract large amounts may exceed it. It depends upon how and how much those numbers are exploiting their habitats and whether the habitats can recover. The presence of habitat degradation itself is perhaps the best operational means to decide whether *K* has been exceeded. If over time a habitat becomes less and less capable of supporting its users at their previous levels of use, then degradation is occurring and overshoot is approaching or is already happening. If *K* has already been overshot, habitat degradation is accelerated and so, too, is overshoot.

Even so, Figure 9.3 is barely adequate to describe the human ecological overshoot observed on Easter Island, for the resolution of the graph is too coarse. It *does* make a population of humans look just like a population of reindeer, which for certain intents and purposes these humans were. But the figure obscures the fact that carrying capacity in the Easter Island case included numerous interacting biophysical and sociocultural dimensions for the population. And this *was* a single biophysical habitat, the degradation of which is easily and directly traceable to the long-term activities of its users, who were isolated, possessed of stone-tool technology, simply organized, and confined to an island, and so collectively became a near-perfect candidate for a wholly disastrous ecological experiment. A simple overshoot model of Easter Island is hardly adequate for linear extrapolation to any case of contemporary interest, however, because contemporary cases are neither Stone Age, simply organized, nor isolated. Further considerations come into play. One is that human ecological carrying capacity is not often tied to a single, geographically well-bounded, biophysical habitat. Another is that human carrying capacity is not just a question of biophysical conditions. A third is that a condition of sociocultural isolation rarely applies. As Hardesty (1977) said, carrying capacity is a dynamic concept.

Multiple Dimensions of Human Carrying Capacity

A fully ecological concept of human carrying capacity suggests a circular and systemic causation in which environmental carrying capacity crashes along with population, because of population and its activities. Even when restricted to a clearly differentiated bioregion, as at Easter Island, the assessment of environmental carrying capacity can be very complicated and difficult because multiple interacting resource limits may come into play.[15] However, also in play when different cultures and societies interact with each other, especially as nation states, is what Hardin (1993) calls cultural carrying capacity and I shall call sociocultural carrying capacity. This enables the concept of carrying capacity, which is a closed-system concept on the population ceiling interpretation, to become an open-system concept—vital for its application to human ecology.

Sociocultural Carrying Capacity

Relax the conditions of geographical isolation and a simple division of labor, as we must for the vast majority of modern human societies and cultures, and we have enormously complicated our treatment by introducing two additional properties. One is the global culture that crystallizes from the interlocking web of connections in which economic trade becomes increasingly significant as political economies become increasingly sophisticated and dominant. The other, a consequence of the first, is that one can no longer identify the carrying capacity of a particular sociocultural system with the particular bioregion in which it is situated—a point sometimes made by geographers (e.g., Ford 1994). With economic trade relations in the modern world system proceeding full bore, carrying capacity has to be conceived in terms of the aggregate of bioregions from which a focal population extracts resources and to which it adds waste products. In modern times, that may include the entire biosphere, but even when it does not, economic trade in effect becomes a means to extend the carrying capacity of otherwise limited bioregions. The reach of human resource withdrawals and waste additions obviously depends upon and varies with technological development, economic influence, and political power.

So, in analyzing human ecological carrying capacity, a variable sociocultural carrying capacity comes into play in addition to biophysical carrying capacity. All the ecological facts one might summon pertaining to a particular bioregion in and of themselves are no indication of the carrying capacity of the population that abides there. It depends on how much the population living there depends upon living there, on how large the population is, and on how the population is living.

Consider three contrasting examples: the United States, Bangladesh, and Japan. Observe that the United States has a rather large geographical region in proportion to the numbers in its population (264 million)—in other words, observe its comparatively low density. Americans live richly, both ecologically and economically, in that they draw upon far more biophysical systems to support their lavish life styles than do most peoples. Yet, the American population appears to be in no danger of approximating the curve in Figure 9.3 because its economic position in the world has so extended its sociocultural carrying capacity that its people are relatively insulated from the immediate limits of biophysical carrying capacity, for theirs extends to bioregions worldwide. Moreover, the American population growth rate is comparatively low. By contrast, Bangladesh, a small nation with large numbers of people, most of whom are destitute, has little sociocultural insulation from immediate biophysical limits, and its bioregion is seriously degraded, in part *because* its people are destitute. The Bangladeshi population, taking into account its high density and population growth rate, may be a candidate for overshoot on the model of Figure 9.3 in the near future. The Japanese, on the other hand, with a low growth rate, are not. A small island nation and demographically dense in proportion to its natural geography, Japan nevertheless is such a prime player in international trade that it can compensate socioculturally for the inherent limits of its bioregion and so shield its population from what otherwise would be some serious ecological limits to well-endowed Japanese life styles. The Japanese can absorb their high population density locally because the environmental impacts of Japanese lifestyles are absorbed globally. The biophysical carrying capacity of the Japanese depends *mostly* upon bioregions elsewhere in the world, where (often) lower density populations can manage to trade some of their indigenous resources and provide waste dumps for resources spent, in return for Japanese capital. Through its command of capital, technology, and trade, Japanese culture provides its population with substantial room to maneuver in the event of adverse consequences of local or even global environmental degradation. As long as Japan maintains economic hegemony in its trade relations, like the United States, the Japanese population has a safety net to protect itself against overshoot at least for a time.

An extensive sociocultural carrying capacity that provides insulation from biophysical limits and a good measure of slack in terms of which to adapt to contingencies, can dampen the effects of increasing environmental degradation by dispersing waste products into different bioregions, reorganize anticipated resource shortages within different sectors of social organization, and distribute the environmental consequences of population' activities over a longer period of time. The difference between alternative cultures in this adaptive capacity is perhaps analogous to a simple versus a complicated food chain. If the grass in the Arctic tundra provides the only nourishment for the lemming, and the lemming the only nourishment for the snowy owl, the snowy owl is immediately endangered if the grass doesn't grow where or when it is supposed to, whereas cousins of that snowy owl can elect alternative prey if they happen to function within the more complicated food chains of forests to the south. Analogously, a nation such as Bangladesh, living on economic and environmental margins with little sociocultural organization to insulate it, is at greater immediate risk than Japan or the United States. These two have a much greater margin for error—much greater room to maneuver. As we shall see in Part B, from an ecological point of view all three are at risk in their own ways, but for different reasons and on different time scales. Especially, the time frames and the particulars should differ according to respective sociocultural carrying capacities. In evaluating conditions for human overshoot, which in the modern world are inordinately complex, it is worth remembering that it took from one to two *centuries*, as measured by upper and lower population bounds, for the full effects of overshoot to course through so simple and isolated a society as that of the Easter Islanders. One should look for nothing less now, and what one sees could be obscured anyhow by an exaggerated sociocultural carrying capacity whose biophysical foundations are not real.

Phantom Carrying Capacity

With the possible exception of Garrett Hardin—owing to the broad influence of his theory of ecological commons (Hardin 1968, 1993)—William R. Catton, Jr., has done more than any other human ecologist to resurrect and develop the earlier range-management concept of carrying capacity. In numerous works Catton (1980, 1983, 1984, 1985, 1986, 1987), developing a suggestion of Wisniewski (1980), has provided a fuller account of human ecological carrying capacity than was heretofore provided by the equating of the concept with the equilibrium value of the logistic. Odum (1989, p. 159) himself eventually acknowledged this, and now it is becoming more common to interpret human carrying capacity, not as a population ceiling but as the maximum sustainable load of an ecological system with reference to some dominant species—in other words, a relation between the size of a population, the uses it makes (resource withdrawals and waste additions) of its environmental systems, and the permanently sustainable uses the systems can tolerate.

With a notion of sustainability brought explicitly to the fore, Catton's distinction between real and phantom carrying capacity takes on added significance. Real carrying capacity refers to the maximum sustainable system load that can be *permanently* endured at a given level of use, for a given population. Phantom carrying capacity is the load that a system can *temporarily* endure at a given level of use. It follows that human populations can sustain themselves indefinitely if, but only if, their activities are within the real carrying capacities of their life support systems. When is that? In theory, populations are living within real carrying capacity if, and only if, exploited resources are renewable and are renewed, and if generated wastes are recyclable and are recycled. But at times and places, in fact, system carrying capacity can be supplemented temporarily by the extraction and exploitation of nonrenewable or unsustainable resources, which defines a phantom condition.

The industrial societies provide the best case in point. In effect, they have exploited a phantom carrying capacity by becoming utterly dependent upon fossil fuels and fossil water. The resources now used to sustain macrosocial industrialism depend very much upon long-term geochemical processes that do not behave on sociocultural time scales. Fossil fuels were transmogrified, and melting glacial ice was deposited, in their respective underground sanctuaries over immense geologic time frames, and industrial societies cannot survive long enough to wait for the further decomposition of flora and fauna that trap solar energy for technology someday to release, or to wait for ice that has yet to form to melt. A phantom condition of carrying capacity exists whenever nonrenewable resources provide the foundation for subsistence organization.

The expansion of phantom capacity may afford temporary relief from the limits of real carrying capacity and create the psychological illusion that the overshoot of real limits is not a serious danger. Typically, relief and its associated illusion are purchased by importing nonindigenous resources (or by exporting wastes). This may be done by importing from the geologic past essentially nonrenewable sources, or by importing them from other regions or habitats in the present, thus putting into production what Catton (1980), following Borgstrom (1965), calls invisible acreage. Such acreage then is no longer available to the region from which it is exported, and so lowers local real carrying capacity and, eventually, the capability to provide exports to the region that has come to depend upon them. With the expansion of phantom carrying capacity, human standards of living may temporarily expand, and population sizes may expand accordingly, but real standards of living figure to stagnate as phantom-based expansion offsets already-sinking real levels, or as phantom capacity itself dissipates.

Since the consumption of nonrenewable resources cannot indefinitely sustain a population, whatever ways of life depend on nonrenewable resource consumption therefore have to change unless substitute resources can be found. To find nonrenewable substitutes is simply to extend phantom capacity—to buy more time. When time runs out and real biophysical carrying capacity limits come into play, as eventually they must if human activities draw down nonrenewable resources, then the effects of overshooting real carrying capacity should be observed. The range and severity of observed effects, we have noted, should differ according to sociocultural carrying capacity. The range of theoretically possible effects includes the same number of people living at lower standards, or fewer people living at the same standards, or fewer living at lower standards.

To develop extensive and long-term phantom carrying capacity by means of social organization, as the macro-industrial societies have done, in effect is to try to finesse the limits of biophysical carrying capacity in order to maintain or enhance standards of living.[16] This, of course, is a prime feature of modern human economic and political organization: the use of a highly developed sociocultural carrying capacity to duck, bob, and weave in response to impending biophysical limits. In one respect, a main *purpose* of social organization is to protect against the effects of just such limits to human subsistence, survival, and well-being— to protect against the realization of Malthusian conditions.

But there comes the question of whether social organization and its cultural rationalizations may be evolving to where together they might actually *cause* Malthusian conditions. To not live within real biophysical carrying capacity in effect is to not live within sustainable ecological means, which is to say, to live in ways that nature's evolutionary design does not permanently enable. There is good reason to think that this is exactly what humans may have undertaken to do.

Human Population Growth and the Increased Utilization of Carrying Capacity

Figure 9.4 presents the curve that is typically used to portray total human population growth for the last 10,000 years. Since this graph appears to replicate the graph in Figure 9.1, before interpreting Figure 9.4 it is important to remember some caveats that apply to any curve that describes population dynamics.

The specific form for a curve of population growth depends entirely upon the time frame and unit of population chosen for analysis. Population growth curves may be coarse-grained or fine-grained and may change shape considerably as one adjusts the time frame or the unit observed. No observed change in population distribution can be validly interpreted without reference to those parameters, in addition to the parameters and implicit assumptions of the specific model employed. One purpose in fitting a curve to data is to smooth out glitches in the data, and that necessarily yields an idealized representation. The population growth curve presented in Figure 9.4 for the entire human population conceals much regional, temporal, and sociocultural variation. That well-known curve is *very* coarse-grained.

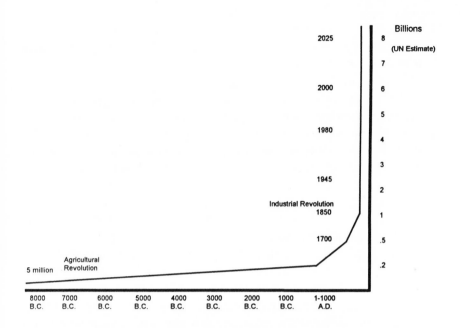

Figure 9.4. Worldwide Human Population Growth
for the Past Ten Thousand Years

In Figure 9.4, an exponential function may be an adequate model for sections of the curve, but the entire curve is really just a segment of a line and, moreover, different segments of it have to be generated with different functions. If we notice the segment where the curve turns sharply upward, roughly between A.D. 1650 and A.D. 1750, we may observe that from there on, human population begins to double *at an increasing rate.* This is no ordinary exponential growth. Rather, human population growth for the past 300 years has been hyperbolic. A hyperbolic function is a variant of an exponential function. The difference is this: With exponential growth, doubling times remain constant, whereas with hyperbolic growth, the doubling time is halved at every doubling. Figure 9.4 clearly shows that something approximating this has been happening until the most recent doubling, which means that human population has been growing much faster than even an ordinary exponential function can describe. The full curve can be completely fitted only when all the data are in, and they will not be until human population growth stabilizes or turns downward, as eventually it must with, which can be said with absolute certainty. Figure 9.4 seems to show that humans have been living in what is a more or less unlimited environment—an impossible ecological condition for a resource-limited species in any but the shortest of time frames. The United Nations has provided various estimates for when human population growth will top out and become sigmoid. Most estimates range deep into the twenty-first century, and they indicate that a virtual doubling in population size is to take place before then.

How can this be? Human population growth from this curve appears to be density-independent when in theory it could not possibly be. In fact, when exponential growth appeared and as it kicked into its hyperbolic phase, the industrialization of society had begun and was proceeding. One consequence, noted before, was that substantial mortality reductions began to be realized. Now, realized r for humans was increasing and tending toward r_{max}, with a doubling each generation (a fact noted by Malthus). Another consequence was the acceleration of a process, begun long before, of the expansion of sociocultural carrying capacity through further differentiation of the division of labor in society, but armed with an energy bonanza that now could be fully exploited—the fossil fuels—to apparently expand biophysical carrying capacity. I say apparently because, to be precise, it is *access* to additional biophysical carrying capacity that was expanded, thus enabling increasing numbers of humans to *utilize* a greater portion of it. The technological means kept pace, for a third consequence, as Hart (1959) showed, was that like population growth, some curves for technological growth also have been more than exponential. For the first and probably the last time in biological evolution, a species was by its sociocultural organization seeming to succeed at turning K into a variable of increasing value. Thus, the size of the total human population could increase along with its density because the expansion of sociocultural carrying capacity served in effect to absorb or offset the density effects that would be expected from approaching limits to biophysical carrying capacity. Thus, there have come into being 5.8 billion members of a single, macrosocially organized, dominant primate species whose population growth becomes resource-limited *even as* it appears to be density-independent. Setting aside empirical reasons for the time being, are there theoretical reasons to suppose that this condition might be just temporary?

The limits to the ecological carrying capacity of the billions turn on human energy requirements and human relationships to food chains and trophic levels. The very existence of the billions represents a concentration of, as well as the extensive environmental expropriation of, energy stored in biological form—biomass. An increase in energy capture by any population through the expropriation of biomass expands the carrying capacity of that population, with respect to its activities in its environment, at least for a time. One interpretive angle on the concept of carrying capacity, employed by many systems and community ecologists, is to evaluate the allocation of biomass in terms of species requirements and the requirements of biomass production, energy flows, and the concentration of energy as biomass in ecological systems. There is a complex order to bioenergetics, with limits set by the first and second laws of thermodynamics.

Here, we may set aside the complexities, for they have not substantially undercut the fundamental simplicities that have been staples of theoretical ecology since the time of Elton (1927, 1933) and Lindeman (1942). The interacting populations of biotic communities can be arrayed, however messily, in terms of trophic levels because of two simple facts: (1) Biomass production originates with autotrophs that fix solar energy, and (2) as autotrophs are consumed by primary heterotrophs, and these in turn by secondary heterotrophs, followed by tertiary heterotrophs, energy is transferred with substantial loss. The magnitude of loss from each trophic level to the next is usually given at 90 percent, although that figure is sometimes challenged (e.g., Slobodkin 1972). Whatever the true rate of loss, there is no doubt that there is much. And because of the energy loss between trophic levels, it becomes possible to array species—again, messily, but not inappropriately—in a pyramidal structure that represents the size of populations that can be sustained, given their energy requirements and their positions in the food chain. This is why, in Colinvaux's (1978) wonderful phrase, big fierce animals are rare: Large numbers of them would require more energy than sustainable natural food chains can produce. There has to be a smaller number of top predators than the number of whatever it is the top predators eat—a substantially smaller number, small enough to accommodate the energy loss rate between trophic levels, whatever its true value, as well as the energy utilized within each level. Ultimately, the bioenergetics of ecological systems fix the sustainable population levels of resource-limited species, because energy limits fix resource limits.

It has not gone unnoticed that humans are positioned as top predators, which the ecological theory of several generations tells us is an inherently unstable condition if the numbers of them get too large. But how large is too large?

When humans have utilized biophysical systems in unsustainable ways, at certain historical periods their technological and social ingenuity has enabled them to adapt so as to expand their resource potential for a time, by developing sociocultural carrying capacity that increased their access to real biophysical carrying capacity in relation to their numbers. Often, with indifference, humans have exploited phantom biophysical carrying capacity until a greater fraction of real capacity could become available from the further development of technology and sociocultural organization. Zigging and zagging so, human population eventually came to grow hyperbolically. The question of whether this population is "too large" depends partly on an answer to the question, "Too large for what?" Too large for carrying capacity? If so, which?

A few basic principles of introductory ecology may be useful for bracketing the problem but not for the solution. We now have a species that is so good at temporarily expanding its carrying capacity through its macrosocial organization, divisions of labor, and technology that its population growth appears to be independent of density when, of course, it is not. Clearly, human ecological carrying capacity has to be analyzed as a multidimensional process for the interaction of sociocultural and biophysical conditions, for over time it has been exactly that.

Much factual analysis of this process in terms of contemporary social, demographic, economic, and biophysical conditions has been provided by numerous ecologists and environmental scientists, and we shall consider some of this in Part B. There, we shall conclude the analysis of human overshoot in terms of current environmental conditions. Next, and last, we complete our analysis of the question in evolutionary perspective. To the extent that current environmental conditions are degrading due to anthropogenic causes, which many have taken to believing, it is plain that the roots must be located in evolving patterns of biosociocultural organization that fundamentally changed human ecology. On that score, humans have come a long way from the savanna.

NOTES

1. Colinvaux (1978) explains why big fierce animals are rare using exactly that title for his highly readable introduction to some basic principles of ecology. They are

rare, as we shall discuss below, because they have to be, so as to conform to the energy flow requirements of functional food chains and trophic levels.

2.   For these three founders of the science of political economy, the issue figured significantly, if variably, in their analyses. In the twentieth century, economic theory would take a different turn, as we shall observe when the issue of limits is considered more fully in Part B.

As to Malthus, his first essay on population appeared in 1798 and the last in 1872 (Malthus died in 1834). There were really two essays. The first, quite brief and not much more than a pamphlet, contained no data, but the second, much longer, marshalled empirical support for the principle of population, which was amplified from the first edition but not much in the later editions. Contrary to common belief, by occupation Malthus was first and foremost a college professor, not a parson of the Anglican Church (with which nonetheless he was closely associated). Malthus' professorship was sufficiently secular that some of his critics denounced him as an atheist. (Karl Marx, one of his most vitriolic critics, was not given to that charge.) Probably the best historical treatment of Malthus is by William Petersen (1979), himself a demographer, who considers the posthumous 1872 version of "the essay" to be definitive.

3.   Pearl was not the first to conceive and fit the logistic curve for population growth (P.F. Verhulst was, in 1838), but Pearl was the first successful promoter of it. The development of the ecological theory of population dynamics, which blossomed early in the twentieth century as the logistic was developed by Lotka and Volterra, has been traced in a marvelous history by Kingsland (1985).

4.   I here follow human demographers instead of population biologists in the use of the terms fecundity and fertility.

5.   We shall not review the controversy, which accelerated with the publication in 1962 of *Animal Dispersion in Relation to Social Behavior* by the British avian biologist Vero Copner Wynne-Edwards. Wynne-Edwards' argument about self-limiting social species derived from his position that populations could be units of natural selection—a position he subsequently seemed to express reservations about (Wynne-Edwards 1977). The natural selection of populations, as biologists see it, is a kind of group selection. That was the controversial part, and Wynne-Edwards' book was a direct stimulus for G.C. Williams' *Adaptation and Natural Selection* (1966), a rebuttal that came to dominate the thinking of evolutionary biologists.

Whatever the reasons may be, and nobody claims to know what they all are, there is no controversy that some populations somehow regulate their own sizes, or have their sizes regulated for them by something other than K. It is quite likely that numerous mechanisms and processes are involved. There is, for instance, no doubt that reproduction in primates is suppressed by social dominance hierarchies which, for laboratory populations of females of some species, can result in complete infertility among subordinates (Abbott 1989). Wynne-Edwards' (1965) idea was that population homeostasis is achieved through the medium of social interaction. If Wynne-Edwards was wrong about group selection, that does not imply that his choice of medium or process was the wrong place to look to find the dynamics of self-regulating populations.

6.   The Lotka-Volterra equations introduce the minimal complication to the system considered above. Add another population of a different species and permit the two to interact in such a way that the density of each affects the density of the other. Then, the growth and decline of each should be a function of the growth and decline of the

other, since each provides environmental resistance to the other. Predators and prey have long been thought to interact in such a way, and their population dynamics have been mathematically modeled with suitable simplifying assumptions.

Lotka-Volterra equations have formed part of the substance of theoretical ecology for three-quarters of a century. However, their utility for applications to natural systems has been seriously questioned of late (see Botkin 1990), and even their fit with the data that traditionally have been used to support them has been challenged (Hall 1988).

7.   The ecological disaster on this small Arctic island was described in an early report by Klein (1968). In a similar experiment conducted not too far away, on St. Paul's Island, 25 reindeer (with a four-to-one ratio of females to males) were introduced, eventually to yield a population around 2,000 individuals—destined also to starve, until only eight remained. But other comparable experiments in the region produced a wider range of results, including almost no population increase at all (Turk and Turk 1984, pp. 166-167).

8.   More differences than these came to be attributed to r-selected and K-selected species, many owing to the influence of Pianka (1970). The r-K concept was conceived apparently by Robert MacArthur, and developed in MacArthur and Wilson (1967), as a model of density-dependent natural selection. The concept has had its detractors and clarifiers. See Boyce (1984), who argues that the original model does not justify many of the differences that came to be attributed to r- and K-strategists.

9.   An observation normally restricted for single animal populations taken as the unit of analysis (Tanner 1966). However, whether the logistic applies well at all—even to single populations—to large animals in their given environments is seriously disputed, and some suggest it may be applicable only to controlled laboratory monocultures (see Dhondt 1988). A related but different observation, sometimes made of entire natural systems, especially coniferous forests, is this: Total biomass typically conforms to a sigmoid growth curve as density increases (Sprugel 1985).

10.   In fact, other species do this too. Over the evolutionary eons, terrestrial fauna expanded their own future carrying capacity as their metabolic processes changed the very environmental conditions that would favor their own selection. Cohen (1995, p. 247) makes the general observation that "the carrying capacity of nonhuman populations may be constant on the time scale of a few generations but not on the time scale of many generations." In his view, this seriously limits *all* the concepts of carrying capacity that theoretical ecology has so far provided.

11.   This rendering of the story of Easter Island is drawn from Mulloy (1967, 1974), Englert (1970), two massive tomes of archaeological detail published under the editorship of Thor Heyerdahl and Edwin N. Ferndon, Jr. (1961)—although some of the interpretations of Heyerdahl have been discredited in the most recent review of evidence—and Bahn and Flenley (1992), which summarizes the current evidence. Catton (1993), unaware of Bahn and Flenley's work but personally acquainted with Mulloy, had used what became Bahn and Flenley's major interpretation of the culture's collapse in earlier work (Catton 1980).

12.   I am oversimplifying this characterization of the social structure and division of labor on Easter Island for expository purposes. I say there were two *principal* roles and social classes, which there were, but in fact there were many derivative supporting roles and variations. Also, I should call attention to the generally accepted fact that the construction of religious monuments was not directed by some central, island-wide

authority but seems, rather, to have been under the control of local kin groups who shared the island-wide culture.

13. Eventually, as Chile claimed the island and Western romantics and entrepreneurs took notice of it, the population began to turn around. Today, there are more than 2,000 people living there, due largely to the fact that Easter Island does not rest in the middle of nowhere anymore. It has its own airport to accommodate jet planes to fly in tourists who want to see all those wondrous statues. Tourism is now central to the modern Easter Island economy.

The widespread fascination with Easter Island dates back a century, when the people and the place became objects of curiosity owing to visiting scientists, journalists, adventurers, do-gooders, and exploiters, some of whom engaged in deliberate mystery-mongering. Mystery-mongering continued even past the middle of the twentieth century, when the silly suggestion was put forward—I will not dignify it with a citation—that the Easter Island statues were built by extra-terrestrials. Since there is massive archaeological evidence pertaining to the construction of the statues and none of it indicates any extra-terrestrial influence, presumably this thesis was suggested for the purpose of advancing the personal gain of pseudo-intellectual hucksters who regard prehistory and the tragedies of a people as something with which to entertain a gullible public.

14. Upon being told of the luxurious rivers and waterfalls of Tahiti, one survivor of the Easter Island slaughter is reported to have then referred to Tahiti as "the country where the water does not die" (Maziere 1968, p. 117). How could a nineteenth-century native of Easter Island even entertain such a concept unless he or she had been so unfortunate as to have lived on a land where the water had died?

Another oral report, consistent with the foregoing, was prepared for a letter presented to the President of the California Academy of Sciences in 1874, by Thomas Croft, who was there. The report tells in a nutshell the same story of the demise of Easter Island that would be confirmed from archaeological and ecological evidence that became available in the next century. Croft was told by natives that once, long ago, their island had been heavily forested but that the forests were cut down because the land was needed for cultivation. And why did that need materialize, according to the natives? Because there were too many people. The letter and its contents are cited by Thor Heyerdahl (Heyerdahl and Ferndon 1961, p. 519).

15. See, for instance, Fearnside's (1986) treatment of the human carrying capacity of the Brazilian rainforest.

16. This, humans have done in the past with startling ingenuity and continue to do with astonishing myopia. No more ludicrous examples can be found than in the American state of California. This state, inherently semi-arid, has fought political water wars since early in the twentieth century. It still does. Now, however, its population exceeds 33 million people. Its principal industry is agriculture, which depends almost entirely upon irrigation. Its main agricultural valleys (the semi-arid San Juaquin, semi-arid Salinas, and fully arid Imperial Valley) consume more than 80 percent of the state's water, in order to produce almost half of domestic American produce. But there is not enough rain to support all those people and all that growing, which includes water-intensive crops such as rice, and not enough melting snow to flow down the high Sierras. The solution? A number have been proposed in the recent past, among them: laying an undersea pipe to Alaska to transport fresh water captured through damming it there,

or transporting Alaskan water by tanker, or building 51 dams in the Canadian Rockies. (The Canadians were not enthralled with that plan.) It has not yet occurred to most Californians to try to live within the limits of their regional carrying capacity. They have always preferred to extend it and depend even further on an ever-expanding phantom capacity—and, thus, maintain the myth of their golden state and so attract even more people to a region that already has thrice too many.

Chapter 10

Human Ecology, Evolution, and Environments

No other species save ours has so changed its way of life, compared to what it once was, and its relations to environments, compared to what they once were, with so little change in its evolved biological endowments. Suppose we reflect upon the social, cultural, and environmental circumstances of humans today and then imagine ourselves to be placed anywhere in the world 15,000 years in the past, before there were settled communities, there to contemplate the human future. Who could have imagined the results? Could anyone have guessed that the human species—then consisting of no more (and possibly far fewer) than five million hunters and gatherers, mostly unknown to each other, organized into small bands according to kinship—would develop formally organized macrosocieties with a total of 5.8 billion people? Or later, upon organizing pristine cities, who among the inhabitants could have predicted the massive urbanization of the nineteenth and twentieth centuries, with the populations of some cities growing to the tens of millions, and the exponential-hyperbolic increase in human population growth that began with the Industrial Revolution? Who would have thought that now the only human competitors left would be a few microscopic organisms? Who could have anticipated that today the social organization of the human race would look more like the social organization of the ants than like the social organization of the primates from which we evolved? Back then, of course, humans did not even possess many of the concepts necessary to entertain such thoughts.

Any attempt to explain this protracted but profound macroscopic change without recourse to the ecological contingencies that human societies and their members confronted back then and that confront us now cannot succeed on its own. Nor can any attempt to explain the ecological contingencies that we now confront possibly succeed without understanding the evolutionary past that put us on the trajectory toward our current station.

RAPPAPORT'S DILEMMA REALIZED

Biological evolution allowed us to be a large-brained primate, with bipedal locomotion and a capacity for speech, whose sheer survival depended upon some modicum of social organization, if only kinship. Implicit in socially organized, large-brained, handed, vocalizers is the capacity for tool-making and language—and for further social organization. Now, if biological evolution provides smart, talking, organized tool-makers, who find themselves hungry and thirsty and cold often enough at different times and places, or find themselves otherwise deprived, then it is not hard to understand how humans got from the savanna to the twenty-first century. No one placed at some point in the beginning of, or even much later in, the process and immersed in its variable details could likely discern much of a pattern, but the general outline is now clear. When we make the reasonable assumptions that social organization and culture are adaptations to environments and that natural selection will favor acculturated, socially organized humans; when we observe a pattern by which subsistence production is intensified as culture and social organization develop; when we keep to some principles of ecology, focusing especially on energy extraction and its concentration in biomass, which eventually gets expressed as human population growth; and when we interpret some principles of sociology, especially concerning the division of labor in society and its connection to population and technological growth; then, the change in human social organization from kinship-based foragers to industrialists hunting for and gathering fossil fuels seems in retrospect to have been a natural (though not inevitable) human ecological development for an acculturated species.

Provided with a surplus of subsistence production, human communities can remain sedentary and can expand their divisions of labor and improve their technology. Improve, in this instance, means to enhance tool kits to obtain an increased capacity for energy extraction and conversions, to further enhance the surplus. This humans began to do as early horticulturalists, when they discovered that a subsistence surplus could be produced because the edible parts of domesticated species were larger than the edible parts of wild species. Political organization developed as a social means for intensifying subsistence production and securing its surplus, along with economic organization, a social means for generating and distributing it. Eventually the economic organization turned from subsistence to political economies, especially as the Industrial Revolution took shape. With the conversion of subsistence production from muscle-based and solar-powered energy inputs to mechanical-based and fossil-fuel powered energy inputs, more energy could be extracted from natural systems because substantially more energy subsidies could be put in to the production process, in order to yield additional surplus. The surplus became expressed in exponential population growth once mortality rates, traditionally quite high, began to drop with the advent of public health measures during the Industrial Revolution. Industrialization, boosted by the full flowering of capitalism, encouraged urbanization, an economically efficient mode for the organization of nonagricultural production.

In the human case, it wasn't just characters of anatomy and physiology that evolved but also our relations to biophysical environments. The interactive effects of an increasingly differentiated division of labor, increasingly specialized technology, an increasing population, and increased energy extraction have changed some of the basic parameters with which the process began—parameters provided by biological evolution that we poised ourselves through sociocultural organization to reset. In the last 10,000 years, as hunters and gatherers were displaced by sedentary agriculturalists and industrialists whose subsistence strategies exploit domesticates, we have conquered most of the natural competitors which our ancestors had to confront. That is the point of domestication: to replace natural selection with human cultural (artificial) selection and, thereby, eliminate competitors. In some cases, our "competitors" were entire biophysical regimes that were culturally defined as obstacles to human subsistence activities, and these were conquered by perpetrating substantial disturbances upon, and sometimes total destruction to, the regimes (see Worster 1977; Simmons 1989; Goudie 1990; Ponting 1991). In other cases, the competitors were pestilential diseases that had provided for high mortality rates once domesticated, sedentary, and especially urban, lifestyles had emerged.

Along the way, we substantially increased our resource expropriation from natural systems, and therein is revealed a record of a single pattern of human ecological adaptation that materialized in different forms. The pattern is the expansion of carrying capacity, through the capture or release of ever more energy for conversion, by means of ever more technology, into ever more resources and surplus wealth for ever more people. The capability to expand carrying capacity is a consequence of acculturation—of advancing technologies and expanding divisions of labor—and of agriculture, which permit more energy to be captured from more environments in more variegated forms. We did not begin abnormal rates of energy capture—abnormal for an ape evolved on the savanna with minimal acculturation—until we turned from foraging to farming. Human carrying capacity has been expanding ever since. We have taken the process so far as to develop new habitats by expanding into geographical regions that could not have been humanly inhabited without the acculturation and technology needed to protect us from unforgiving geoclimatic conditions. We have exploited biophysical materials, systems, and processes that earlier could not be utilized and transformed natural conditions that otherwise would have been out of reach and, by converting them into resources, have fundamentally changed the conditions of human existence. The increased exploitation of biophysical environments in the last 10,000 years, but especially in the last few hundred, has been converted into higher standards of living, longer life spans, and more people. The story of sociocultural development has been the story of humans pushing their carrying capacity ever upwards.

But if all this is a natural human ecological development, it has produced what appears to be an unnatural result for a resource-limited species: an increasing population size together with an increasing population density. Human population growth is not intrinsically independent of its density, although for a long time now it seems to have been as we have been caught up in the expansion of a phantom carrying capacity licensed by sociocultural organization for the express purpose of providing subsistence for expanding numbers of people and their expanding per capita appetites. Expanding numbers and appetites produce expanding environmental impacts on biophysical systems that are not themselves infinitely expandable. Therefore, density-dependent effects eventually must show up in the population curve. U iless humans are not resource-limited and real carrying capacity *is* infinitely expandable, the exponential-hyperbolic population increase of the last few centuries cannot continue indefinitely and must top off. The question is whether it will top off before—or *because*—human sociocultural systems become environmentally unsustainable.

There is nothing in the evolved human being itself to render us environmentally unsustainable; we know the genus was sustainable for two-and-one-half million years. But, in the received view, we can easily locate the phases of recent human history in which there began to occur fundamental transitions in the ecological relationships of our species that, in the full course of time, would raise serious questions about long-term human sustainability. The first phase was farming; the second, industrialization—both paradoxically essential to the near-term sustainability of so many. Industrialization substantially increased the downside risk, for it compounded and accelerated a process that had begun long before. With the adoption of sophisticated technologies for releasing the energy potential of fossil hydrocarbons, the weight of control in human ecology shifted from biophysical to sociocultural systems. With the application of fossil hydrocarbon technologies to agriculture itself, natural environments now seem to be exerting less control on humans and humans more control on them. Human ecological dominance on such a scale has never existed before.

Traditional agro-ecosystems are solar powered and have built-in biogeochemical controls to ensure that human interference, substantial though it may be, is checked. The deliberate intent of humans to farm the land in traditional organic ways, and so convert a natural system into one that is socioculturally organized, is restricted by the differential capacity of crops to host nitrogen-fixing bacteria, by nutrient cycles, by competing species, by the geography of the land, and, of course, by the seasons and the weather. To adapt to these and other restricting conditions of agro-ecosystems, traditional agrarian social organization learned to rotate crops, set land aside for fallow periods, irrigate, utilize draft animals for additional energy inputs and dung for fertilizer, and, for the prime power needs of its people, utilize wood.

These and related adaptations were grounded thus: Traditional agro-ecosystems have to be managed by social organization in terms of the cycles of natural systems that are just within the power of traditional social organization to manipulate. Given the levels of technology and the sources of energy invested in traditional agriculture, only so much control of natural systems can fall within the human reach. If the biogeochemical cycles of natural systems are not respected when agro-ecosystems are designed, the land talks back and traditional agrarian cultural adaptations come to grief. A traditional agrarian economy is environmentally based—it has to be—and its culture has to adapt to the cycles that govern the agro-ecosystems it manages, if the mode of subsistence is to succeed.

This all changes when the amplified potential of the fossil fuels is developed in the context of an energy system whose derivative technologies have application to agriculture. In agro-industrial ecosystems, synthetic organic compounds are added; natural competitors are eliminated with herbicides and insecticides; new genetic strains are introduced; nitrogen fertilizers are applied; planting seasons are extended, and growing is undertaken in locales that normally would not permit it, by means of massive water control projects; and, of course, the internal combustion engine replaces draft animals. The agro-industrial ecosystem is still solar powered, but with a difference. Now, from a system out of which energy is to be extracted, a technologically derived energy subsidy is *put in*. The point in doing that is to finesse the governing cycles of natural systems, for a longer time than the systems would ordinarily permit, thus enabling the systems to produce enhanced energy outputs. Of course, this succeeds, to a degree that additional muscle-power inputs never could, partly because of a physical property of the fossil fuels themselves. They are so concentrated in their energy content that their exploitation (presuming their abundance) affords substantial economic returns for the energy subsidies invested to get the returns.

It also succeeds at adapting a natural system to a sociocultural system, where before, sociocultural systems had been adapted to natural systems. Traditional agro-ecosystems may represent socially organized disturbances of natural systems, but here the natural systems exert more control than the social organization. With agro-industrial ecosystems, it is the other way round. The balance of control now passes to social organization, whose economic institutions and derivative cultural adaptations become no longer environmentally but, rather, technologically based. With this shift, humans need no longer be impressed by the natural signs of ecosystem disturbance and impending system failure that appear when system limits are finessed and the land talks back. More energy subsidies can always be introduced, and more efficient extractive technologies employed, to maintain yields—in effect, seeming to extend the capacity of the system. Now, biogeochemical cycles do not have to be respected so much, at least in the short or intermediate term, because fossil hydrocarbon technologies enable the messages of the signs to be conveniently ignored.

The whole point of agriculture is to redesign undisturbed macroscopic ecosystems—in effect, to disturb them in the service of human ends. The point has been made: Humans can now boast of having the highest biomass of any animal. This was accomplished by replacing complex organic communities with simpler ones, thus destabilizing affected ecosystems, and shortening the food chain in such a way that biotic productivity, normally dispersed, became concentrated in a few forms for use by humans now positioned at the end of the chain—thus establishing a primate as a dominant species when plant species normally are. Among the ecological results may be listed a reduced number of organic species, severely perturbed population equilibria for various surviving species, lowered total biomass relative to pre-agricultural conditions, a decreased efficiency of nutrient cycling, increased acidification of the land, and altered regimes of hydrologic cycling.

Today, as we noted at the outset of this work, humans expropriate or waste an estimated 40 percent of the net primary production of terrestrial ecosystems (Vitousek, Ehrlich, Ehrlich, and Matson 1986). Were it not so, there could not possibly be more than 5.8 billion humans present to experience and sometimes suffer the implications of it. Worse for portents, the survival and well-being of the billions present and yet to come now depend upon the technologies and social organizations responsible for all that expropriation. The only way to get and keep 8 to 15 billion dominant primates at the end of the food chain is to provide them with culture, social organization, technology, agriculture, and surplus wealth in measures that correspond to their numbers.

That package of attributes, of course, was not designed from biological evolution. As the biophysical systems in which we evolved and on which we depend begin now to "talk back" to this top predator whose summed biomass and expropriation of net primary production far exceed those of any other animal, and whose population growth appears to be density-independent when in theory and fact it cannot sustainably be, we have to conclude that humans may have developed socioculturally along a trajectory that makes their continued functioning incompatible with the environments in which and in relation to which they biologically evolved. Carrying capacity that can expand because of the sociocultural exploitation of biophysical processes is carrying capacity that can contract when exploitation becomes degradation. In many ways and places it has so become, to the point where the natural asset base is not enlarging as fast as the human population. Toward what does this trajectory lead?

It is possible to interpret the entire history of human sociocultural development, given our biological phenotypes, as a long procession down an ecological avenue of no return, into an ecological trap closed by our own adaptations to the material conditions of subsistence (Freese 1995). Catton (1995), so inclined, and with special reference to industrialization, perhaps the ultimate socioecological trap, calls *this* a natural development of a culture-bearing species. For our purpose, we need not now commit to that, for there is more to consider in Part B, but clearly the question of long-term human sustainability is real. Rappaport's Dilemma is realized.

PROLOGUE TO PART B

Generally speaking, ecology is the link between evolution and environments. What becomes of some evolutionary trajectory depends upon the characteristics of environments, for these are the sites of evolution. The characteristics of environments and the processes that change them are the subject of ecology. Evolution sets parameters in terms of which ecological processes behave; it provides the material, so to speak, of environments; and, according to how ecological processes behave with respect to the particular material at various sites of evolution, the future course of evolution is affected. But evolutionary and ecological processes behave at different rates and on different scales. Moreover, evolutionary change, while contingent, for the most part is irreversible, whereas ecological change, often necessary, sometimes can be reversed. All this is true whether we are talking about humans or not.

If we are talking about humans, then perforce human ecology is the link between human evolution and human environments. But there are some unrecognized implications. One is that human ecology is rooted in biophysical conditions, since evolution is a biological and physical affair, as are the assorted environments in which humans are given to function. Another is that human ecology encompasses social and cultural phenomena insofar as they relate to biophysical conditions, because some social and cultural phenomena are transparent adaptations to biophysical conditions, and the adaptations change the conditions. A third is that *contemporary* human relationships to biophysical environments, processes, and phenomena cannot be comprehended without relating the human condition to its evolutionary past.

But some investigations try to do this—some try, with a single-minded pursuit, to understand current human environmental predicaments, and even try to suggest how to correct them, uninformed by any consideration of the human evolutionary past. On the other hand, there are some investigations in which the pursuit of an understanding of human evolution stops there, as if evolution had stopped and none of it had any bearing on the present and future environmental predicaments of humans. This bifurcation of interest in evolutionary patterns as they historically developed or in topical environmental issues of the present, but not in both, to me is puzzling and curious. Evolution is about the past; environments in the present and the future *connect* to what happened in the past. Where we are depends upon where we were, not just historically speaking, but evolutionarily and ecologically speaking. To understand human environmental connections, we have to understand human evolutionary connections. And to understand human evolutionary prospects, we have to understand human environmental connections.

A third possible attitude, expressed throughout social science and rather astonishing, is to suppose that human evolutionary and environmental connections do not matter much. And, in the psychological experience of many people, indeed they do not.

With the shifting weight of control in human ecological interactions that was afforded by the development of fossil hydrocarbon technologies, substantially greater numbers of the human population, through its evolving social organizations, were now placed at some remove from the immediate feedback that biophysical systems inherently provide when they are exploited by simpler technologies using less efficient energy inputs. It was intended that political economies effect this—intended that they develop markets for goods, services, and labor that came to be several orders removed from any direct connection to biophysical, material processes, intended that technological and economic growth reduce the need for agricultural labor and provide for higher standards of living by means of economic and occupational specialization. But a concomitant effect—unintended—has been to insulate human sociocultural and politico-economic spheres of activity from ecosystem interactions, not in objective fact but in the subjective experience of the affected human populations, who no longer directly experience human life as lived on the ground but who, rather, experience life more in symbolic than material terms. That subjective experience seems perfectly natural, and its supporting attitude perfectly logical, because modern political economies are such vast networks of highly specialized exchange that their material bases can be ignored without penalty in many sectors of transaction. My tax accountant, pushing paper, might not recognize any indication of ecological penalties coming due.

But human life *is* lived on the ground, where survival and well-being are at issue always, precisely because of the material basis. So, the subjective experience of macrosocial industrialists and any attitude to rationalize the experience, is wholly delusionary.[1] With the rise and spread of macrosocial industrialism, human sociocultural development has proceeded at odds from human biological evolution to the point where, with respect to the material basis, we may have become evolutionarily cornered. Humans have embarked on a grand ecological experiment to test biospheric carrying capacity by substantially increasing their environmental impacts on increasingly disorganized biophysical systems and processes. The outcome of the experiment depends upon sustainable ecological connections between human evolution and human environments. If biosociocultural regimes do not get rended to the point where human ecological connections become unsustainable, then the material basis of human survival and well-being can be taken for granted, and a science of human ecology might have no significant problem to address.[2] But they do get rended, and the connections may indeed be unsustainable.

NOTES

1.   Apart from the false psychological comfort afforded within societies having vast surplus wealth, the delusion of disconnectedness is supported and often fully rationalized in social science theory. Here can be found Whitehead's fallacy of misplaced concreteness in the extreme. Here, theory so thoroughly confuses symbols with realities that it becomes an article of unyielding faith to suppose that symbolic constructions can be investigated *instead of* the realities the constructions are supposed to symbolize, or to suppose that the only realities worthy of investigation for the human case are symbolic, as if sociocultural systems were self-sustaining and not affected by any biophysical processes, conditions, or phenomena, or as if the symbolic meanings attributed to events were somehow more significant than the events. That such a theoretical posture is so widespread in social science is a testament to how much we have neglected the fact that humans, like every other living species, are material beings—the foundation of human ecology. The misplaced concreteness of social science theory is addressed in Chapter 1 of *Environmental Connections*.

2.   If the prophecies of the "apocalypse literature" are accepted as valid, then again there may be no problem to address. Price (1995), for instance, after briefly construing the role played by energy capture in human evolution and noting its significance for population growth, in roughly the manner we do in this work, concludes "this cannot

go on forever; collapse is inevitable. The only question is when" (p. 309). Perhaps, but if massive system collapse is inevitable in the manner that Price and other doomsdayers envision, with nothing remaining but relict human populations to subsist on the leavings, then further human ecological analysis is moot. I find the analyses of the doomsdayers too slanted and their conclusions too simple, and the analyses of what Catton (1980) calls cornucopians to be chock full of wishful thinking and dangerous delusions. Therefore, further human ecological analysis is necessary.

APPENDIX

Modern Evolutionary Systems Theory

The general theoretical frame for investigating dynamical, evolving, complex, self-organizing systems consists of a body of ideas whose unification is embryonic.[1] Dynamical, complex, self-organizing systems that are far from thermodynamic equilibrium are said to be dissipative:[2] able to maintain a temporary state of internal order by importing free energy and exporting wastes to a sink. The physical theory of nonequilibrium thermodynamics is, therefore, significant for conceiving and analyzing such systems. The acronym NET is sometimes used for nonequilibrium thermodynamics, but the terminology is far from settled. Because different sciences wishing to investigate different kinds of complex systems can benefit from the application of NET, some writers speak of the sciences of complexity. The domain over which the sciences of complexity can range is not yet settled either, but hypotheses range from the molecular to the astrophysical. More significantly, perhaps, the domain is potentially capable of including microscopic and macroscopic processes by integrating different scales and rates of interaction. The framework is potentially capable of describing systems defined so as to contain entities, relations, and processes of inherent interest to assorted different scientific disciplines at once—capable of defining new classes of phenomena that within current convention would be given the timid title of interdisciplinary. How this all plays out is a matter for the future, for this amalgamated body of ideas represents an unconventional paradigm for scientific knowledge that is just now gaining momentum. I refer to it all as evolutionary systems theory just so as not to prejudice arguments about fundamental properties, not all of which are yet matters of consensus. Nonlinear dynamical systems theory might be a better name, but that name does not advertise the evolutionary feature. There were evolutionary systems theory and dynamical systems theory before nonlinear, self-organizing systems became the rage of current theoretical interest.[3]

EVOLUTIONARY THEORY OLD AND NEW

In the new paradigm of evolutionary systems theory, naturally, still, the process of evolution is central. However, in case that reminds one of the theory of evolution by natural selection, the thought should be set aside. At issue is the evolution of complex, open systems far from thermodynamic equilibrium, and the theory of natural selection is useless to describe that. Instead, we must think of evolutionary theory applicable to entire systems, not just to populations of individuals. Systems evolution is not inconsistent with natural selection theory, but rather, we should say, is in some respects incommensurable. The incommensurability comes in so: Natural selection is about entities that respond to external conditions, whereas the evolution of self-organizing systems is about entities that respond to their own internal conditions. How does a system maintain an integrated state over time as it evolves from changes caused by its own internal interactions? How does it maintain its unity and integrity while its structures are changing? How does it reconstitute its structures, integrity, and process in the face of internally generated evolutionary changes?

With questions like these at issue, the theory of evolution by natural selection comes to be bracketed within a framework more general and fundamental than neo-Darwinism. This project has occupied many. Thus, Swenson (1991a, 1992, 1997) is able easily to interpret natural selection as just one facet of the evolutionary process by which order is produced out of disorder in dynamically open, far-from-equilibrium systems. Kauffman's (1993) extensive analysis, with more tortuous maneuvering, is able also to situate selection in a larger, evolutionary, complex, systems context. Wicken (1987) attempts to bracket and to extend neo-Darwinian selection theory with nonequilibrium thermodynamics. Numerous other angles for using NET to develop a general evolutionary theory, and the implications of such a theory for neo-Darwinism, can be found in Weber, Depew, and Smith (1988) and Brooks and Wiley (1986). And associates of the Sante Fe Institute, devoted to studies of complexity, have surrounded neo-Darwinian evolutionary adaptation (Cowan, Pines, and Meltzer 1994). Allowing for individual differences, the common tactic is to bring biological evolution into the framework of physical theory, and the common strategy is to develop the theory to describe evolutionary change as endogenetic, or internally driven. While some efforts, such as Kauffman's, are so broad-based as to consider nothing less than the origins of order (!), some are more specific. Thus, Ulanowicz (1986) developed an application to ecosystems, and Adams (1988), an application to sociocultural systems.

The modern developments in evolutionary systems theory have created a patchwork quilt that is coming to have its own complex order. But much of it is, in a way, a revitalization of an early tradition in evolutionary theory. The first recognizably scientific general theory of evolution that was applicable to entire systems, without regard for whether the systems were physical or biological, was formulated by Herbert Spencer (1862). Spencer's work is quaintly compatible with some of the fragments of the modern framework which bring back his concept of end-directed evolution (see Swenson 1991a, 1991b). Spencer continues to inspire efforts to construct general theories of progressive evolution applicable across sociocultural, biological, and physical domains—for example, Corning's (1983).

Neo-Darwinism provides a theory of the natural selection of adaptations (Williams 1966), and adaptation is a fundamental ecological process. So is interaction (Young 1996), which we may think of as the organized multilateral adaptations. But so is integration, which we may think of as the organized, multilateral, functional interactions that maintain the integrity of systems whose structures are undergoing internally generated evolutionary change. Evolutionary systems theory, being so comprehensive, provides a framework for models that can demonstrate, for ostensibly different kinds of system, common origins through homologous principles rather than just the formally similar or analogous evolutionary principles that are sometimes inferred by generalization from the theory of natural selection. With an evolutionary systems theory frame, we are in principle enabled to discover, and with a neo-Darwinian theory frame we are not, evolutionary and developmental principles that describe the ecological integration or disintegration of biophysical, economic, cultural, and social systems as historically situated—enabled to discover how they combine, or did combine, to function or to dysfunction ecologically as a biosociocultural system.[4]

There follows a brief sketch of the language commonly used to characterize some of the major properties of the frame of evolutionary systems theory. Readers familiar with the paradigm will know that the literature in question, to say nothing of specific modeling efforts, is highly technical once one goes beyond the broad generalities mentioned here—a difference clearly visible, for instance, when one compares Prigogine and Stengers'(1984) introduction to the theory frame with Nicolis and Prigogine's (1989) introduction to modeling within the frame. Our purpose here is pedagogical not technical, and if nothing else, perhaps we can get a sense of why some philosophers regard this body of ideas as providing, in effect, the underpinnings of a new scientific cosmology.[5]

FRAGMENTS OF THE EVOLUTIONARY SYSTEMS THEORY FRAME

The most general property of self-organizing systems—a view currently being refined by Swenson (1992, forthcoming)—is generally thought to be autopoiesis. This refers to the tendency of living systems to renew themselves, not in response to external perturbations but in a continuous process by which the systems regulate their own functioning in such a way as to preserve the integrity of their structures. This does not mean that system structures will not change. It means that the integrity of the system can be preserved through continuity in its functional processes *as* structures are changing. Specific structures dissolve into processes that give rise to new structures that evolve as the system regulates and renews itself over time. Thus, the term process-structure.

One ought not to think of process-structures as reified or reifiable. They are temporary structures-in-process, which means they represent dynamic regimes in which system organization may unfold through a variety of different organizational forms that an interaction process may generate. New organizational forms can emerge from a sequence of instabilities and their regimes can become stable for a time—until new instabilities initiate further change and new process-structures evolve. These process-structures are dissipative in that they regulate the relative proportions of free energy and entropy (energy lost) in the system. The function served by the evolution of dissipative process-structures is the importation of free energy or the exportation of entropy. Autopoietic systems are thus self-referential, and the point of self-reference is the energy state of the system. The evolution of new regimes of dissipative process-structures enables the system to maintain its order and organization—and, thus, its functioning. That's why we may talk about self-renewal. It can happen with, but only with, an exchange of energy through the system from and to its operating environment in such a way that the system is able to control, in something of an opportunistic manner, the production of entropy. The system's internal kinetic organization accomplishes this, and thus reinforces itself and maintains and renews the system, by importing from the system's environment resources for the system's own production process.

Attributing the property of autopoiesis (which we did implicitly to biosociocultural systems in Chapter 6) is not a backhanded way of imputing teleological purpose. When the organization of a system is geared to self-renewal, that is more correctly called teleonomic (cf. O'Grady and Brooks 1988), which need not imply goal-seeking activity. It should also be noted that self-renewal is not just another word for a tendency to return to a condition of homeostasis. The tendency is for system process-structures to evolve in a coherent way, in which new regimes of organization emerge from fluctuations that become accentuated, or from periodic instabilities.

Self-renewal becomes necessary whenever instabilities emerge in existing regimes of system organization, but why should there be instabilities in the first place? Simply because complex systems are subject to feedback from their own accumulated interactions. This property is called autocatalysis, which is an impetus for autopoiesis. Originally a technical term that referred to the condition in which a chemical molecule is necessary for a reaction that produces other molecules of its kind, autocatalysis is not limited to chemical reactions. The term applies to any system that changes from fluctuations initiated by the accumulation of its own internal interactions. Fluctuations may be expected to occur when feedback from system interactions beyond some critical threshold changes the conditions for future system interactions. Then the behavior of the system is propelled into a nonlinear range. Thus, self-organizing systems are said to be characterized by autocatalytic nonlinearities.

Any open system far from equilibrium that accumulates a sufficient interaction history—a well-functioning biosociocultural system, for instance—should be an autocatalytic, nonlinear, evolving, self-organizing system with an unfolding dynamic that, provided a sufficient threshold for fluctuations, drives it to reconstitute itself with new structures. When systems do that, they are said to be self-referential with respect to their own evolution.

Systems are self-referential when their own past interactions are incorporated into conditions that alter future system trajectories. When we understand this to be dependent upon energy exchanges with some environment and, with that, understand that entropy must be exported to that environment, we understand another fundamental property: the irreversibility of system processes. Time and the Second Law of thermodynamics, operating on a macroscopic scale, ensure that the overall effects of the processes of energetically open systems are irreversible. Ultimately, this is because the evolution and behavior of the energetic mass of the universe itself is thermodynamically irreversible. Energetic processes in macroscopic, open systems are time-directed, with nonlinear phase transitions. That leads to qualitative changes in system functioning when new dissipative-process structures emerge as adaptations to system instabilities. Systems whose interactions involve a large number of diffusely coupled nonlinear elements are driven far from equilibrium as free energy is increasingly imported. And its importing tends to increase in nonlinear systems because energetic processes favor structural regimes that import more. In other words, entropy tends to *decrease* not increase with time. New forms of order, represented by new dissipative structures, tend to arise spontaneously as the opportunity permits. Their evolution depends on the forms that preceded them. That evolution can go forward in time but cannot reverse because system processes will have undergone energetic phase transitions. A macroscopic description of a dissipative system with energetic phase transitions requires equations the structure of which is not invariant if time is reversed. So, as the system evolves there is no going back.

We are, of course, talking now about a system as a whole—its history and its evolution—and not about microscopic processes that may be embedded within it. Microscopic processes contained within may be reversible; indeed, the localized fluctuations of a self-organizing system are often microscopic and reversible. However, when a newly evolved macroscopic regime appears in response to a cascade of microscopic fluctuations or the amplified effects of a small number, the system's evolutionary trajectory becomes increasingly irreversible as time and the effects accumulate. Repetitive microscopic behavior in the system can generate feedback that is internally absorbed but, as it is, it gradually changes system conditions, propelling the behavior of macroscopic processes into a nonlinear range. This forces the system to bifurcate—to adopt alternative regimes and trajectories in the process of self-renewal. Once a bifurcation point is crossed, deterministic description is no longer possible; stochastic description now applies. Depending upon the choice of bifurcation alternatives, yet another system property may be observed: chaos.[6]

Chaos is a name for nonlinear motion in a system that is sensitive to its own initial conditions. The idea of sensitivity to initial conditions, first remarked upon by Henri Poincare, is that small differences or errors in the values for the initial state of a system may accumulate exponentially over time, with increasingly amplified effects on system processes, such that the system does not repeat its past behavior. Thus, future states of the system are not exactly predictable from initial conditions because the amplification of the effects of the initial parameter values produces irregular behavior that forms the intrinsic— chaotic—dynamics of the system. This does not imply that chaotic dynamics are random; to the contrary, they are determinate (which is not to say determinable). Chaos is not a name for disorganized behavior or chance fluctuations.

How important is chaos? Although chaos theory is only about thirty years old and in itself supplies no new physical hypotheses about the world, one authority calls chaos "a basic mode of motion underlying almost all natural phenomena ... neither exceptional nor peripheral" (Tomita 1986, p. 211). The operative word there is "underlying." "Overriding" might work, too. Speaking loosely, there are times when chaotic dynamics come to "control" the evolution of a system. But not all the time.

Chaotic dynamics do not always override system behavior because nonlinear systems may have regimes characterized by stable equilibria or stable cycles. But chaotic fluctuations may appear during phase transitions from normal periodicities. Chaotic system behavior is normally understood with respect to periodic system behavior. As an example of periodicity, we may think of the Lotka-Volterra equations for predator-prey interactions, and how they describe regular oscillations in the mortality of two species. Because the oscillations seem to be steady over time periods, one could calculate some average value for this periodicity, interpreting the average as an initial value for a system. But now imagine a community in which there were thousands of such interactions on varying scales each of which also represented an initial value for the system (community). If we consider that bilateral interactions are not isolated but are part of a network of multilateral interactions, we have now a great many initial values for this system—

too many really to estimate[7]—and we have not included any values for biogeochemical interactions. Still, for quite a while we could observe periodic behavior in the overall system, however extraordinarily complex it might be, aggregated of the various periodicities. But what is going to happen in the long run as these initial system values are subject to the effects of their own interactions? The values could change in such a way that system dynamics become chaotic, and that would permanently change the periodicities.

Chaos arises when periodicity fails. Periodicity can fail when parameter values are changed in certain respects, and autocatalytic systems in particular are subject to those respects. They provide their own input to naturally change parameter values and, thus, to alter the course of system evolution. The trajectory that represents the evolution of a system from its initial conditions to an end state may gravitate toward a single set of states, called attractors, and remain there. But a system that is sensitive to changes in its initial values, even though it may behave periodically for a time, can be driven into nonlinear ranges in which one or more of its trajectories bifurcate. At a bifurcation point, the system adopts an irregular pattern (irregular compared to its past behavior) as it undergoes a phase transition in response to the fluctuations that have accumulated from the amplified, time-dependent effects of its changed control parameters. Values that enable periodicity, when adjusted to sufficient extremes, become disturburances that can instigate a transition from a periodic to a chaotic state—a state of regular irregularity that may persist so long as the pattern of accumulated disturbances underlying it persists, and until a new and stable regime is organized when the phase transition is complete.

Thus nonlinear dynamical systems can exhibit chaotic motion out of which order is "spontaneously" generated from apparent disorder. A system's own interaction history may change the values for the initial conditions of interaction to a point where periodic fluctuations, in a condition far from equilibrium, introduce nonlinear discontinuities in system trajectories that eventually settle into new organizational regimes having new and unpredictable parameters in terms of which future system behavior proceeds. In this new regime, different periodicities may be established and previous periodicities may be changed or eliminated, because the system is now reorganized with new process-structures or new arrays of them. In a word, the system has evolved.

There is nothing to guarantee that a system will evolve. Systems can devolve as well. Dissipative systems that evolve, though their structures and organization may change, are order- and function-preserving. Devolution is the process of structure, order, and function decay. This will happen to any open system whose energy exchanges are inadequate to maintain the system far from equilibrium. A devolving system is one that is tending to equilibrium, which in energetic terms is heat death. In that event, we can expect structures, functions, and processes to break down. A complex, dynamical system can renew itself through evolution only if its continually changing initial conditions enable its functions to be sustained with reference to its energetic boundary conditions. These boundary conditions must be such as to permit the functions continually to create order out of disorder. Otherwise the functions degrade. Beyond critical thresholds, which will vary according to particular system characteristics, degraded functions may be unable to renew themselves. That turns the trajectory of the system toward increased entropy production, thus toward devolution, disintegration and, possibly, massive system collapse.

Clearly, the potential value of modeling evolutionary phenomena at a system level using the frame of nonlinear dynamical systems theory lies in the capability of models to incorporate parameter values that represent changes in the system's historical development. In this respect, assuming proper circumspection in the application of the theory frame and in model development, the possibility now presents itself for advancing a theory of developmental evolution for once adequate to connect sociocultural and biophysical systems. For both sorts of system, it is not risky to assume that, as time proceeds, autocatalytic effects introduce nonlinearities that change the conditions for evolution. Evidence for this is all over the board. The important fact for theory to note is that the changed conditions include the initial conditions themselves, which get peeled away. If what gave rise to what is no longer is, then whatever is cannot return to what it was. This is characteristic of biological evolution over the long term. The developmental evolution of biosociocultural regimes, penetrated and altered by social organizations and technologies, considered over a broad time frame, also ought to exhibit autocatalytic, nonlinear, dynamic effects in which the instituting of new regimes of system organization is both consequence and cause. The presumption of all this in Chapter 6 led to a counterintuitive theoretical implication, namely, that biosociocultural systems may evolve by descent with modification but without a preserved inheritance. Such an implication, if empirically true, introduces enormous complications to the study of systemic evolution in so far it has sociocultural components—which may explain why the theory of the subject, so old, is yet so new.

NOTES

1. Embryonic, but not all parts of which have recent origin. One of the major connections of the theory—between self-organization and nonequilibrium—is credited to the preeminent pathfinding theoretician in the line, Ilya Prigogine, in 1945 (Laszlo 1987, p. 28).

2. Self-organizing systems may be dissipative or conservative (see Jantsch 1980, chap. 2). Here, we consider only dissipative self-organization because of its significance for system evolution and for suggesting evolutionary connections between biophysical and sociocultural systems—the point in bringing up the subject.

3. It is instructive to observe the evolution of the thought and pedagogy of Ervin Laszlo in this regard. Laszlo, once a member of the infamous Club of Rome, in 1972 produced a useful but now-dated pedagogical introduction to a systems theory world view. The book contains only vague hints of some concepts that by 1987, in a book with similar purpose, Laszlo was now taking to be prominent if not definitive. In the earlier work, he had said, "The systems view of nature is one of harmony and dynamic balance" (p. 75). In the later work, in which fragments of the modern frame are introduced, he is much more cautious. Using a completely modern frame, he couldn't possibly say that, except by mistake.

4. But for now, applications that might further human ecological theory are only suggestive, for the social sciences have yet to become coupled to the complexity train. What few attempted couplings there have been should, with time, come to be regarded as naive and stupid—brave may be the nicest adjective anyone ever uses. But, we start where we must. With modesty, Dyke (1988) provided thoughtful insights, coherent analyses, and some closure for a variety of issues pertinent to theorizing about the evolution of biosociocultural systems, and he included fragments of a human ecological analysis of cities. With immodesty, I tried to identify an evolutionary process common to ecosystems and social systems in order to show how the two might be integrated (Freese 1988). With grandeur befitting a classic tradition (see Part B, chap. 4), Adams (1988) described social evolution in terms of the self-organization of energy. Olsen (1993a, 1993b) connected the immodest with the grand to suggest how sociocultural organization interfaces with socioecological organization. The idea in all cases was to develop a theory frame that would enable one to connect biophysical with sociocultural systems in ways that would enable a description of their evolutionary dynamics in nonlinear terms. But all of these efforts, including the qualitative model of Chapter 6, which occasioned this appendix, would depend upon substantial mathematical development if they were to have any cumulative results. It simply does not suffice to "picture" the evolution of complex systems, then tell a plausible story intended to describe their dynamics, and frame the story with vague language that evokes a sense of general laws—all of which I did in Chapter 6. The fundamental problem is those supposed general laws. Kauffman (1993) put the current consensus this way: "we have no general laws concerning the behavior of open, far-from-equilibrium systems. Indeed,

for apparently good reasons, we could not hope to have such laws" (p. 387). The "complexity revolution" which some take to augur the foundations of the science of the twenty-first century itself stands to generate some very complex science, which current related discourse in the social sciences only dimly comprehends. An exception is the combination of theory and application found in Giampietro (forthcoming) and Giampietro, Bukkens, and Pimentel (forthcoming).

5. Modern evolutionary systems theory requires fundamental changes in thoughtways—fundamental departures from the models of science that we have inherited from the past. For sheer simplicity, clarity, and quality of pedagogical discourse by which one may grasp for purposes of theorizing the necessary changes in thoughtways and world views, and comprehend how fundamental they really are, I unhesitatingly call the work of Chuck Dyke (1988, 1990, 1992, 1994, forthcoming) without peer.

6. Gleick's (1987) well-known and entertaining introduction of this subject to general audiences remains useful, and so is Kellert's (1993), but chaos too becomes mathematically technical very quickly. See Baker and Gollub (1990) for a technical introduction, Holden's (1986) anthology for some complications, and Glass and Mackey (1988) for an application to biological problems.

7. The behavior of a chaotic system is governed by equations that must contain at least three independent dynamical variables coupled with at least one nonlinear term. Periodic functions are useful for describing periodic system behavior, but periodic solutions to linear differential equations become unstable for certain parameter choices when a nonlinear term is introduced. Thus, chaotic dynamics require solutions to nonlinear differential equations.

References

Abbott, D.H. 1989. "Social Suppression of Reproduction in Primates." Pp. 285-304 in *Comparative Socioecology: The Behavioural Ecology of Humans and Other Mammals*, edited by V. Standen and R.A. Foley. Oxford: Blackwell Scientific Publications.

Adams, R.N. 1988. *The Eighth Day: Social Evolution as the Self-Organization of Energy*. Austin: University of Texas Press.

Alexander, R.D. 1979. *Darwinism and Human Affairs*. Seattle: University of Washington Press.

Anderson, J.N. 1973. "Ecological Anthropology and Anthropological Ecology." Pp. 179-239 in *Handbook of Social and Cultural Anthropology*, edited by J.J. Honigmann. Chicago: Rand McNally.

Aoki, K. 1985. "Reciprocal Altruism and Reciprocal Alliance Between Relatives." Pp. 429-441 in *Population Genetics and Molecular Evolution*, edited by T. Ohta and K. Aoki. Tokyo: Japan Scientific Societies Press.

Ashburn, P.M. 1947. *The Ranks of Death: A Medical History of the Conquest of America*. New York: Coward-McCann.

Axelrod, R. 1984. *The Evolution of Cooperation*. New York: Basic Books.

Axelrod, R., and D. Dion. 1988. "The Further Evolution of Cooperation." *Science* 242(December 9): 1385-1390.

Bahn, P., and J. Flenley. 1992. *Easter Island Earth Island*. London: Thames and Hudson.

Baker, G.L., and J.P. Gollub. 1990. *Chaotic Dynamics: An Introduction*. Cambridge: Cambridge University Press.

Bamforth, D.B. 1988. *Ecology and Human Organization on the Great Plains*. New York: Plenum.

Barinaga, M. 1992. "'African Eve' Backers Beat A Retreat." *Science* 255 (February 7): 686-687.

Basalla, G. 1988. *The Evolution of Technology*. Cambridge: Cambridge University Press.

Bell, R.W., and N.J. Bell, eds. 1989. *Sociobiology and the Social Sciences*. Lubbock: Texas Tech University Press.

Bennett, J.W. 1993. *Human Ecology As Human Behavior: Essays in Environmental and Development Anthropology*. New Brunswick, NJ: Transaction.

Berry, B.J., and J.M. Kasarda. 1977. *Contemporary Urban Ecology*. New York: Macmillan.

Bettinger, R.L. 1991. *Hunter-Gatherers: Archaeological and Evolutionary Theory*. New York: Plenum.

Bettinger, R.L., and M.A. Baumhoff. 1982. "The Numic Spread: Great Basin Cultures in Competition." *American Antiquity* 47: 485-503.

Bickerton, D. 1990. *Language and Species*. Chicago: University of Chicago Press.

Binford, L.R. 1980. "Willow Smoke and Dog's Tails: Hunter-Gatherer Settlement Systems and Archaeological Site Formation." *American Antiquity* 45: 4-20.

Black, F.L. 1992. "Why Did They Die?" *Science* 258(December 11): 1739-1740.

Bloom, B.R., and C.J.L. Murray. 1992. "Tuberculosis: Commentary on a Reemergent Killer." *Science* 257(August 21): 1055-1062.

Bodley, J.H. 1994. *Cultural Anthropology: Tribes, States, and the Global System*. Mountain View, CA: Mayfield.

Bonner, J.T. 1980. *The Evolution of Culture in Animals*. Princeton, NJ: Princeton University Press.

Bonner, J.T. 1988. *The Evolution of Complexity by Means of Natural Selection*. Princeton, NJ: Princeton University Press.

Borden, R.J. 1986. "Forward and Acknowledgements." Pp. v-vi in *Human Ecology: A Gathering of Perspectives*, edited by R.J. Borden, J. Jacobs, and G.L. Young. College Park, MD: Society for Human Ecology.

Borgstrom, G. 1965. *The Hungry Planet*. New York: Collier.

Boserup, E. 1965. *The Conditions of Agricultural Growth*. Chicago: Aldine.

Botkin, D.B. 1990. *Discordant Harmonies: A New Ecology for the Twenty-first Century*. Oxford: Oxford University Press.

Bowler, P.J. 1984. *Evolution: The History of an Idea*. Berkeley, CA: University of California Press.

Box, H.O. 1984. *Primate Behaviour and Social Ecology*. London: Chapman and Hall.

Boyce, M.S. 1984. "Restitution of r- and K-Selection as a Model of Density-Dependent Natural Selection." *Annual Review of Ecology and Systematics* 15: 427-447.

Boyd, R., and P.J. Richerson. 1985. *Culture and the Evolutionary Process*. Chicago: University of Chicago Press.

Bramwell, A. 1989. *Ecology in the Twentieth Century: A History*. New Haven, CT: Yale University Press.

Brandon, R.N. 1990. *Adaptation and Environment*. Princeton, NJ: Princeton University Press.

Brooks, D.R., and D.A. McLennan. 1991. *Phylogeny, Ecology, and Behavior*. Chicago: University of Chicago Press.

Brooks, D.R., and E.O. Wiley. 1986. *Evolution As Entropy: Toward A Unified Theory of Biology*. Chicago: University of Chicago Press.

Brown, W.L. 1984. "Hybrid Vim and Vigor." *Science* 84(November): 77-78.

Campbell, B. 1995. *Human Ecology*, 2nd ed. New York: Aldine de Gruyter.

Cann, R.L. 1988. "DNA and Human Origins." *Annual Review of Anthropology* 17: 127-143.

Cann, R.L., M. Stoneking, and A.C. Wilson. 1987. "Mitochondrial DNA and Human Evolution." *Nature* 325: 31-36.

Carneiro, R.L. 1970. "A Theory of the Origin of the State." *Science* 169: 733-738.

Catton, W.R., Jr. 1980. *Overshoot: The Ecological Basis of Revolutionary Change.* Urbana: University of Illinois Press.

———. 1983. "Social and Behavioral Aspects of the Carrying Capacity of Natural Environments." Pp. 269-306 in *Human Behavior and Environment: Advances in Theory and Research*, Vol. 6: *Behavior and the Natural Environment*, edited by I. Altman and J.F. Wohlwill. New York: Plenum.

———. 1984. "Probable Collective Responses To Ecological Scarcity." *Sociological Perspectives* 27(January): 3-20.

———. 1985. "On the Dire Destiny of Human Lemmings." Pp. 74-89 in *Deep Ecology*, edited by M. Tobias. San Diego, CA: Avant Books.

———. 1986. "Homo Colossus and the Technological Turn-Around." *Sociological Spectrum* 6: 121-147.

———. 1987. "The World's Most Polymorphic Species." *Bioscience* 37(June): 413-419.

———. 1993. "Carrying Capacity and the Death of a Culture: A Tale of Two Autopsies." *Sociological Inquiry* 63(May): 202-223.

———. 1995. "From Eukaryotic Cells to Gaia: The Range of Symbiosis and Its Relevance to Human Ecology." Pp. 1-34 in *Advances in Human Ecology*, Vol. 4, edited by L. Freese. Greenwich, CT: JAI Press.

Cavalli-Sforza, L.L., and M.W. Feldman. 1981. *Cultural Transmission and Evolution: A Quantitative Approach.* Princeton, NJ: Princeton University Press.

Chagnon, N.A., and W. Irons (eds.). 1979. *Evolutionary Biology and Human Social Behavior: An Anthropological Perspective.* North Scituate, MA: Duxbury Press.

Cheney, D., R. Seyfarth, and B. Smuts. 1986. "Social Relationships and Social Cognition in Nonhuman Primates." *Science* 234(December 12): 1361-1366.

Childe, V.G. 1952. *New Light on the Most Ancient East.* London: Routledge and Kegan Paul.

Cleveland, C.J. 1991. "Natural Resource Scarcity and Economic Growth Revisited: Economic and Biophysical Perspectives." Pp. 289-317 in *Ecological Economics: The Science and Management of Sustainability*, edited by R. Costanza. New York: Columbia University Press.

Cohen, J.E. 1995. *How Many People Can The Earth Support?* New York: W.W. Norton.

Cohen, M.N. 1977. *The Food Crisis in Prehistory.* New Haven, CT: Yale University Press.

———. 1989. *Health and the Rise of Civilization.* New Haven, CT: Yale University Press.

Cohen, M.L. 1992. "Epidemiology of Drug Resistance: Implications for a Post-Antimicrobial Era." *Science* 257(August 12): 1050-1055.

Coimbra, C.E.A. 1991. "Environmental Changes and Human Disease: A View From Amazonia." *Journal of Human Ecology* 2: 15-21.

Colinvaux, P. 1978. *Why Big Fierce Animals Are Rare: An Ecologist's Perspective.* Princeton, NJ: Princeton University Press.

Collins, F.H., and N.J. Besansky. 1994. "Vector Biology and the Control of Malaria." *Science* 264(June 24): 1874-1875.

Cook, E. 1971. "The Flow of Energy in an Industrial Society." *Scientific American* 224(3): 134-144.

Corning, P.A. 1983. *The Synergism Hypothesis: A Theory of Progressive Evolution.* New York: McGraw Hill.

Cowan, G.A., D. Pines, and D. Meltzer (eds.). 1994. *Complexity: Metaphors, Models, and Reality.* Reading, MA: Addison-Wesley.

Cowan, C.W., and P.J. Watson. 1992. *The Origins of Agriculture: An International Perspective.* Washington, DC: Smithsonian Institution Press.

Crosby, A.W. 1972. *The Columbian Exchange: Biological and Cultural Consequences of 1492.* Westport, CT: Greenwood Press.

_____. 1986. *Ecological Imperialism: The Biological Expansion of Europe, 900-1900.* Cambridge: Cambridge University Press.

Culotta, E. 1991. "How Many Genes Had to Change to Produce Corn?" *Science* 252(June 28): 1792-1793.

Daly, H.E., and J.B. Cobb, Jr. 1989. *For The Common Good.* Boston: Beacon Press.

Dawkins, R. 1976. *The Selfish Gene.* Oxford: Oxford University Press.

_____. 1982. *The Extended Phenotype: The Gene As The Unit of Selection.* Oxford: Oxford University Press.

_____. 1989 [1977]. *The Selfish Gene.* Oxford: Oxford University Press.

Debeir, J-C., J-P. Deleage, and D. Hemery. 1986. *In The Servitude of Power: Energy and Civilisation Through The Ages,* trans. J. Barzman. London: Zed Books.

Depew, D.J., and B.H. Weber (eds.). 1985. *Evolution At A Crossroads: The New Biology and the New Philosophy of Science.* Cambridge, MA: MIT Press.

_____. 1995. *Darwinism Evolving: Systems Dynamics and the Genealogy of Natural Selection.* Cambridge, MA: MIT Press.

Dhondt, A.A. 1988. "Carrying Capacity: A Confusing Concept." *Acta Oecologica* 9: 337-346.

Dobson, A.P., and E.R. Carper. 1996. "Infectious Diseases and Human Population History." *Bioscience* 46(February): 115-126.

Dobzhansky, T. 1962. *Mankind Evolving: The Evolution of the Human Species.* New Haven, CT: Yale University Press.

Douglas-Hamilton, I., and D. Douglas-Hamilton. 1975. *Among the Elephants.* New York: Viking Press.

Dunnell, R.C. 1988. "The Concept of Progress In Cultural Evolution." Pp. 169-194 in *Evolutionary Progress,* edited by M.H. Nitecki. Chicago: University of Chicago Press.

Durham, W.H. 1990. "Advances in Evolutionary Culture Theory." *Annual Review of Anthropology* 19: 187-210.

_____. 1991. *Coevolution: Genes, Culture, and Human Diversity.* Stanford, CA: Stanford University Press.

Durkheim, É. 1933. *The Division of Labor in Society.* New York: Free Press.

Dyke, C. 1988. *The Evolutionary Dynamics of Complex Systems: A Study In Biosocial Complexity.* Oxford: Oxford University Press.

_____. 1990. "Strange Attraction, Curious Liaison: Clio Meets Chaos." *The Philosophical Forum* 21: 369-392.

_____. 1992. "From Entropy to Economy: A Thorny Path." Pp. 149-176 in *Advances in Human Ecology,* Vol. 1, edited by L. Freese. Greenwich, CT: JAI Press.

————. 1994. "The World Around Us and How We Make It: Human Ecology As Human Artifact." Pp. 1-22 in *Advances in Human Ecology*, Vol. 3, edited by L. Freese. Greenwich, CT: JAI Press.

————. Forthcoming. "The Heuristics of Ecological Interaction." In *Advances in Human Ecology*, Vol. 6, edited by L. Freese. Greenwich, CT: JAI Press.

Eaton, G.G. 1976. "The Social Order of Japanese Macaques." *Scientific American* 235(October): 97-106.

Edgar, B. 1995. "Digging Up The Family Bones." *Bioscience* 45(November): 659-662.

Eldredge, N. 1985. *Unfinished Synthesis: Biological Heirarchies and Modern Evolutionary Thought.* New York: Oxford University Press.

Eldredge, N. 1989. *Macroevolutionary Dynamics.* New York: McGraw-Hill.

Elton, C. 1927. *Animal Ecology.* London: Sidgwick and Jackson.

————. 1933. *The Ecology of Animals.* London: Methuen.

Endler, J.A. 1986. *Natural Selection in the Wild.* Princeton, NJ: Princeton University Press.

Endler, J.A., and T. McLellan. 1988. "The Process of Evolution: Toward A Newer Synthesis." *Annual Review of Ecology and Systematics* 19: 395-421.

Englert, S. 1970. *Island At The Center of the World: New Light On Easter Island*, trans. W. Mulloy. New York: Schribner's.

Ereshefsky, M. (ed.). 1992. *The Units of Evolution: Essays on the Nature of Species.* Cambridge, MA: MIT Press.

Ewald, P.W. 1994. *Evolution of Infectious Disease.* Oxford: Oxford University Press.

Fearnside, P.M. 1986. *Human Carrying Capacity of the Brazilian Rainforest.* New York: Columbia University Press.

Fiorito, G., and P. Scotto. 1992. "Observational Learning in *Octopus vulgaris*." *Science* 256(April 24): 545-547.

Fogle, T. 1990. "Are Genes Units of Inheritance?" *Biology and Philosophy* 5: 349-371.

Foley, R.A. 1989. "The Evolution of Hominid Social Behavior." Pp. 473-494 in *Comparative Socioecology: The Behavioural Ecology of Humans and Other Mammals*, edited by V. Standen and R.A. Foley. Oxford: Blackwell Scientific Publications.

Foley, R.A., and P.C. Lee. 1989. "Finite Social Space, Evolutionary Pathways, and Reconstructing Hominid Behavior." *Science* 243(February 17): 901-906.

Ford, R.E. 1994. "A Geographer Comments on 'Sex and the Single Planet.'" *Human Ecology Review* 1(Summer/ Autumn): 240-244.

Freese, L. 1988. "Evolution and Sociogenesis, Parts 1 and 2." Pp. 53-118 in *Advances in Group Processes*, Vol. 5, edited by E. Lawler and B. Markovsky. Greenwich, CT: JAI Press.

————. 1994. "Evolutionary Tangles for Sociocultural Systems: Some Clues from Biology." Pp. 139-171 in *Advances in Human Ecology,* Vol. 3, edited by L. Freese. Greenwich, CT: JAI Press.

————. 1995. "From Commons to Traps: Natural Balance and Human Ecological Series." Pp. 117-140 in *Advances in Human Ecology*, Vol. 4, edited by L. Freese. Greenwich, CT: JAI Press.

Fried, M.H. 1978. "The State, the Chicken, and the Egg: Or, What Came First." Pp. 35-48 in *Origins of the State: The Anthropology of Political Evolution*, edited by R. Cohen and E.R. Service. Philadelphia, PA: Institute for the Study of Human Issues.

Garnett, G.P., and E.C. Holmes. 1996. "The Ecology of Emergent Infectious Disease." *Bioscience* 46(February): 127-135.

Garrett, L. 1995. *The Coming Plague: Newly Emerging Diseases in a World Out of Balance.* New York: Farrar, Straus, and Giroux.

Ghiselin, M.T. 1981. "Categories, Life, and Thinking." *Behavioral and Brain Sciences* 4: 269-313.

Giampietro, M. Forthcoming. "Linking Technology, Natural Resources, and Socioeconomic Structure of Human Society: A Theoretical Model." In *Advances In Human Ecology,* Vol. 6, edited by L. Freese. Greenwich, CT: JAI Press.

Giampietro, M., S.G.F. Bukkens, and D. Pimentel. Forthcoming. "Linking Technology, Natural Resources, and Socioeconomic Structure of Human Society: Examples and Applications." In *Advances in Human Ecology,* Vol. 6, edited by L. Freese. Greenwich, CT: JAI Press.

Gibbons, A. 1991. "Yanomami People Threatened." *Science* 252(June 21): 1616.

_____. 1995. "The Mystery of Humanity's Missing Mutations." *Science* 267(January 6): 35-36.

Glass, L., and M.C. Mackey. 1988. *From Clocks to Chaos: The Rhythms of Life.* Princeton, NJ: Princeton University Press.

Gleick, J. 1987. *Chaos: Making A New Science.* New York: Viking.

Goodall, J. 1986. *The Chimpanzees of Gombe: Patterns of Behavior.* Cambridge, MA: Harvard University Press.

_____. 1990. *Through A Window: My Thirty Years with the Chimpanzees of Gombe.* Boston: Houghton Mifflin.

Goudie, A. 1990. *The Human Impact on the Natural Environment,* 3rd edition. Cambridge, MA: MIT Press.

Gould, S.J. 1977. *Ontogeny and Phylogeny.* Cambridge, MA: Harvard.

Grant, V. 1991. *The Evolutionary Process: A Critical Study of Evolutionary Theory,* 2nd edition. New York: Columbia University Press.

Gregg, S.A. 1988. *Foragers and Farmers: Population Interaction and Agricultural Expansion in Prehistoric Europe.* Chicago: University of Chicago Press.

Hall, C.A.S. 1988. "An Assessment of Several of the Historically Most Influential Theoretical Models Used in Ecology and of the Data Provided in their Support." *Ecological Modeling* 43: 5-31.

Hallpike, C.R. 1986. *The Principles of Social Evolution.* Oxford: Clarendon Press.

_____. 1992. "Illusions of Darwinism." Report #15/92 of the Research Group on Biological Foundations of Human Culture, University of Bielefeld, Center for Interdisciplinary Research.

Hamilton, W.D. 1964. "The Genetical Evolution of Social Behavior, Parts 1 and 2." *Journal of Theoretical Biology* 7: 1-32.

Haraway, D. 1989. *Primate Visions: Gender, Race and Nature in the World of Modern Science.* New York: Routledge.

_____. 1991. *Simians, Cyborgs, and Women: The Reinvention of Nature.* New York: Routledge.

Hardesty, D.L. 1977. *Ecological Anthropology.* New York: John Wiley.

Hardin, G. 1968. "The Tragedy of the Commons." *Science* 162: 1243-1248.

————. 1993. *Living Within Limits: Ecology, Economics, and Population Taboos.* Oxford: Oxford University Press.

Harris, M. 1977. *Cannibals and Kings: The Origins of Cultures.* New York: Random House.

Hart, H. 1959. "Social Theory and Social Change." In *Symposium On Sociological Theory*, edited by L. Gross. New York: Harper and Row.

Hawley, A.H. 1971. *Urban Society: An Ecological Approach.* New York: Ronald Press.

Hayes, K.C., and C. Hayes. 1952. "Imitation in a Home-Raised Chimpanzee." *Journal of Comparative and Physiological Psychology* 45: 450-459.

Hedges, S.B., S. Kumar, K. Tamura, and M. Stoneking. 1992. "Human Origins and Analysis of Mitochondrial DNA Sequences." *Science* 255(February 7): 737-739.

Heltne, P.G., and L.A. Marquardt (eds.). 1989. *Understanding Chimpanzees.* Cambridge, MA: Harvard University Press.

Henderson, D.A. 1976. "The Eradication of Smallpox." *Scientific American* 235(October): 25-33.

Henige, D. 1992. "Standards of Proof and Discursive Strategies in the Debate over Native American Population at Contact." Paper presented at the Annual Meeting of the American Association for the Advancement of Science, February 8, Chicago.

Heyerdahl, T., and E.N. Ferndon, Jr. (eds.). 1961. *Archaeology of Easter Island.* London: Allen and Unwin.

Holden, A.V. (ed.). 1986. *Chaos.* Princeton, NJ: Princeton University Press.

Hopkins, D.R. 1983. *Princes and Peasants: Smallpox in History.* Chicago: University of Chicago Press.

Hunt, G.R. 1996. "Manufacture and Use of Hook-tools by New Caledonian Crows." *Nature* 379(January 18): 249-251.

Huxley, J. 1942. *Evolution: The Modern Synthesis.* London: Allen and Unwin.

Inhorn, M.C., and P.J. Brown. 1990. "The Anthropology of Infectious Disease." *Annual Review of Anthropology* 19: 89-117.

Jaeger, C.C. 1993. "Sustainable Regional Development: A Path for The Greenhouse Marathon." Pp. 163-190 in *Advances in Human Ecology*, Vol. 2, edited by L. Freese. Greenwich, CT: JAI Press.

Jantsch, E. 1980. *The Self-Organizing Universe: Scientific and Human Implications of the Emerging Paradigm of Evolution.* Oxford: Pergamon Press.

Johnson, A.W., and T. Earle. 1987. *The Evolution of Human Societies: From Foraging Group to Agrarian State.* Stanford, CA: Stanford University Press.

Joklik, W.K., B. Moss, B.N. Fields, D.H.L. Bishop, and L.S. Sandakgshiev. 1993. "Why the Smallpox Virus Stocks Should Not Be Destroyed." *Science* 262(November 19): 1225-1226.

Kaplan, H., and K. Hill. 1992. "The Evolutionary Ecology of Food Acquisition." Pp. 167-201 in *Evolutionary Ecology and Human Behavior*, edited by E.A. Smith and B. Winterhalder. New York: Aldine De Gruyter.

Kauffman, S. 1993. *The Origins of Order: Self-Organization and Selection in Evolution.* Oxford: Oxford University Press.

Kaye, H.L. 1986. *The Social Meaning of Modern Biology.* New Haven, CT: Yale University Press.

Kellert, S.H. 1993. *In The Wake of Chaos.* Chicago: University of Chicago Press.

Kimura, M. 1983. *The Neutral Theory of Molecular Evolution.* Cambridge: Cambridge University Press.

Kingsland, S.E. 1985. *Modeling Nature: Episodes in the History of Population Ecology.* Chicago: University of Chicago Press.

Kinzey, W.G. (ed.). 1987. *The Evolution of Human Behavior: Primate Models.* Albany, NY: State University of New York Press.

Kipple, K.F. (ed.). 1988. *The African Exchange: Toward A Biological History of Black People.* Durham, NC: Duke University Press.

Kitcher, P. 1984. "1953 and All That: A Tale of Two Sciences." *The Philosophical Review* 93: 335-373.

_____. 1985. *Vaulting Ambition: Sociobiology and the Quest for Human Nature.* Cambridge, MA: MIT Press.

Klein, D.R. 1968. "The Introduction, Increase, and Crash of Reindeer on St. Matthew Island." *Journal of Wildlife Management* 32: 350-367.

Kolberg, R. 1994. "Finding 'Sustainable' Ways to Prevent Parasitic Diseases." *Science* 264(June 24): 1859-1861.

Krause, R.M. 1992. "The Origin of Plagues: Old and New." *Science* 257(August 21): 1073-1078.

Krebs, J.R., and N.B. Davies (eds.). 1991. *Behavioural Ecology: An Evolutionary Approach,* 3rd ed. Oxford: Blackwell.

Kroeber, A.L. 1948. *Anthropology: Culture Patterns and Processes,* rev. ed. New York: Harcourt, Brace, and World.

Laszlo, E. 1972. *The Systems View of the World.* New York: Braziller.

_____. 1987. *Evolution: The Grand Synthesis.* Boston, MA: Shambhala.

Lawrence, D.L., and S.M. Low. 1990. "The Built Environment and Spatial Form." *Annual Review of Anthropology* 19: 453-505.

Lenski, G., J. Lenski, and P. Nolan. 1991. *Human Societies: An Introduction to Macrosociology,* 6th ed. New York: McGraw Hill.

Leopold, A. 1933. *Game Management.* New York: Charles Scribner's Sons.

Levins, R. 1968. *Evolution in Changing Environments: Some Theoretical Explorations.* Princeton, NJ: Princeton University Press.

Levins, R., and R.C. Lewontin. 1985. *The Dialectical Biologist.* Cambridge, MA: Harvard University Press.

Lindeman, R.L. 1942. "The Trophic-Dynamic Aspect of Ecology." *Ecology* 23: 399-417.

Livingstone, F.B. 1958. "Anthropological Implications of Sickle-Cell Gene Distribution in West Africa." *American Anthropologist* 60: 533-562.

_____. 1971. "Malaria and Human Polymorphisms." *Annual Review of Genetics* 5: 33-64.

Lockhard, J.S. (ed.). 1980. *The Evolution of Human Social Behavior.* New York: Elsevier.

Lopreato, J. 1984. *Human Nature and Biocultural Evolution.* Boston, MA: Allen and Unwin.

Lotka, A.J. 1922. "Contribution to the Energetics of Evolution." *Proceedings of the National Academy of Science* 8: 147-151.

_____. 1956 [1924]. *Elements of Mathematical Biology.* New York: Dover.

Low, B.S., A.L. Clarke, and K.A. Lockridge. 1992. "Toward An Ecological Demography." *Population and Development Review* 18(March): 1-31.

Lumsden, C.J., and E.O. Wilson. 1981. *Genes, Mind, and Culture: The Coevolutionary Process.* Cambridge, MA: Harvard University Press.

MacArthur, R.H., and E.D. Wilson. 1967. *The Theory of Island Biogeography.* Princeton, NJ: Princeton University Press.

Machalek, R. 1992. "The Evolution of Macrosociety: Why Are Large Societies Rare?" Pp. 33-64 in *Advances in Human Ecology*, Vol. 1, edited by L. Freese. Greenwich, CT: JAI Press.

————. 1995. "Basic Dimensions and Forms of Social Exploitation: A Comparative Analysis." Pp. 35-68 in *Advances in Human Ecology*, Vol. 4, edited by L. Freese. Greenwich, CT: JAI Press.

————. 1996. "The Evolution of Social Exploitation." Pp. 1-32 in *Advances in Human Ecology*, Vol. 5, edited by L. Freese. Greenwich, CT: JAI Press.

Machalek, R., and L.E. Cohen. 1991. "The Nature of Crime: Is Cheating Necessary for Cooperation?" *Human Nature* 2: 215-233.

Mahy, B.W.J., J.W. Almond, K.I. Berns, R.M. Chanock, D.K. Lvov, R.F. Pettersson, H.G. Schatzmayr, and F. Fenner. 1993. "The Remaining Stocks of Smallpox Virus Should Be Destroyed." *Science* 262(November 19): 1223-1224.

Mainardi, D. 1980. "Tradition and the Social Transmission of Behavior in Animals." Pp. 227-255 in *Sociobiology: Beyond Nature/Nurture?*, edited by G.W. Barlow and J. Silverberg. Boulder, CO: Westview Press.

Malthus, T.R. 1872. *An Essay on the Principle of Population*, 7th ed. London: Reeves and Turner.

Maryanski, A. 1992. "The Last Ancestor: An Ecological Network Model on the Origins of Human Sociality." Pp. 1-32 in *Advances in Human Ecology*, Vol. 1, edited by L. Freese. Greenwich, CT: JAI Press.

Maryanski, A., and J.H. Turner. 1992. *The Social Cage: Human Nature and the Evolution of Society.* Stanford, CA: Stanford University Press.

Mascie-Taylor, C.G.N. 1993. "The Biological Anthropology of Disease." Pp. 1-72 in *The Anthropology of Disease*, edited by C.G.N. Masci-Taylor. Oxford: Oxford University Press.

Maurice, J. 1995. "Virus Wins Stay of Execution." *Science* 267(January 27): 450.

May, J.M. 1958. *The Ecology of Human Disease.* New York: MD Publications.

Maynard Smith, J. 1974. "The Theory of Games and the Evolution of Animal Conflict." *Journal of Theoretical Biology* 47: 209-221.

————. 1978. "The Evolution of Behavior." *Scientific American* 239: 176-192.

————. 1982. *Evolution and the Theory of Games.* Cambridge: Cambridge University Press.

Mayr, E. 1982. *The Growth of Biological Thought: Diversity, Evolution, and Inheritance.* Cambridge, MA: Harvard University Press.

————. 1988. *Toward A New Philosophy of Biology: Observations of an Evolutionist.* Cambridge, MA: Harvard University Press.

Maziere, F. 1968. *Mysteries of Easter Island.* New York: Norton.

McElroy, A., and P.K. Townsend. 1989. *Medical Anthropology in Ecological Perspective*, 2nd ed. Boulder, CO: Westview Press.

McGrew, W.C. 1989. "Why Is Ape Tool Use So Confusing?" Pp. 457-472 in *Comparative Socioecology: The Behavioural Ecology of Humans and Other Mammals*, edited by V. Standen and R.A. Foley. Oxford: Blackwell Scientific Publications.

_____. 1992. *Chimpanzee Material Culture: Implications for Human Evolution.* Cambridge: Cambridge University Press.

_____. 1994. "Tools Compared: The Material of Culture." Pp. 25-39 in *Chimpanzee Cultures,* edited by R.W.C. Wrangham, W.C. McGrew, F.B.M. de Waal, and P.G. Heltne. Cambridge, MA: Harvard University Press.

McIntosh, R.P. 1985. *The Background of Ecology: Concept and Theory.* Cambridge: Cambridge University Press.

McNeill, W.H. 1976. *Plagues and Peoples.* Garden City, NY: Anchor Books.

Mead, G.H. 1934. *Mind, Self, and Society.* Chicago: University of Chicago Press.

_____. 1936. *The Philosophy of the Act.* Chicago: University of Chicago Press.

Meddin, J. 1979. "Chimpanzees, Symbols, and the Reflective Self." *Social Psychology Quarterly* 42: 99-109.

Micklin, M., and H.M. Choldin. 1984. *Sociological Human Ecology: Contemporary Issues and Applications.* Boulder, CO: Westview Press.

Modahl, K.B., and G.G. Eaton. 1977. "Display Behaviour in a Confined Troop of Japanese Macaques (*Macaca fuscata*)." *Animal Behavior* 25: 525-535.

Moore, J.A. 1985. "Science as a Way of Knowing—Human Ecology." *American Zoologist* 25: 483-637.

Morgan, L.H. 1887. *Ancient Society.* Chicago: Charles H. Kerr.

Mulloy, W. 1967. "Easter Island." *Natural History* 76(December): 74-81.

_____. 1974. "Contemplate The Navel of the World." *Americas* 26(April): 25-33.

Neu, H.C. 1992. "The Crisis in Antibiotic Resistance." *Science* 257(August 21): 1064-1073.

Nicolis, G., and I. Prigogine. 1989. *Exploring Complexity.* New York: Freeman.

Odum, E.P. 1953. *Fundamentals of Ecology.* Philadelphia, PA: Saunders.

_____. 1989. *Ecology and Our Endangered Life-Support Systems.* Sunderland, MA: Sinauer Associates.

O'Grady, R.T., and D.R. Brooks. 1988. "Teleology and Biology." Pp. 285-316 in *Entropy, Information, and Evolution: New Perspectives on Physical and Biological Evolution,* edited by B.H. Weber, D.J. Depew, and J.D. Smith. Cambridge, MA: MIT Press.

Olsen, M.E. 1992. "The Energy Consumption Turnaround and Socioeconomic Well-Being in Industrial Societies in the 1980s." Pp. 197-234 in *Advances in Human Ecology,* Vol. 1, edited by L. Freese. Greenwich, CT: JAI Press.

_____. 1993a. "Components of Socioecological Organization: Tools, Resources, Energy, and Power." Pp. 35-67 in *Advances in Human Ecology,* Vol. 2, edited by L. Freese. Greenwich, CT: JAI Press.

_____. 1993b. "A Socioecological Perspective on Social Evolution." Pp. 69-92 in *Advances in Human Ecology,* Vol. 2, edited by L. Freese. Greenwich, CT: JAI Press.

Orians, G.H. 1980. "Micro and Macro in Ecological Theory." *Bioscience* 30: 79.

Oster, G.F., and E.O. Wilson. 1978. *Caste and Ecology in the Social Insects.* Princeton, NJ: Princeton University Press.

Packer, C. 1986. "The Ecology of Sociality in Felids." Pp. 429-451 in *Ecological Aspects of Social Evolution: Birds and Mammals,* edited by D.I. Rubenstein and R.W. Wrangham. Princeton, NJ: Princeton University Press.

Parkinson, C.N. 1957. *Parkinson's Law and Other Studies in Administration.* Boston: Houton Mifflin.

Peirce, C.S. 1958. *Selected Writings: Values In A Universe of Chance.* New York: Dover.

Petersen, W. 1961. *Population.* New York: Macmillan.

————. 1979. *Malthus.* Cambridge, MA: Harvard University Press.

Pianka, E.R. 1970. "On *r*- and *K*-selection." *American Naturalist* 106: 592-597.

————. 1994. *Evolutionary Ecology,* 5th ed. New York: Harper Collins.

Plotkin, H.C. (ed.). 1988. *The Role of Behavior in Evolution.* Cambridge, MA: MIT Press.

Ponting, C. 1991. *A Green History of the World.* New York: St. Martin's Press.

Potts, R. 1987. "Reconstructions of Early Hominid Socioecology: A Critique of Primate Models." Pp. 28-47 in *The Evolution of Human Behavior: Primate Models,* edited by W.G. Kinzey. Albany: State University of New York Press.

————. 1991. "Untying the Knot: Evolution of Early Human Behavior." Pp. 41-59 in *Man and Beast Revisited,* edited by M.H. Robinson and L. Tiger. Washington, DC: Smithsonian Institution Press.

Povinelli, D.J. 1994. "What Chimpanzees (Might) Know about the Mind." Pp. 285-300 in *Chimpanzee Cultures,* edited by R.W.C. Wrangham, W.C. McGrew, F.B.M. de Waal, and P.G. Heltne. Cambridge, MA: Harvard University Press.

Price, D. 1995. "Energy and Human Evolution." *Population and Environment: A Journal of Interdisciplinary Studies* 16(March): 301-319.

Prigogine, I., and I. Stengers. 1984. *Order Out of Chaos: Man's New Dialogue With Nature.* Toronto: Bantam Books.

Pyke, G.H. 1984. "Optimal Foraging Theory: A Critical Review." *Annual Review of Ecology and Systematics* 15: 523-575.

Ramenofsky, A.F. 1987. *Vectors of Death: The Archaeology of European Contact.* Albuquerque: University of New Mexico Press.

Rappaport, R.A. 1990. "Ecosystems, Populations, and People." Pp. 41-72 in *The Ecosystem Approach In Anthropology,* edited by E.F. Moran. Ann Arbor: University of Michigan Press.

Reynolds, V., V.S.E. Falger, and I. Vine (eds.). 1986. *The Sociobiology of Ethnocentrism.* Athens: University of Georgia Press.

Roberts, L. 1988. "Disease and Death in the New World." *Science* 246(December 8): 1245-1247.

Rosenberg, A. 1985. *The Structure of Biological Science.* Cambridge: Cambridge University Press.

Rumbaugh, D.M., E.S. Savage-Rumbaugh, and R.A. Sevick. 1994. "Behavioral Roots of Language: A Comparative Perspective of Chimpanzee, Child, and Culture." Pp. 319-334 in *Chimpanzee Cultures,* edited by R.W.C. Wrangham, W.C. McGrew, F.B.M. de Waal, and P.G. Heltne. Cambridge, MA: Harvard University Press.

Sale, K. 1990. *The Conquest of Paradise: Christopher Columbus and the Columbian Legacy.* New York: Plume.

————. 1995. *Rebels Against The Future.* Reading, MA: Addison-Wesley.

Sanderson, S.K. 1990. *Social Evolutionism: A Critical History.* Cambridge, MA: Basil Blackwell.

Sebiok, T.A. 1991. *A Sign Is Just A Sign.* Bloomington: Indiana University Press.

Service, E.R. 1975. *Origins of the State and Civilization: The Process of Cultural Evolution.* New York: W. W. Norton.

Simmons, I.G. 1989. *Changing the Face of the Earth: Culture, Environment, History.* New York: Basil Blackwell.

Simons, E.L. 1989. "Human Origins," *Science* 245(September 22): 1343-1350.

Slobodkin, L.B. 1972. "On The Inconstancy of Ecological Efficiency and the Form of Ecological Theories." Pp. 291-306 in *Growth By Intussusception: Ecological Essays in Honor of G. Evelyn Hutchinson*, edited by E. Deevey. *Transactions of the Connecticut Academy of Sciences*, Vol. 44.

Smith, A. 1964 [1776]. *The Wealth of Nations*, Vol. 1. London: Dent.

Smith, E.A., and B. Winterhalder (eds.). 1992. *Evolutionary Ecology and Human Behavior*. New York: Aldine de Gruyter.

Snipp, C.M. 1986. "Who Are American Indians?: Some Observations About the Perils and Pitfalls of Data for Race and Ethnicity." *Population Research and Population Review* 5: 237-252.

Sober, E. 1984a. *The Nature of Selection: Evolutionary Theory In Philosophical Focus*. Cambridge, MA: MIT Press.

———— (ed.). 1984b. *Conceptual Issues in Evolutionary Biology: An Anthology*. Cambridge, MA: MIT Press.

Sober, E., and R.C. Lewontin. 1984. "Artifact, Cause, and Genic Selection." Pp. 210-231 in *Conceptual Issues in Evolutionary Biology: An Anthology*, edited by E. Sober. Cambridge, MA: MIT Press.

Spencer, H. 1862. *First Principles*. London: Williams and Norgate.

Sprugel, D.G. 1985. "Natural Disturbance and Ecosystem Energetics." Pp. 335-352 in *The Ecology of Natural Disturbance and Patch Dynamics*, edited by S.T.A. Pickett and P.S. White. Orlando, FL: Academic Press.

Stannard, D.E. 1992. *American Holocaust: Columbus and the Conquest of the New World*. New York: Oxford University Press.

Stebbins, G.L., and F.J. Ayala. 1981. "Is A New Evolutionary Synthesis Necessary?" *Science* 213: 967-971.

Stern, P.C. 1993. "A Second Environmental Science: Human-Environmental Interactions." *Science* 260(June 25): 1897-1899.

Strong, D.R., D. Simberloff, L.G. Abele, and A.B. Thistle (eds.). 1984. *Ecological Communities: Conceptual Issues and the Evidence*. Princeton, NJ: Princeton University Press.

Swenson, Rod. 1991a. "End-Directed Physics and Evolutionary Ordering: Obviating the Problem of the Population of One." Pp. 41-59 in *The Cybernetics of Complex Systems: Self-Organization, Evolution and Social Change*, edited by F. Geyer. Salinas, CA: Intersystems Publications.

————. 1991b. "Order, Evolution, and Natural Law: Fundamental Relations in Complex Systems Theory." Pp. 125-148 in *Cybernetics and Applied Systems*, edited by C. Negoita. New York: Marcel Dekker.

————. 1992. "Autocatakinetics, yes—Autopoiesis, no: Steps Towards A Unified Theory of Evolutionary Ordering." *International Journal of General Systems Research* 21: 207-228.

————. 1997. *Spontaneous Order, Evolution, and Natural Law: An Introduction to the Physical Basis for an Ecological Psychology*. Hillsdale, NJ: Lawrence Earlbaum Associates.

————. Forthcoming. "Autocatakinetics, Evolution, and the Law of Maximum Entropy Production: A Principled Foundation Towards the Study of Human

Ecology." In *Advances in Human Ecology*, Vol. 6, edited by L. Freese. Greenwich, CT: JAI Press.

Tanner, J.T. 1966. "Effects of Population Density on Growth Rates of Animal Populations." *Ecology* 47: 733-745.

Templeton, A.R. 1992. "Human Origins and Analysis of Mitochondrial DNA Sequences." *Science* 255(February 7): 737.

Theodorson, G.A. (ed.). 1961. *Studies in Human Ecology*. Evanston, IL: Row, Peterson.

Tomita, K. 1986. "Periodically Forced Nonlinear Oscillators." Pp. 211-236 in *Chaos*, edited by A.V. Holden. Princeton, NJ: Princeton University Press.

Tooby, J., and I. DeVore. 1987. "The Reconstruction of Hominid Behavioral Evolution Through Strategic Modeling." Pp. 183-237 in *The Evolution of Human Behavior: Primate Models*, edited by W.G. Kinzey. Albany: State University of New York Press.

Trinkhaus, E., and P. Shipman. 1993. *The Neandertals: Changing the Image of Mankind*. New York: Alfred A. Knopf.

Trivers, R.L. 1971. "The Evolution of Reciprocal Altruism." *Quarterly Review of Biology* 46: 35-57.

Turk, J., and A. Turk. 1984. *Environmental Science*, 3rd ed. New York: Saunders.

Turnbull, C.M. 1972. *The Mountain People*. New York: Simon and Schuster.

————. 1978. "Rethinking the Ik: A Functional Non-Social System." Pp. 49-75 in *Extinction and Survival in Human Populations*, edited by C.D. Laughlin, Jr., and I.A. Brady. New York: Columbia University Press.

Turner, J.H. 1985. *Herbert Spencer: A Renewed Appreciation*. Newbury Park, CA: Sage.

Ulanowicz, R. 1986. *Growth and Development: Ecosystems Phenomenology*. New York: Springer-Verlag.

van den Berghe, P.L. 1979. *Human Family Systems: An Evolutionary View*. New York: Elsevier.

van Hoof, J.A.R.A.M. 1994. "Understanding Chimpanzee Understanding." Pp.267-284 in *Chimpanzee Cultures*, edited by R.W.C. Wrangham, W.C. McGrew, F.B.M. de Waal, and P.G. Heltne. Cambridge, MA: Harvard University Press.

Vasey, D.E. 1992. *An Ecological History of Agriculture: 10,000 B.C.-A.D. 10,000*. Ames: Iowa State University Press.

Vayda, A.P. 1995a. "Failures of Explanation in Darwinian Ecological Anthropology: Part 1." *Philosophy of the Social Sciences* 25(June): 219-249.

————. 1995b. "Failures of the Explanation in Darwinian Ecological Anthropology: Part 2." *Philosophy of the Social Sciences* 25(September): 360-375.

Vitousek, P.M., P.R. Ehrlich, A.H. Erhlich, and P.A. Matson. 1986. "Human Appropriation of the Products of Photosynthesis." *Bioscience* 36(June): 368-380.

Walker, S. 1983. *Animal Thought*. London: Routledge and Kegan Paul.

Weber, B.H., D.J. Depew, and J.D. Smith (eds.). 1988. *Entropy, Information, and Evolution: New Perspectives on Physical and Biological Evolution*. Cambridge, MA: MIT Press.

White, L. 1949. *The Science of Culture*. New York: Farrar, Strauss, and Giroux.

Wicken, J.S. 1987. *Evolution, Thermodynamics, and Information*. New York: Oxford.

Wiegele, T.C. (ed.). 1982. *Biology and the Social Sciences: An Emerging Revolution*. Boulder, CO: Westview Press.

Wiens, J.A. 1984. "Resource Systems, Populations, and Communities." Pp. 397-436 in *A New Ecology: Novel Approaches To Interactive Systems*, edited by P.W. Price, C.N. Slobodchikoff, and W.S. Gaud. New York: Wiley.

Williams, G.C. 1966. *Adaptation and Natural Selection: A Critique of Some Current Evolutionary Thought*. Princeton, NJ: Princeton University Press.

Wilson, E.O. 1975. *Sociobiology*. Cambridge, MA: Harvard University Press.

Wilson, F.D. 1984. "Urban Ecology: Urbanization and Systems of Cities." *Annual Review of Sociology* 10: 283-307.

Wisniewski, R.L. 1980. "Carrying Capacity: Understanding Our Biological Limitations." *Humboldt Journal of Social Relations* 7: 55-70.

Wittfogel, K. 1957. *Oriental Despotism*. New Haven, CT: Yale University Press.

Wolpoff, M.H., and J. Radovcic. 1992. "The Place of the Neandertal in Human Evolution." Paper presented at the 158th Annual Meetings of the American Association for the Advancement of Science, February 6-11, Chicago.

Woodwell, G.M. 1974. "Short-Circuiting the Cheap Power Fantasy." *Natural History* (October): 16-20, 88.

Worster, D. 1977. *Nature's Economy: A History of Ecological Ideas*. Cambridge: Cambridge University Press.

Wrangham, R.W. 1987. "The Significance of African Apes for Reconstructing Human Social Evolution." Pp. 51-71 in *The Evolution of Human Behavior: Primate Models*, edited by W.G. Kinzey. Albany: State University of New York Press.

Wrangham, R.W., W.C. McGrew, F.B.M. de Waal, and P.G. Heltne (eds.). 1994. *Chimpanzee Cultures*. Cambridge, MA: Harvard University Press.

Wynne-Edwards, V.C. 1962. *Animal Dispersion In Relation To Social Behaviour*. Edinburgh: Oliver and Boyd.

_____. 1965. "Self-Regulating Systems in Populations of Animals." *Science* 147(March 26): 1543-1548.

_____. 1977. "Society vs. The Individual in Animal Evolution." Pp. 5-17 in *Evolutionary Ecology*, edited by B. Stonehouse and C. Perrins. London: Macmillan.

Young, G.L. 1989. "A Conceptual Framework For An Interdisciplinary Human Ecology." *Acta Oecologiae Hominis: International Monographs in Human Ecology*, No. 1. Lund: University of Lund.

_____. 1994. "The Case for a 'catholic" Ecology." *Human Ecology Review* 1(Summer/Autumn): 310-319.

_____. 1996. "Interaction As A Concept Basic to Human Ecology: An Exploration and Synthesis." Pp. 157-211 in *Advances in Human Ecology*, Vol. 5, edited by L. Freese. Greenwich, CT: JAI Press.

Zeder, M.A. 1991. *Feeding Cities: Specialized Animal Economy in the Ancient Near East*. Washington, DC: Smithsonian Institution.

INDEX

Abbott, D.H., 219n.5
Aberle, L.G., 41n.4
Acculturation, 96, 139, 151, 163, 226
   as a human phenotype, 6
   irreversibility of macrosocial, 188-190
   population growth and, 193
   social organization and, 163-164
   sociological dynamics of, 163
   urbanization and, 180
   See also Culture; Social organization
Adams, R.N., 130, 237, 244n.4
Adaptation, 120-121
   of cultures to conditions of disease, 87,
      98-100, 103, 106-107, 110-111,
      115
   to energy capture/extraction rates, 141
   to environments, 18-19, 118, 125-126
   to habitat changes, by humans, 146
   interpretations of, 18-19, 117, 137n.1
   to mortality rates, 140-141
   See also Culture; Social organization
Agrariansim. *See* Agriculturalism; Sub-
      sistence organization
Agricultural revolution, 148. *See also*
      Agriculturalism
Agriculturalism, 193
   energy subsidies and, 149-50, 165n.6,
      227-228
   environmental impacts of, 148, 151,
      164n.3, 165n.5, 225, 227-228
   as environmentally based, 227-228
   nutrition levels and, 152-153
   population growth and, 149-153
   poverty and, 152-153, 159
   See also Industrialized agriculture

Alexander, R.D., 122
Anderson, J.N., 15n.3
Aoki, K., 53
Ashburn, P.M., 113n.14
Axelrod, R., 49
Ayala, F.J., 42n.9

Bahn, P., 202, 204-05, 220n.11
Baker, G.L., 245n.6
Bamforth, D.B., 111n.1
Barinaga, M., 84n.8
Bassala, G., 188
Baumhoff, M.A., 92
Bell, R.W. 138n.2
Bennett, J.W., 15n.5
Berry, B.J., 186
Besansky, N.J., 105
Bettinger, R.L., 92-93
Bickerton, D., 73, 84n.5
Binford, L.R., 92
Biological evolution, 12-14, 17-19, 36-40,
      224-25, 229, 232
   as allelic substitutions, 24-26
   as connected to ecology, 17-22, 230-
      231
   as descent with modification, 46, 55-
      57, 117, 127
   disconnections between microscopic
      and macroscopic processes of,
      36-40, 42-43n.9, 52
   distinguished from development, 117
   Hardy-Weinberg equilibrium and, 24,
      35, 38, 42n.6
   human phenotypes and, 45-47, 229
   "jumping genes" and, 35, 39

Research in Rural Sociology and Development

Series Editor: **Harry K. Schwarzweller,**
Department of Sociology, Michigan State University

Rural sociology, as a field of study, is experiencing some exciting new directions in research and scholarship. Contributions from younger scholars are encouraged in building this series into an effective forum for assessing the new wave of challenging ideas and approaches. Thematically organized, this series addresses problems relating to population turn around in rural America, the changing structure of agriculture, rural poverty and crime, social impacts of technology, and developmental processes in Third World nations.

Volume 6 - Sustaining Agriculture and Rural Communities
1995, 270 pp. $73.25
ISBN 1-55938-458-1

Edited by **Harry K. Schwarzweller,** *Department of Sociology, Michigan State University* and **Thomas A. Lyson,** *Department of Rural Sociology, Cornell University*

CONTENTS: Preface. Introduction: Researching the Sustainability of Agriculture and Rural Communities, *Harry K. Schwarzweller and Thomas A. Lyson.* Twentieth Century Agricultural and Environmental Transitions: A Preliminary Analysis, *Frederick H. Buttel.* Competing Paradigms: An Overview and Analysis of the Alternative Conventional Agricultural Debate, *Curtis E. Beus.* Missouri Farmers and Pesticide Use: A Diversity of Viewpoints, *Douglas H. Constance, Jere L Gilles, J. Sanford Rikoon,* and *Ernest B. Perry.* Prospects for a Sustainable Agriculture in the Northeast Rural/Urban Fringe, *Max J. Pfeffer and Mark B. Lapping.* Fighting an Uphill Battle: Population Pressure and Declining Land Productivity in Rwanda, *Daniel C. Clay.* Policy Instruments Designed to Foster Sustainable Agriculture: An Appraisal, *Alan W. Black.* Seasonal and Local Diets: Consumers' Role in Achieving a Sustainable Food System, *Jennifer L. Wilkins.* Sustainable Agriculture and Prospects for Rural Community Development in the United States, *Gilbert W. Gillespie, Jr..* Labor Exchange Among Dairy Farmers: Lessons from the Past for a More Sustainable Future, *Douglas Harper* and *Thomas A. Lyson.* Reinvigorating Rural Economies, *Frederick Kirschenmann.* Social Capital and Sustainability: Agriculture and Communities in the Great Plains and Corn Belt, *Cornelia Butler Flora.* Some South Asian Illustrations of Policy Issues in Sustainable Rural Development, *Nancy W. Axinn* and *George H. Axinn.* Biographical Sketches.

Also Available:
Volumes 1-5 (1984-1991) $73.25 each

J A I P R E S S

Research in Urban Sociology

Edited by **Ray Hutchison,** *Department of Urban and Public Affairs, University of Wisconsin—Green Bay*

"This new research series addresses the major subject areas of urban sociology—ethnic and minority groups within the city, social network of urban residents, location of retail and industrial activities within the metropolitan complex, decline of the central cities and emergence of suburban lifestyles, and the core question of community integration itself. The goal is to provide an outlet for original research which may be passed up in the more usual urban studies journals. Future volumes will focus on new research in urban sociology in Europe and an evaluation of classic models and new paradigms of theory and research in the United States."

— *From the Preface*

Volume 3, Urban Sociology in Transition
1993, 253 pp. $73.25
ISBN 1-55938-580-4

CONTENTS: Introduction. The Crisis in Urban Sociology, Ray Hutchison. Human Ecology and Social Ecology. Recent Empirical and Theoretical Developments in Sociological Human Ecology, *William A. Schwab.* Neighborhood Succession: Theory and Patterns, *David J. Hartmann.* Embattled Neighborhoods: The Political Ecology of Neighborhood Change, *Kent Schwirian and Gustavo S. Mesch.* Spacial Structure and the Urban Experience: Ecology and the New Urban Sociology, *Mark LaGory.* The New Urban Sociology. All the Discomforts of Home: The Political Economy of Housing, Gregory Squires. Protest Movements and Urban Theory, *Eric Hirsch.* World Cities: A Political Economy/Global Network Approach, *David A. Smith and Michael Timberlake.* Marxian Urban Sociology and the New Approaches to Space, *Mark Gottdiener.* The Question of Convergence in Urban Sociology. The Structural Roots of Action and the Question of Convergence, *William Flanagan.*

Also Available:
Volumes 1-2 (1989-1992) $73.25 each

Research in Community Sociology

Edited by **Dan A. Chekki,** *Department of Sociology, University of Winnipeg*

Volume 6, New Communities in a Changing World
1996, 315 pp. $73.25
ISBN 0-7623-0040-X

CONTENTS: PART I. INTRODUCTION. The Social Landscape of New Communities in North America, *Dan A. Chekki.* PART II. THEORETICAL PERSPECTIVES. Using Classical Theorists to Reconceptualize Community Dynamics, *Jonathan H. Turner and Norman A. Dolch.* PART III. NEW IMMIGRANT COMMUNITIES. New Immigrant Communities in the United States and the Ideology of Exclusion, *Carol Schmid.* Blurring Borders: Constructing Transnational Community in the Process of Mexico-U.S. Migration, *Luin Goldring.* New Immigrant Communities in a Suburban Region, *Mark Baldassare.* The Attainment of Neighborhood Qualities among British, Chinese, and Black Immigrants in Toronto and Vancouver, *Eric Fong and Milena Guila.* PART IV. THE AIDS COMMUNITY. The Uncertainty, Diversity, and Change: The Aids Community in New York City, *Susan M. Chambré.* PART V. COMMUNITY IN CYBERSPACE. Lawyers on Line: Professional Identity and Boundary Maintenance in Cyberspace, *Debra J. Schleef.* PART VI. ENCLOSED COMMUNITY LIFE. Enclosure, Community, and Public Life, *Dennis R. Judd.* PART VII. COMMUNES - UTOPIAN COMMUNITIES. The Contemporary Communal Movement, *William L. Smith.* PART VIII. COMMUNITY DYNAMICS IN A NEW MILIEU. A New Community of Old Members: Old Order Mennonites in Upstate New York, *Daniel B. Lee.* Cultural Dynamics and Futuristic Scenarios of the Virásaiva Community in North America, *Dan A. Chekki.*

Also Available:

Volumes 1-5 (1990-1995)
  + Supplement 1 (1994) $73.25 each

J A I   P R E S S

Research in the Sociology of Work

Edited by **Ida Harper Simpson,**
Department of Sociology, Duke University
and **Richard L. Simpson**, *Department of
Sociology, University of North Carolina, Chapel Hill*

Volume 5, The Meaning of Work
1994, 288 pp. $73.25
ISBN 0-89232-971-8

CONTENTS: Introduction, *Richard L. Simpson and Ida Harper Simpson.* The Concept of Work on the Rack: Critique and Suggestions, *Jan Ch. Karlsson.* The Meanings of Work, *Curt Tausky.* Some Effects of Gender on the Meaning of Work: An Empirical Examination, *Elizabeth A. Martin, Jennifer Hess, and Paul M. Siegel.* Work Orientation, Job Discrimination, and Ethnicity: A Focus Group Perspective, *Lawrence Bobo, Camille L. Zubrinsky, James H. Johnson, Jr., and Melvin L. Oliver.* Trends in Job Satisfaction in the United States by Race, Gender, and Type of Occupation, *Glenn Firebaugh and Brian Harley.* From the Instinct of Workmanship to Gift Exchange: Employment Contracts, Social Relations of Trust, and the Meaning of Work, *Margaret L. Krecker.* Cohesion or Conflict? Race, Solidarity, and Resistance in the Workplace, *Randy Hodson.* Job Satisfaction Theories and Job Satisfaction: A China and U.S. Comparison, *Shanhe Jiang, Richard H. Hall, Karyn L. Loscocco, and John Allen.* Researchers, Cultural Boundaries, and Organizational Change, *Tim Turpin and Stephen Hill.* Costs and Opportunities of Marketization: An Analysis of Russian Employment and Unemployment, *Susan Goodrich Lehmann.* Organizational Commitment and Job Performance in the U.S. Labor Force, *Arne L. Kalleberg and Peter V. Marsden.* Objective and Subjective Parental Working Conditions Effects on Child Outcomes: A Comparative Test, *Laura E. Geschwender and Toby L. Parcel.*

Also Available:
Volumes 1-4 (1981-1988) $73.25 each